THE HUTH LIBRARY.

LIFE AND WORKS

OF

ROBERT GREENE, M.A.

VOL. IX.

ALCIDA : GREENES METAMORPHOSIS.
GREENES MOURNING GARMENT.
AND
GREENES FAREWELL TO FOLLY.
1588—1591.

Days of old,
Ye are not dead, though gone from me ;
Ye are not cold,
But like the summer-birds gone o'er. the sea.
The sun brings back the swallows fast,
O'er the sea :
When thou comest at the last,
The days of old come back to me.

GEORGE MACDONALD, LL.D.

The Huth Library.

THE

LIFE AND COMPLETE WORKS

IN

PROSE AND VERSE

OF

ROBERT GREENE, M.A.

CAMBRIDGE AND OXFORD.

IN FIFTEEN VOLUMES

FOR THE FIRST TIME COLLECTED AND EDITED
WITH NOTES AND ILLUSTRATIONS, ETC.,

BY THE REV.

ALEXANDER B. GROSART, LL.D. (EDIN.), F.S.A.,
St. George's, Blackburn, Lancashire.

VOL. IX.—PROSE.

ALCIDA: GREENES METAMORPHOSIS.

GREENES MOURNING GARMENT.

AND

GREENES FAREWELL TO FOLLY.

1588-1591.

New York

RUSSELL & RUSSELL

1964

Reissued in 1964 by Russell & Russell, Inc.,
in an Edition Limited to 400 Sets
L. C. Catalog Card No: 64-23465

PRINTED IN THE UNITED STATES OF AMERICA

CONTENTS.

***

False world, thou ly'st : Thou canst not
    lend
      The least delight :
Thy favours cannot gain a Friend,
      They are so slight :
Thy morning pleasures make an end
      To please at night :
Poore are the wants that thou supply'st,
And yet thou vaunt'st, and yet thou vy'st
With heav'n ; Fond earth, thou boasts ;
    false world, thou ly'st.

Thy babbling tongue tels golden tales
    Of endlesse treasure ;
Thy bountie offers easie sales
    Of lasting pleasure ;
Thou ask'st the Conscience what she ails,
    And swear'st to ease her ;
There's none can want where thou
    supply'st :
There's none can give where thou deny'st.
Alas, fond world, thou boasts ; false
    world, thou ly'st.

What well-advisèd ease regards
    What earth can say ?
Thy words are gold, but thy rewards
    Are painted clay ;
Thy cunning can but pack the cards,
    Thou can'st not play :

Thy game at weakest, still thou vy'st ;
If seen, and then revy'd, deny'st ;
Thou art not what thou seem'st : false
    world, thou ly'st.

Thy tinsel-bosome seems a mint
    Of new-coin'd treasure,
A Paradise, that has no stint,
    No change, no measure ;
A painted cask, but nothing in't,
    Nor wealth, nor pleasure :
Vain earth ! that falsly thus comply'st
With man : Vain man ! that thus rely'st
On earth : Vain man, thou dot'st : Vain
    earth, thou ly'st.

What mean dull souls, in this high mea-
    sure
      To haberdash
In earth's base wares ; whose greatest
    treasure
      Is drosse and trash ?
The height of whose inchaunting pleasure
      Is but a flash ?
Are these the goods that thou supply'st
Us mortals with ? Are these the highest ?
Can these bring cordiall peace ? False
    world, thou ly'st.

FRANCIS QUARLES ('Chertsey Worthies' Library, vol. iii. p. 59).

ALCIDA:
GREENE'S METAMORPHOSIS.

1588—1617.

NOTE.

'Alcida Greene's Metamorphofis,' was licensed for the press in 1588, and probably printed in the same year, or shortly thereafter ; but the earliest and only edition now known is of 1617. I am indebted for it to the 'Huth Library' as before. See annotated Life in Vol. I.—G.

ALCIDA

GREENES

Metamorphofis,

VVherein is difcouered, a pleafant
tranfformation of bodies into fundrie fhapes,
fhewing that as vertues beautifie the mind, fo vani-
ties giue greater ftaines, than the perfection
of any quality can rafe out :

The Difcourfe confirmed with diuerfe
merry and delightfull Hiftories ; full of graue
Principles to content Age, and fawfed with pleafant
parlees, and witty anfweres, to fatisfie youth :
profitable for both, and not of-
fenfiue to any.

By R. G.

Omne tulit punctum, qui mifcuit dulci.

LONDON,
Printed by George Purflowe. 1617.

The Epiſtle Dedicatory.

To the Right Worſhipfull, Sir *Charles Blount,*
Knight, indewed with perfeɛtions of learning, and
titles of nobility : *Robert Greene* wiſheth
increaſe of honour and vertue.

Chilles, the great Commander of the
Mirmidones, had no ſooner (Right
Worſhipfull) encountred the hardie
Troian with his Courtelax, and regiſtred his valour
on the helme of his enemie, but returning to his
tents, hee pourtraied with his pen the praiſe of
Polixena, ioyning Amors with Armors, and the
honor of his Learning with the reſolution of his
Launce. In the *Olympiades* the Laurell ſtriued as
well for the Pen, as the Speare : and *Pallas* had
double Sacrifice, as well perfumes of torne papers,
as Incenſe of broken truncheons. Entring (right
worſhipfull) with deep inſight into theſe premiſſes,
I found [Fame] blazoning your reſolute indeuors in
deeds of Armes, and report figuring out your euer-

intended fauours to good letters : prefuming vpon
the courteous difpofition of your Worfhip, I
aduentured to prefent you, as *Lucius* did *Cæfar*,
who offered him an Helmet topt with Plumes in
warres, and a booke ftuffed with precepts in peace,
knowing that *Cæfar* held it as honorable to be
counted an Orator in the Court, as a Souldier in
the field. So (right worfhipfull) after your returne
from the Low Countries, (paffing ouer thofe praife-
worthy refolutions executed vpon the enemie)
fee / ing abfence from armes had transformed
Campus Martius to Mount *Helicon*, I ouerboldned
my felfe to trouble your Worfhip, with the fight
of my Metamorphofis : A pamphlet too fimple
to patronage vnder fo worthy a *Mæcenas*, and
vnworthy to be viewed of you, whofe thoughts
are intended to more ferious ftudies. Yet *Auguftus*
would read Poems, and write Roundelayes, rather
to purge melancholly with toyes, then for any
delight in fuch trifles. So I hope your Worfhip
wil, after long perufing of great volumes, caft a
glance at my poore pamphlet: wherein is difcouered
the Anatomy of womens affections : fetting out as
in a mirror, how dangerous his hazard is, that fets
his reft vpon loue : whofe enemie (if it haue any)
is momentany, and effects variable. If either the
method, or matter miflike, as wanting fcholarifme
in the one, or grauity in the other : yet if it fhall

ſerue your Worſhip as a trifle to paſſe away the
time, and ſo ſlip with patience, as a boord Ieſt, I
ſhall be leſſe grieved : if any way it pleaſe, as to
procure your delight, I ſhall be glad and ſatisfied,
as hauing gained the end of my labours : but
howſoeuer, hoping your Worſhip will pardon my
preſumption in preſenting ; and weigh more of the
well affected will, then of the bad labored worke,
I wiſh your Worſhip ſuch fortunate fauours, as
you can deſire, or I imagine.

Your Worſhip to command,

Robert Greene. /

To the Gentlemen Readers, HEALTH.

*F*ALLING *(Gentlemen) by chance amongſt a company of no meane Gentlewomen : after ſuppoſes and ſuch ordinary ſports paſt, they fell to prattle of the qualities incident to their owne Sexe : one amongſt the reſt, very indifferent, more addicted to tell the truth, then to ſelfe conceit, ſaid, That woman that had fauours, had moſt commonly contrary faults : for (quoth ſhee) beauty is ſeldome without pride, and wit without inconſtancie. The Gentlewomen began to bluſh, becauſe ſhee ſpake ſo broad, be ſure, and blamed her that ſhee would ſo fondly ſoyle her owne neſt. Shee ſtill maintained it, that what ſhe had ſpoken was true : and more, that ſhe had forgotten their little ſecrecie. Whereupon there grew arguments : and a Sophiſticall diſputation fell out among the Gentlewomen, about their owne qualities. I ſate ſtill as a cypher in Algoriſme, and noted what was ſpoken : which after I had peruſed in my chamber, and ſeeing it would be profitable for yong Gentlemen, to*

know and forefee as well their faults as their fauours,
I drew into a fiction, the forme and method, in manner
of a Metamorphofis: which (Gentlemen) I prefent
vnto your wonted curtefies, defiring you not to looke
for any of Ouids *wittie inuentions, but for bare and*
rude difcourfes: hoping to finde you, as hitherto I haue
done, whatfoeuer in opinion, yet fauorable and filent
in fpeech. In which hope fetting downe my reft, I
bid you farewell.

Yours euer, as he is bound
ROBERT GREENE.

Authoris ad librum fuum carmen Ouidianum,
cum diutina febri rure laboraret.

Parue (nec inuideo) fine me liber ibis in vrbem:
Hei mihi, quod domino non licet ire tuo. |
Et palma tu dignus, & hic, & quisquis in altam,
Pluribus vt profit, doctus defcendit arenam.

R. A. Oxon.

In praife of the Author.

The bufie Bee, that rifeth with the Sunne,
Hies forth her hiue, to end her daily tafke :
With weary wings fhe plies into the fields,
And Natures fecrets fearcheth by her fkill,
From flower to flower her carefull way doth flie:
To fucke her hony from her natiue fweet;

Loden, ſhe rich beſtirres her to her home,
And there ſhe workes and tilles within her hiue:
Not for her ſelfe thus buſily ſhe romes,
But for vs men, that feed vpon her combes.
So GREENE hath ſought into the depth of Art,
With weary labours toyling at his bookes
For fruits, ſuch as the learned Authors yeeld ;
Searching the ſecrets that their wits haue pen'd,
Toſſing amongſt their learned principles
Their Rhethoricke and deepe Philoſophy :
Gathering the ſweet that euery Science giues,
To carry pleaſant hony to his hiue.
Not for himſelfe alone the Author lookes,
But for ſuch men as daigne to read his bookes,

Sic vos non vobis mellificatis apes.

                              Ed. Percy. /

To the Authour his Friend.

Well haft thou painted in thy learned Profe,
The perfect portraiture of womens workes :
How many fcapes they fhadow with a glofe,
What mortall faults amongft their fauours lurkes.
How if they haue a vertue to entice,
A cooling card comes following with a vice :
Beautie doth grace, and yet is ftain'd with pride,
Faire is abaf'd by being ouer-coy :
It is a gemme, but if inconftant try'd,
Account it for a trifle and a toy.
Conftant and kinde are vertues that do grace :
But babling dames fuch glories doe deface.
Vertue[s] thus fet oppof'd vnto their vice,
Giues vs a light to fettle fafe our loues :
To feare left painted fhewes may vs entice.
Subtill are women, then it men behoues
To read, fweet friend, and ouer-read thy bookes,
To teach vs 'ware of womens wanton lookes.

Bubb Gent. /

In ROBERTI GRENI Metamorphoſin carmen
ENKOMIASTIKON.

Bellica pacificæ concedat lancea linguæ,
 Seu tibi profa magis, feu tibi metra placent.
Sæpe Duces inter laudem meruere Poetæ,
 Hoſtibus in medijs arma virofq canunt.
Inter Philofophos laudem meruere Poetæ,
 Qui leuibus mifcent feria metra iocis.
Bella Ducum, & claros multi fcripfere triumphos,
 Inter quos primas Maro Poeta tenet.
Sunt qui mutatas ſtuduerunt dicere formas,
 Quales quæ quondam Nafo Poeta dedit.
Poſt Metamorphoſin Nafonis, carmine fcriptam,
 Mutatas formas carmine nemo dedit.
Grenus adeſt tandem, rhetor bonus atque Poeta,
 Qui fua cum profis carmina iunƈta dedit
Si cupis ingratæ pœnas perfoluere amicæ,
 Hic exempla legas, moribus apta fuis.
Orabis Venerem (folet exaudire precantem)
 Inque nouam formam vertet amica Venus.
Dura eſt? in faxum : leuis eſt? in Chameleontem :
 Inque rofam vertet, garrula fi fuerit.

        G. B. Cant.

In laudem Roberti Greni *Cantab. in*
Artibus Magiſtri.

Olim præclaros fcripfit *Chaucerus* ad Anglos,
 Aurea metra fuis patrio fermone refundens:
Poſt hunc *Gowerus*, poſt hunc fua carmina *Lydgate*,
Poſtque alios alij fua metra dedere Britannis.
Multis poſt annis, coniungens carmina profis,
Florint *Afcamus, Chekus, Gafcoynus,* & alter
Tullius Anglorum nunc viuens *Lillius,* illum
Confequitur *Grenus,* præclarus vterque Poeta.
          Alci-/

ALCIDA

GREENES

Metamorphosis.

Oosing from *Tripoly*, to make for *Alexandria*, as we thought to crosse the Seas with a speedy cut, our Ship had not long gone vnder saile, scarce past two hundred Leagues vpon the maine ; but whether our vnhappy Fortune, the frowardnesse of the Fates, the Constellation of some contrary Aspect, or the particular destinie of some vnhappy Man had so decreed : when the calme was smoothest, the sea without storme, the skie without clouds ; then *Neptune*, to shew he was God of the seas, and *Æolus* master of the windes, either of them seuerally and both of them coniointly, so conspired, that they first drew a foggie vale ouer *Phœbus* face, that the heauens appeared

all gloomie, the Trytons daunced, as forefhewing
a rough fea : and *Æolus* fetting his winds at
libertie, hurled fuch a gale into the Ocean, that
euery furge was ready to ouertake our fhip, and
the barke ready to founder with euery waue : fuch
and fo miferable was our eftate, that wee fhooke
all our Sailes, weighed our Ankers, and let the fhip
hull at winde and weather, from our handy labours
falling to heartie praiers. Thus looking euery
houre to commit / our Soules to the gods, and our
bodies to the feas, after we had floted by the fpace
of fiue dayes without hope of life, our barke by
chance fel vpon the coaft of *Taprobane*, an Iland
fituated far South, vnder the pole *Antarticke*, where
Canapus the faire ftarre gladdeth the hearts of
the inhabitants : there wee fuffered fhipwracke, all
perifhing in the fea, except my infortunate felfe :
who count my mis-fortune greater in furueying
[= furviving] the reft, than if I had beene partner
with them of their deftinies. Well, the gods would
haue me liue to be more miferable, and defpaire I
would not, left I fhould proue guiltie of mine owne
mifhap, but taking heart at graffe, wet and weary
as I was, I paffed vp into the Iland, which I found
inhabited and fruitfull, the aire paffing temperate,
the fituation pleafant, the foyle abounding with
trees, hearbes, and graffe, fowles and beafts of all
kind : the Champion fit for corne and graine, the

wood-land full of thickets, the meades full of
fprings and delightfull fountaines : that the foyle
and the aire equally proportioned, the Ile feemed
a facred Eden, or Paradife : much like that faire
England the flower of *Europe,* ftored with the
wealth of all the Wefterne world, which as *ex
oppofito* is contrarily placed farre North, vnder the
pole *Articke.* Well, crept vp the clyffes into the
maine continent of this Iland, I wandred farre, and
found no village, til at laft, vnder a hill I fpied
a little cottage, at the door whereof fate an old
woman decrepit, ouer worne with yeares, her haire
as white as the Downe found vpon the fhrubbes of
Arabia, her face full of wrinckles, furrowed fo
with age, as in her vifage appeared the very map
of antiquitie : yet might I perceiue by the lineaments of her face, that fhe had beene beautifull
and well featured; and that fhe was defcended from
fome good parentage, fuch fparkes of Gentilitie
appeared in her countenance. Mufing at this
old Matron, that fate paffing melancholy, my teeth
for cold beating in my head, I faluted her in this
manner.

Mother : for this Title I may vfe in refpeƈt of
your age, crauing / pardon if I impart not what
reuerence belongs to your eftate, in that I am
a ftranger : I falute you, wifhing as many good
fortunes may end your dayes, as you haue paft ill

2

fortunes in the courfe of your life. My name, or
Countries, little auailes now to reueale, time being
too fhort, and my ftate too miferable : let it fuffice,
I am a ftranger that haue fuffered fhipwracke on
your coaft, my fellow conforts drowned, ending
their forrowes : I efcaped, referued to great misfortunes. The weather is cold, and I am wet,
might I craue harbour this night, I fhould bee
bound to make fuch requitall as diftreffe can
affoord, which is thankes, and pray to the gods
that you may die as fortunate as the mother of
Cleotis and *Byton*. The old beldam lifting vp
her head, and feeing mee ftand fhaking for colde,
vttered not a word, but taking vp her ftaffe, and
me by the hand, confirmed my welcome with
filence, and led mee into her Cottage : where ftum-
bling about on her three legges, fhee made me a
luftie fire, that cheered my halfe dead limbes, and
reuiued what the Sea had halfe mortified. After
fhe perceiued I began to waxe warme, and that my
colour grew to be frefh, fhe began to make me
anfwere in this manner.

Since now that the fire hath made thee frolicke,
and the warmth of my poore Cottage hath beene
as good as houfhold Phyficke to cure thy weather-
beaten loynes, let mee fay as thou fhalt finde, that
thou art welcome : for I hold it a religion to honor
ftrangers, efpecially diftreft, fith comfort in miferie

is a double gift. I know not thy degree, nor I
recke not : fuffice I vfe thee as thou feemeft, and
entertaine thee as my abilitie can : thy eftate may
bee great, for the Hood makes not the Monke, nor
the apparrell the man. *Mercurie* walked in the
fhape of a Country Swaine, *Apollo* kept *Midaes*
fheep, and poore *Philemon* & *Bawcis* his wife,
entertained *Iupiter* himfelfe, fupt him & lodged
him : they honored an vnknowne gheft : he not
vngratefull to fo kinde an Oaft, for hee turned
their Cottage to a Temple, and made them
Sacrificers at his Altars. Thus I may be deceiued
in thy degree, / but howfoeuer, or whofoeuer, this
cottage, & what is in it, is mine and thine : leffe
thou fhalt not find, and more in confcience thou
canft not craue. Sonne, I fpeake thus frankly, for
that I am olde, for age hath that priuiledge, to be
priuate & familiar with ftrangers : for were I as I
haue been, as beautifull as now I am withered : as
young as I am olde : I would bee leffe prodigall
and more churlifh, left with *Phillis* I might inter-
taine *Demophon*, which did make account of the
trothleffe Troian, or with *Ariadne* tye my felfe to
the proportion of *Thefeus*. But age hath put water
in the flame, & many yeeres turned the glowing
fparkes to cold windes. Time (fonne) is like the
worme *Tenedes*, which fmoothly lying on the barke
of the tree, yet eateth out the fappe. It ftealeth

on by minutes, and fareth like the Sunne, whofe
fhadow hafteth on, yet cannot be perceiued: but
letting this parle paffe, feeing thou art weary and
hungrie, two fruits that grow from fhipwracke,
reft thee till I prouide Supper, which how homely
foeuer it be, yet muft thou account it dainty, for
that it is my delicates, and accept it as a prodigall
banket, for that euery difh fhall bee fauced with
welcome.

With this, fhee rofe from her ftoole and went to
prouide fupper, leauing me amazed at her gracious
reply, making me to coniecture by her words, that
as fhe was wife, fo fhee had beene well brought vp
and was defcended of no fmall Parentage: I fate
in a mufe till fhee had made ready our cates:
which being fet on the table, we fell to make tryall
of our teeth, as before we had done of our tongues,
that we began and ended fupper without any great
chat. Well, our repaft taken, the old woman
feeing me fitter for fleepe than for prattle, gaue
me leaue to goe to bedde, where I paft away the
night in golden flumbers, lying fo long in the
morning till *Phœbus* glimmering on my face, bade
me good day.

Awakt by the fummons of the Sunne, I arofe,
and found mine old Oafteffe fitting at her doore in
her old melancholly mood, fighing and forrowfull:
an interchange of falues paffed, / betweene her and

me, I with thankes for my great and courteous intertainment, and fhee with oft repetitions of welcomes: taking a ftoole and fitting down by [t]his old dame, feeing fhee fell againe to her dumpes, I began to bee thus inquifitiue.

Mother, if I may without offence prefume to vfe a queftion, I would inquire what I mufe at, and be abfolued in a darke Enigma that I haue found in your cottage: but rather had I ftill hold my thoughts in fufpence, than bee offenfiue either to your age, or to fo courteous an Oaftefle. The old woman fmiling at my feare, or at my folly, bade me fay on: and I boldly profecuted my purpofe thus.

Since my arriuall in your Cottage, I haue noted your thoughts to be pafſionate, and your pafſions to be violent: I haue feene care lurking midft the wrinkles of your age, and forrow breath'd out with broken fighes. I do not deny but age is giuen to melancholy, and many yeeres acquainted with many dumps: but fuch farre fetcht grones, the heralts of griefes, fuch deepe fighes, the Ambafſadors of forrow, make me thinke either you grieue at your finnes with repentance, or elfe recount fome great forepafſed mifsfortunes: this is the doubt, and here lies the queftion.

I had no fooner vttered thefe words, but the old woman leaning her head againft her ftaffe, fell

into fuch bitter teares, as did difcouer a multitude
of forrowes and perplexed paffions : infomuch as
taking pittie of her griefes, I lent her a fewe
lukewarme drops, to fhew how in minde I did
participate of her vnknowne doloures. After fhee
had filled the furrows of her face with the ftreams
of her teares, ending the cataftrophe of her paffions,
with a volee of fighes, fhe blubbered out this reply.
Ah fon, ill haue thofe painters deciphered time
with a pumice ftone, as rafing out both ioyes and
forrowes with obliuie : feeing experience tels mee,
that deepe conceiued forrowes are like the Sea
Iuie, which the older it is, the larger rootes it
hath : refembling the Eagle, which in her oldeft
age reneweth her bill. Paffions / (my fonne) are
like the arrowes of *Cupid*, which if they touch
lightly prooue but toyes, but piercing the fkin,
prooue deep wounds, as hardly to be rafed out as
the fpots of the Leopard : I was, fonne, (and with
that fhee entred her narration with a deepe figh)
once young and buxfome as thou art, beauty
difcouering her pride, where now a tawny hiew
pulleth downe my plumes: the lineaments of my
face were leueld with fuch equall proportion, as I
was counted full of fauour : and of fo faire a Dye
had Nature ftained my cheekes, that I was thought
beautifull: yea (fon) giue me leaue a little to
fauour of felfe loue, I tell thee I was called the

Venus of *Taprobane* : my parentage did no whit difgrace what nature had imparted vpon mee, for I was the daughter of an Earle. To be briefe (my fonne) as well the qualities of my mind, as my exteriour fauours were fo honored in *Taprobane*, that the Prince of the Iland called *Cleomachus* took me to wife, and had by me foure children, one fon and three daughters : and with this fhe fell afrefh to her teares, pouring forth many paffionate plaints, til at laft the forrow of her teares ftopping, fhe went forward in her tale: My Hufband in the prime of yeeres dyed, my fonne fucceeded in the gouernment, and I and my daughters courted it, as their youth and my direction would permit. Liuing thus contentedly, and as I thought armed againft fortune, in that we foregarded all our actions with vertue, the Fates, if there be any, or the deftinies, fome ftar or planet, in fome infortunate and curfed afpect, calculated fuch ill hap to all my daughters natiuities, as they proued as miferable, as I would haue wifhed them happy. And here multiplying figh vpon figh with double and trebble reuies, fhee ceafed: but I defirous to know the fequell of their misfortunes, afked her the caufe and manner of their mifhaps: fhe replyed not, but taking mee by the hand, fhee led mee from her cottage, to a valley hard by, where fhe brought me to a marble piller, fafhioned and pourtraied like a woman, which made me remember *Pigmalions* picture, that hee carued with his hand and / doted on with his heart. No fooner were wee come to the ftone, but *Alcida* (for fo was the old ladies name) taking it in her armes, kiffed it, and wafht it with her teares. I amafed at this ftrange greeting of *Alcida* and the ftone, drew more nigh, and there I might perceiue the Image to hold in either hand a table. In the right hand was depainted the portraiture of *Venus*, holding the ball that brought *Troy* to ruine, and vnder were written thefe verfes.

When Nature forged the faire vnhappy mould,
Wherein proud beauty tooke her matchleffe
 fhape:
She ouer-flipt her cunning and her fkill,
And aym'd to farre, but drew beyond the marke ;
For thinking to haue made a heauenly bliffe,
For wanton gods to dally with in heauen,
And to haue fram'd a precious iem for men,
To folace all their dumpifh thoughts with glee,
She wrought a plague, a poyfon, and a hell :
For gods, for men, thus no way wrought fhe well.
Venus was faire, faire was the queene of loue,
Fairer then *Pallas*, or the wife of *Ioue* ;
Yet did the Gigglets beauty greeue the Smith,
For that fhe brau'd the Creeple with a horne.
Mars faid, her beauty was the ftarre of heauen,

Yet did her beauty ftaine him with difgrace :
Paris for faire, gaue her the golden ball ;
And brought his, and his fathers ruine fo :
Thus nature making what fhould farre excell,
Lent gods, and men, a poifon and a hell.

In her left hand, was curioufly pourtraied a Peacocke, clad glorioufly in the beauty of his feathers ;
vnder was written as followeth :

The bird of *Iuno* glories in his plumes,
Pride makes the Fowle to prune his feathers fo,/
His fpotted traine, fetcht from old *Argus* head,
With golden rayes, like to the brighteft funne :
Inferteth felfe-loue in a filly bird,
Till midft his hot an[d] glorious fumes,
He fpies his feete, and then lets fall his plumes.
Beauty breeds pride, pride hatcheth forth difdaine,
Difdaine gets hate, and hate calls for reuenge,
Reuenge with bitter prayers vrgeth ftill :
Thus felfe-loue nurfing vp the pompe of pride,
Makes beautie wracke againft an ebbing tide.

After I had viewed the pictures, and read the
poefies, I grew to be more defirous to know what
this image ment : intreating *Alcida* to difcourfe
vnto me what this portraiture did meane : fhee
fitting downe at the foot of the ftone, began to
tell her tale in this manner.

ALCIDA, her firſt Hiſtorie.

While I liued in the Court, honoured of all, as mother to the Prince and loued of euery one, as one that laide the methode of my ſonnes happy and vertuous gouernment, beeing princely wedded to the higher, and affable to the lower, a Mother to them that were in want, and a Nurſe to the diſtreſſed ; I counted my glorie the more, and my fortune the greater, in that I was guarded with my three daughters, Virgins adorned ſo with excellent qualities both of mind and body, I meane as well exteriour fauours as interiour vertues, that fame made report of their honors, not only through all *Taprobane,* but through all the Ilands adiacent, eſpecially of my eldeſt daughter, called (for her beauty in her cradle) *Fiordeſpine* : Nature had ſo inricht her with ſupernaturall beauty, that ſhee / ſeemed an immortall creature, ſhrowded in a mortall carcaſe, inſomuch that if her times had been equall with *Troy, Paris* had left *Greece,* and come to *Taprobane* for her loue.   Liuing thus loued and admired of all : ſelfe-loue the moth that creepeth into young mindes, ſo tickled her with the conceit of her owne beauty, that ſhee counted no time well ſpent which ſhe beſtowed not in ſetting out that

more glorious by Art, which Nature had made fo
abfolute and excellent: no drugges from *Arabia*,
that might cleere the fkinne, were vnfought for:
no herbes nor fecrets that any Philofopher in
Phyficke had found out, which might increafe
beautie, but fhe made experience of : following
Venus euery way in fuch vanities, and playing the
right woman : for, to confeffe the truth, their fexe
careth more for the tricking of their faces, than the
teaching of their foules, fpending an houre rather
in righting the treffes of their haire, than a moment
in bending their thoughts to deuotion. The fouleft
muft be faire, if not in deed, yet in conceit : and
fhe that is faire muft venter her foule to keep her
beauty inuiolate: but leauing off this digreffion, my
daughter *Fiordefpine* being thus felfe conceited, was
more curious than wife, and could fooner afford a
pound of pride, then an ounce of humility : for
diuers Noble men reforted from all the bordering
Ilands to be futors vnto her, but her beauty made
her fo coy, that happy was hee that might haue
a glance of her perfection. So that many came
ioyful in hope to haue fauor, but departed forrowfull, anfwered with difdaine. For as none pulleth
vp the barran root, but he is ftifled with the fauour:
as none looketh into the poole of *Babylon*, but he
hafardeth his health : as none gafeth againft the
Cockatrice, but either hee lofeth his fight, or his

life; fo none tooke view of the beauty of *Fiorde-fpine*, but they returned either frantike in affection, fond with fancy, or pained with a thoufand perplexed paffions. Yet fhe taking delight in their griefes, refembled the Cryfolite, which the more it is beaten with hammers, the harder it is, and as the Palme / tree can by no meanes be depreffed, nor the Margarites of *Europe* wrought into no other forme, than Nature hath fram'd them: fo no praiers, promifes, paffions, fighes, forrowes, plaints, teares nor treaties could preuaile, to make her fhowe fome fauour to any of her futors. In fo much that the poore Noble men finding themfelues fettered, without hope of freedome, feeing their liberties reftrained within an endleffe labyrinth, and no courteous *Ariadne* to giue them a clew of threed to draw them out of their miferies, cried out againft loue, againft *Venus*, againft women, as mercileffe monfters, hatched to torture the mindes of men: and at laft fpying their owne follies, fhaking off the fhackles of loue with difdaine, went home, and at their departure pronounced with *Demofthenes*, that they would not *Pœnitentiam tanti emere*. *Cupid* feeing how his fchollers flocked from his fchoole, thought hee would retaine fome one, with whom to dally ; and therefore pulling forth a fierce inflamed arrow, hee ftrooke the fonne of a Noble man here in *Taprobane* to the quicke, that he

of all the reft remained faft fnared in her beauty :
his name was *Telegonus*, a youth euery way equall
to *Fiordefpine*, except in parentage, and yet he was
no meaner man than the fon of an Earle. This
Telegonus (omitting his proportion and qualities,
for that it fhall fuffice to fay they were excellent)
hauing had a fight of *Fiordefpine*, ftood as the
Deere at the gaze, fwallowing vp greedily the
inuenomed hooke that *Venus* fo fubtilly had baited
for him: for after the Idea of her perfon and
perfection had made a deepe impreffion on his
minde, and that hee had paffed three or foure
daies in ruminating her excellency, and debated
in his bed with many [a] betweene flumber, how
fweete a faint fhe was, he fell from liking to
fo deepe loue, that nothing but death did rafe it
out.

And thus he marched vnder the ftandard of
fancy, being but a frefh water fouldier, to abide
the alarums of affection, feeling a reftleffe paffion
that fretted his minde, as the caterpiller the fruit,
he could not tell on which eare to fleep, but /
builded Caftles in the ayre, and caft beyond the
moone: firft, hee began to confider with himfelfe,
how many braue Noble men of fundry Ilands, rich
in poffeffions, honourable in parentage, in qualities
rare, in property excellent, had fought her loue,
and yet miffed. When hee had made comparifon

betweene himfelfe and them, defpaire began with
darke perfwafions to diffwade him from attempting
fuch high loues, knowing, that *Aquila non capit
mufcas* : Ladies of great beauty looke not at
meane perfonages: that *Venus* frowned on the
fmith with a rinkle on her forehead, when fhe
fmiled on *Mars* with a dimple on her chin.

Thefe premifes confidered, poore *Telegonus* fad,
nipped on the pate with thefe new thoughts, refembling the melancholy difpofition of *Troilus*, for the
inconftancy of *Creffida*, yet after hee had mufed
awhile, and paft ouer a fewe dreaming dumpes ;
Hope clad in purple futed robes, tolde him that
Cupid had but one ftring to his bowe, one head to
one arrow; that *Venus* greateft number was an
vnity, how the heart could harbour but one fancy
and one woman be wedded but to one man.
Therefore though they mift, as either infortunate,
or croffed by fome contrary influence, fith loues
fee fimple was regiftred in the court of their
deftinies, there was no caufe of his defpaire, but
that hee might bee the man that fhould enioy
Fiordefpine, and fet vp the trophee of loue, maugre
all the finifter determinations of *Cupid*. Floting
thus between defpaire and hope, he paffed ouer
three or foure dayes, melancholy and paffionate,
taking his only content in being folitary: fo that
at laft finding himfelfe all alone, feeling the fire too

great to fmother in fecrecy, he burft forth into
thefe flames.

Ah *Telegonus,* miferable in thy life, and infortunate in thy loues : is thy youth blafted with fancy,
or the prime of thy yeeres daunted with affeċtion :
canft thou no fooner fee *Paphos,* but thou muft
prouide facrifice for *Venus?* Canft thou not heare
the Syrens fing, but thou muft bend thy courfe to
their mufike? may not beauty kindle a fire, but
thou muft / ftraight ftep to the flame : wilt thou
dally with the flye in the candle, fport with the
Salamander in the heate of *Aetna,* and with *Troilus*
hazard at that which will breede thy harme?
Knoweft thou not loue is a frantike frenzie that fo
inforceth the minds of men, that vnder the tafte of
nurture, they are poifoned with the water of *Stix* :
for as hee which was charmed by *Laon,* fought ftill
to heare her inchauntment : or as the Deere after
he once broufeth on the Tamarifke, he will not be
driuen away untill he dyeth : fo Louers haue their
fenceleffe fences fo befotted with the power of this
lafciuious god, they count not themfelues happy,
but in their fuppofed vnhappineffe : beeing at moft
eafe in difquiet ; at greateft reft, when they are
moft troubled : feeking contentation in care, delight
in mifery, and hunting greedily after that which
alwaies breedeth endleffe harme. Yea but *Telegonus,*
beauty is therefore to be obeyed becaufe it is

beauty : and loue to be feared of men, becaufe it
is honoured of the gods. Dare reafon abide the
brunt, when beauty bids the battell : can wifedome
win the field, where loue is captaine ? No, no,
loue is without law, and therefore aboue all lawe :
honoured in heauen, feared in earth, and a very
terror to the infernall ghofts : Bow then vnto that
Telegonus, whereunto lawleffe neceffity doth bend :
be not fo fond, as with *Zeuxes* to bind the Ocean
in fetters : fight not with the *Rafcians* againft
the wind : bark not with the Wolues againft the
Moone : feeke not with them of *Scyros* to fhoot
againft the Starres : ftriue not with *Thefides* againft
Venus: for loue being on[ce] [al]lowd, lookes to command by power, and to be obeyed by force : truth
Telegonus, for *Iuno* ftroue but once with *Venus*, and
hee was vanquifhed : *Iupiter* refifted *Cupid*, but
hee went by the worft. It is hard for thee with
the Crabbe to ftriue againft the ftream, or to wraftle
with a frefh wound, left thou make the fore more
dangerous. Wel *Telegonus*, what of all this prate ?
thou doft loue : thou honoreft beauty as fuper-
natural : thou fayft, *Venus* amongft al the goddeffes
is moft mighty : that / there is no Iland like *Paphos*,
no bird like the doues, no god like *Cupid* : what
of this ? but why doft yᵘ loue no meaner woman
than *Fiordefpine*, the daughter of the Prince, the
faireft in *Taprobane* ? Ah *Telegonus*, derogate not

from her beauty, the faireſt in the world: vnhappy man in recounting her beauty, in reckoning
her perfections, thou doeſt imblaze thine owne
misfortunes: for the more ſhee is excellent, the
leſſe will be her loue, and the greater her diſdaine.
Can the Eagle and the blind Oſyphrage build in
one tree : will the Falcon & the Doue couet to
ſit on one pearch: will the Ape and the Beare be
tyed in one tedder : will the Fox and the Lambe
be in one den ; or *Fiordeſpine*, who thinketh her-
ſelfe fairer then *Venus*, ſtoope to the lure of one ſo
baſe as I ?   No, for the more beauty, the more pride
and the more pride, the more precifeneſſe.   None
muſt play on *Ormenes* harpe, but *Orpheus* : none
rule *Lucifer* but *Phœbus* : none weare *Venus* in a
tablet but *Alexander*, nor none enioy *Fiordeſpine*, but
ſuch a one as farre exceedeth thee in perſon and
perſonage.   Tuſh *Telegonus*, enter not into theſe
doubts : *Sapho* a Queene loued *Phao* a Ferri-man ;
ſhee beautiful and wiſe, he poore and ſeruile: ſhe
holding a ſcepter, hee an Oare; the one to gouerne,
the other to labour.   *Angelica* forſooke diuers
Kings and tooke *Medon* a mercenary Souldier :
Loue *Telegonus* hath no lack ; *Cupid* ſhooteth his
ſhafts at randon; *Venus* as ſoone looketh at the ſun,
as at a ſtar.   Loue feareth a Prince as ſoone as a
peaſant, and fancy hath no reſpect of perſons.

Then *Telegonus* hope the beſt : *Audaces fortuna*

3

*adiuuat : Loue and fortune fauoreth them that are
refolute.* The ftone *Sandaftra* is not fo hard, but
being heat in the fire it may be wrought : nor
Iuory fo tough, but feafoned with *Zathe* it may be
ingrauen. The gates of *Venus* temple are but halfe
fhut : *Cupid* is a churle and peremptory, yet to be intreated : women are wilful, but in fome meanes they
may be won : were fhe as full of beauty as *Venus*,
or as great in Maiefty as *Iuno.* Hope then the beft
and be bold : for cowards are admit/ted to put in
no plea at the barre of loue. *Telegonus* hauing, by
vttering thefe paffions, difburdened fome part of
his paines, and yet not in fuch fort, but his temples
were reftleffe, his griefe much, his content none at
all, his care in his fleepe inceffant, his mind melancholy, fo that his only delight was to be in dumpes ;
in fo much that he gadded folitary vp and downe
the Groues as a Satyre enamoured of fome Country
Nymph. *Cupid* feeing his art did well, thought
to fhewe him fome fport ; for on a day as hee
walked, contemplating the beauty of *Fiordefpine*,
being fore athirft with inward forrow, he went to
a fountaine hard by to coole his heate, where he
found his heart fet on fire with a great flame : for
there he efpied *Fiordefpine*, and her other two
fifters fitting folacing themfelues about the fpring :
which fodaine fight fo appalled his fenfes, as if he
had been appointed a new Judge to the three

goddeſſes in the valley of *Ida* : yet ſeeing before
his eyes the miſtris of his thoughts, and the ſaint
vnto whom he did owe his deuotion : hee began
to take heart at graſſe, thinking that by this fit
opportunity, Loue and Fortune began to fauour
his enterpriſe : willing therfore not to omit ſo good
an occaſion, he ſaluted them in this ſort.

Muſe not, faire creatures, if I ſtand in a maze,
ſith the ſight of your ſurpaſſing beauties makes me
doubt, whether I ſhould honour you as earthly
ladies, or adore you as heauenly goddeſſes : for no
doubt *Paris* neuer ſaw fairer in *Ida*. But now
noting with deep inſight the figure of your diuine
faces ; I acknowledge your honours to be ſiſters
to our prince, whom I reuerence, as allyed to my
ſouereigne, and offer my ſeruice, as a ſeruant euer
deuoted to ſuch faire and excellent ſaints.

The ladies hearing this ſtrange and vnlooked for
ſalutation, began to ſmile : but *Fiordeſpine* frowning, as halfe angry he ſhould preſume into her
preſence, with a coy countenance returned him this
anſwere.

If ſir *Telegonus*, for ſo I ſuppoſe is your name,
your eye/ſight be ſo bad, perhaps with peering too
long on your bookes, or your ſelfe ſo far beſide
your ſences, as to take vs for Nymphes : I would
wiſh you to read leſſe, or to prouide you a good
Phyſition, elſe ſhall you not iudge colours for me :

and yet fince I would you fhould know wee count our penny good filuer, and thinke our faces, if not excellent, yet fuch as may boote compare.

Telegonus taking opportunity by the forehead, and thinking to ftrike the yron at this heat, made reply.

Maiden, hee might be thought either blinde or enuious, that would make a doubt of *Venus* beauty, and he be deemed either frantike or foolifh, that cannot fee and fay, as you are fuperior to moft, fo you are inferiour to none. Pardon Madam, if my cenfure be particular, I meane of your fweet felfe, whofe fauours I haue euer loued and admired, though vnworthy to fet my fancy on fuch glorious excellency.

Fiordefpine hearing her felf thus praifed, was not greatly difpleafed, yet paft fhe ouer what was fpoken, as though her eares had beene ftopt, with *Vliffes* : but *Eriphila*, the fecond, who was as wife as her fifter was beautifull, defired *Telegonus* to reft him by them on the graffe, and that they would at their departure afke him as a guard to the court: *Telegonus* as glad of the command, as if he had been willed by the gods to haue been chamberlaine to *Venus*, fate downe with a mind full of paffions, hauing his eye fixed ftill on the beautie of *Fiorde-fpine* : which *Eriphila* efpying, thinking to be pleafant with *Telegonus*, fhe began thus to prattle.

Your late paffionate fpeech *Telegonus*, to my fifter *Fiordefpine*, makes me think that *Venus* is your chiefe goddeffe, and that loue is the lord, whofe liuery your weare : if it be fo, neighbour take heede (for fancie is a Shrew) : many like, that are neuer loued : *Apollo* may cry long after *Daphne* before fhe heare him : and *Troilus* may ftand long enough on the walls before *Crefida* waue her gloue for a falue. I fpeak *Telegonus* againft our felues : take heed, we be coy, and wily : we with our lookes can change men, though *Venus* will weare / the target, and *Mars* the diftaffe, *Omphalo* handle the club, and *Hercules* the fpindle : *Alexander* muft crouch and *Campafpe* looke coy : women will rule in loues, howfoeuer men bee lofty in courage. Indeed Madam, quoth *Telegonus*, him whom no mortall creature can controll, loue can command : no dignity is able to refift *Cupids* deitie. *Achilles* was made by his mother *Thetis* invulner- able, yet wounded by fancie : *Hercules* not to be conquered of any, yet quickly conquered by affection : *Mars* able to refift *Iupiter*, but not to withftand beautie. Loue is not onely kindled in the eye by defire, but ingrauen in the minde by deftinie, which neither reafon can efchew, nor wifedome expell : the more pittie I confeffe Madam, for poore men, and the greater impietie in the gods, that in giuing loue free libertie, they

grant him a lawleffe priuiledge : but fince *Cupid*
will bee obeyed, I am contented to bowe: efpecially,
feeing I haue chanced to fet my affection on fo
excellent a creature.

And who might that be, I pray you, (quoth
Fiordefpine) (taking the matter in dudgen, that
Telegonus fhould make report) that is of fuch
great excellencie ? dwelleth fhee in *Taprobane* ? In
Taprobane Madam, replied *Telegonus*, but with fuch
a peale of fighes, bewraying his loues in filence : that
Eriphila fmiling, fayd ; I fee fire cannot be hidden
in the Flaxe without fmoke, nor Mufke in the
bofome without fmell, nor loue in the breft without
fufpition : I perceiue, in faith neighbour, by your
lippes what lettice you loue : the faint that you
account of fuch excellency, whofe perfection hath
fo fnared your fences, is my fifter *Fiordefpine*. I,
quoth *Fiordefpine*, filling her Iuory browes full of
Shrewifh wrinkles, I hope the young lord *Telegonus*
knowes what Suters I haue fhaken off : and therefore not inferring comparifons, becaufe they bee
odious, I may giue him his anfwere with an &c.
There are more Maydes then Maulkin, and more
birds for the Faulcon to pearch with, then the
Eagle : the Lyon is a bloudy / beaft, for that he
knoweth his ftrength : I will not conclude, but lord
Telegonus, if I be the woman you mean, ceafe from
your fute : for in faith fo well I doe loue you,

that you cannot more difpleafe mee, then in feeking
to pleafe mee: for if I knew no other caufe to
miflike, yet this might fuffice, that I cannot loue.
At this flat and peremptorie anfwere, *Telegonus* fate
nipped on the pate, like to them which tafte of the
fifh *Mugra*, whofe operation maketh them for a
time fenceleffe : which *Eriphila* efpying, thinking
to iumpe euen with the Gentleman, pittying his
paffions, in that *Fiordefpine* was fo coy to fo
courteous a Youth, fayd : You may fee now
Telegonus, that *Venus* hath her frownes, as fhee
hath fmiles: that *Cupid* hath arrowes headed with
lead to procure difdaine, as well as with golde
to increafe loue: heare mee that am a Virgin, as
dutifull to *Vefta*, as reuerent to *Venus*.

The paines that louers take, for hunting after
loffe, if their mindes were not confirmed with fome
fecret inchantment, were able to keepe their fancies
from being inflamed, or elfe to coole defire alreadie
kindled : for the daies are fpent in thoughts and
the nights in dreames : both in danger, either of
beguiling vs of that wee had, or promifing vs that
wee haue not. The head fraught with fantafies,
fiered with ielofie, troubled with both : yea fo
many inconueniences waite vpon loue as to reckon
them all, were infinite : and to tafte but one of
them were intollerable, being alwaies begun with
griefe, continued with forrow, and ended with

death: for it is a paine fhadowed with pleafure,
and a ioy ftuffed with mifery. So that I cõclude,
that as none euer fawe the altars of *Bufiris* without forrow, nor banqueted with *Phœbus* without
furfetting : fo as impoffible it is to deale with
Cupid, and not either to gaine fpeedie death, or
endleffe danger : As I was ready in defence of
loue to make reply, there came a little page from
their lady mother, to call them home to dinner :
wherupon they all rofe, and would haue taken
their leaue, but boldly I ftood / to my tackling, and
told them : Ladies you paffe not fo ; for conftrue
my meaning how you pleafe, or accept of my repay
how you lift, I will not bee fo difcourteous to
leaue you fo flenderly garded, as in the guard of
this little page : and with that I conducted them
vnto the court, and there with a loth to depart,
tooke my leaue, hauing a courteous farewell of all
but *Fiordefpine* : who frowning like *Iuno*, in her
maieftie gaue mee a niggardly *A dio* with a nod :
which notwithftanding, loue commanded me to
take as a prodigall courtefie. Well, *Telegonus* thus
left alone, fearing too much folitarineffe might
breede intemperate paffions, went home, mufing
on the ftrange qualities of his miftreffe : where
cafting himfelfe on his bed, he began to confider,
that as fhe was beautifull, fo fhe was proud ; and
that her exteriour fauour was blemifhed with an

interiour difdaine : that *Venus* was as much defpifed
for her lightneffe, as honoured for her deity : that
the blacke violet was more efteemed for her fmell,
then the Lilly for her whiteneffe : that the darkeft
Topas was held more precious then the brighteft
Cryftall : and women are to bee meafured by their
vertues, and not by their beauties : And why doft
thou vrge this *Telegonus,* for that fhee hath not
fawned on thee at the firft meeting, giuen ouer the
fort at the firft affault, and confented to thy loue
at the firft motion ? wouldeft thou haue her fo
light, fond youth, as to ftoope to the lure at the
firft call ? *Helena* was wanton, yet was fhee long
in wooing : *Paris* courted her before he caught
her : if a ftraggler made it ftrange, blame not her
that is vertuous and a Virgin, if fhe be fomewhat
coy : refting in this hope, he fomewhat appeafed
his paffions, driuing away his melancholy and
defpairing humours, by fetting his reft on this
point. But loue that is impatient, was in the day
his companion, and in the night his pillow : *Venus*
commanded her fonne to be beaten with Rofes,
which as they are faire coloured, and fauour fweet,
fo they are full of prickes, and pierce the fkin :
Loue, thus hammering in the head of *Telegonus,*
hee was doubt / full what to do, or how beft to
profecute his purpofe : to repaire to the court, and
there to court her, was to attempt an aduenture

very perilous and halfe impoſſible: to ſeeke meanes to parle with her, was to offer blank papers to *Venus*: therefore he reſolued to write vnto her, and therupon entering into his ſtudie, hee tooke pen and paper, and ſent vnto her in this effect.

Telegonus, to Fiordeſpine, health.

THey (honourable *Fiordeſpine*) that are in-uenomed with the *Hidaſpis*, if they preſently diſcouer not their paine, periſh : ſuch as are ſtung with the *Tarantula*, muſt haue muſicke at their eare before the poiſon come at their heart : *Venus* temple is neuer ſhut: *Cupids* regiſter euer vnfolded, and the ſecrets of loue, if they bee concealed, breed either danger by ſilence, or death by ſecrecy : I ſpeake this by experience, for the deepe impreſſion of your diuine beauty, counited with the admira-tion of your excellent vertues, haue printed ſuch a character in my thoughts, ſince firſt I ſawe your ſweet ſelfe, as either muſt bee confirmed with your mercie, or I ſhall be confounded with miſery : where *Cupid* ſtriketh, there no ſalues can preuaile, where loue ſerueth his writ of commaund, there a Superſedeas of reaſon is of no auaile.

Beauty forceth the gods, and therefore may fetter men : but perhaps your honor will ſay, that

the Fox is no phere for the Lion : none fo meane
a man as I worthy to gaze at fo glorious a perfonage, fo that I may rather be counted impudent
than paffionate, in attempting that which fo many
my betters haue miffed.

To this obiection giue mee leaue to fay, that
Venus refpecteth not the robes, but the minde : not
the parentage but the / minde : not the Parentage,
but the perfon : not the wealth, but the heart :
not the honours but the loyaltie : if then faith in
fancie, not poffeffions, are to bee refpected, I hope,
as Nature by her fecret iudgement hath endewed
al creatures with fome perfect quality, where want
breeds miflike : as the Mole depriued of fight, hath
a wonderful hearing : the Hare being very feareful,
is moft fwift : the Fifh hauing no eares, hath moft
cleere eyes : fo I, of parentage meane, of wealth
little, of wit leffe; yet haue I giuen mee, by nature,
fuch a loyall heart, as I hope the perfection of the
one fhall fupply the want of the other, coueting
not to rule as a Hufband, but to liue dutifull and
louing euer to the Lady *Fiordefpine.*

Blame me not Madame, if I pleade with my
penne, for euer fince I fell into the labyrinth of
your lookes, I haue felt in my heart, as in a little
worke, all the paffions and contrarieties of the
elements : for mine eyes (I call the gods to witneffe,
I fpeake without fayning) almoft turne into water,

through the continuall ſtreames of teares, and my ſighes flie as winde in the ayre, proceeding from the flaming fire which is kindled in my heart, as that without the droppes of your pittie, it will turne my bodie into drie earth and cinders.

Then *Fiordeſpine*, ſith your beauty hath giuen the wound, let it like *Achilles* ſpeare, cure the ſame ſore : couet not to ſet out the trophe of diſdaine, where already you are conquered: ſtriue not for life, ſith you haue any liberty, but fetch water from the fountaine of *Alcidalie*, ſimples from the hill *Erecius*, conſerues from the temple of *Venus*, to appeaſe that paſſion that otherwiſe cannot be cured : render but loue for loue, yea Madame, ſuch loue as time ſhall neuer blot out with obliuion, neither any ſiniſter fortune diminiſh. So that if the world wondred at the loyalty of *Petrarch* to his *Lawra,* or of *Amadis* to his *Gryance*, they ſhall haue more cauſe to maruell at the loue of *Telegonus* to *Fiordeſpine*, whoſe life and death ſtandeth in / your anſwere, which I hope ſhall bee ſuch as belongeth to the deſert of my loue, and the excellencie of your beautie.

Yours, if he be

Telegonus of *Taprobane*.

*T*Elegonus hauing finiſhed this letter, cauſed it to be deliuered to *Fiordeſpine* with great truſtineſſe and ſecrecie, who receiuing it with a frowning

looke, as halfe fufpecting the contents, yet vnripped
the feales and read it : which when fhee had
throughly perufed, draue her into fuch a furie,
that fhee in a rage rent it, and flung it into the fire,
faying : There end his letters and his loues. But
as the Sea once hoyfed with a gale, calmeth not till
it hath paffed with a ftorme : as the ftone *Pyrites*
once fet on fire burneth in the water : fo a womans
ftomacke once ftirred, ceafeth not to be difcontent,
till it bee glutted with reuenge : for, *Fiordefpine*
not fatisfied with tearing the letter of *Telegonus*,
could take no reft, till either fhee had breathed
out fome hard fpeeches with her tongue, or fet
downe bitter taunts with her pen : feeing therefore
no fit meanes for the one, fhee ftept in great choller
to her ftandifh, and wrote to him thus fatyrically.

Fiordefpine to Telegonus.

THough *Vulcan* with his polt foote prefumed to
couet the queene of beauty : though *Ixion*
aduentured to attempt the loue of *Iuno*: yet lord
Telegonus, no offence to your perfon, thefe paltring
prefidents are no conclufions that perfons vnworthy
fhould difgrace, by their impudent and worthleffe
motions, the honours of excellent perfonages.
How I am greeued at your letters, geffe by my

fharp reply: how I like of your lines, examine in my writing : how I difdaine them both, time fhall put you in euidence. My beautie, you fay, hath made an impreffion in your heart: a man of foft metall, that fo foone takes the ftampe; a louer of great conceit, that is fixed at the firft looke : but fince it is your gentle nature to be fo full of fancie, I would haue the gods to make you either *Venus* chamberlaine, or *Cupids* chaplaine, or both : becaufe being fo amorous, you fhould not want offices : you foreftalled me in red letters, / with an obiection that many your betters haue courted me and mift: then good louely lord *Telegonus*, thinke not, if I delighted not to gaze at ftars, that I meane to ftumble at ftones : if I vouchfafe not to fmel to moft fragrant flowers, that I mean to make me a nofegay of weeds. If honorable princes offered to *Venus*, and could not be heard, and fought for my fauours but found them not, I thinke : fuppofe the reft, for I lift not to be tedious, left I fhould weary my felfe, and grace thee with writing fo much. For thy loyalty keep it for thy equals : for thy loue, lay it not on me, left as I difdaine thy perfon, fo I reuenge thy prefumption. And fo my hand was weary, my eyes fleepie, and my heart full of contempt, and with that I went to bed.

Her owne *Fiordefpine*

of *Taprobane*.

This letter was no fooner fealed, but (as women are impatient of delaies) it was conuied with all poffible fpeed to *Telegonus* ; who receiuing it, kiffed and rekiffed it, as comming from the hands of his goddeffe, changing colour oft, as one betweene feare and hope : at laft vnripping the feales, he read fuch a corafiûe, as cut him to the heart. The Afpis ftingeth not more deadly, the ferpent *Porphirius* inuenometh not more deepely, neither did euer the fight of *Medufas* head more amaze a man, than the contents of this fatyricall letter did *Telegonus* : yea it draue the poore Gentleman into fo many paffions, that he became halfe lunaticke, as if hee had eaten of the feed of fputanta, that troubleth the braine with giddineffe : he fell to exclaime againft *Venus* and her deitie, blaming the gods that would fuffer fuch a gigglet to remaine in heauen, repeating her lawleffe loues with *Adonis*, and her fcapes with *Mauors*. *Cupid* he called a boy, a fondling, blind in his ayme, and accurfed in hitting the marke : rageth againft women, faying, they were mercileffe, cruell, vniuft, deceitfull, like vnto the Crocodile in teares : in fight, they feem to be Carnations ; in fmelling, Rofes ; in hearing, Syrens ; in tafte, worme-wood ; in touching, nettles : Thus he rayled and raged, cafting himfelfe on his bed, and there forging a thoufand perplexed paffions, one while accufing loue as a lunacie, and then againe faying : Beautie was diuine, and the richeſt iewell that euer nature beſtowed vpon men. Lingring a day or two in this frenzie, he thought not to giue ouer the Caſtle at the firſt repulſe, nor to prooue ſo lewd a Huntſman as to giue ouer the chaſe at the firſt default : therefore he once again armed himſelfe with his pen and paper, and gaue a freſh alarum to his friendly foe in this manner. /

Telegonus to faire Fiordeſpine, of Taprobane.

H Onourable Ladie, the Phyſicians ſay, ſalues feldome helpe an once long ſuffered ſore, and too late it is to plant Engines to batter, when the walls are already broken.   Autumne ſhowres are euer out of ſeaſon, and too late it is to diſlodge loue out of the breſt, when it hath infeſted euery part of the body.   The ſore, when the feſtering fiſtula hath by long continuance made the ſound fleſh rotten, can neither with lenitiue plaiſters, nor cutting coraſiues, be cured : ſo loue craueth but onely time to bring the body and mind to ruine.   Your honor ſeeing how deeply I am deuoted to your beauty and vertue, hath ſent mee pilles of hard digeſtion, to aſſwage the force of my loue, and qualifie the flame ſet on fire by fancy ; but as the biting of the Viper rankleth, til it hath brought the body bitten

to bane: fo your exquifite perfection hath fo pierced
euery veine with the fting of loue, that neither
your bitter reply, nor fatyrical inuectiue, can in any
wife preuaile / : only the mild medicine of your
mercie may falue the fore, and cut away the caufe
of my carefull difeafe.

The extremity of my loue, and the violence of
my paffions, hath forced mee to hazard my felfe on
your clemencie : for I was neuer of that minde to
count him martiall, that at the firft fhoot would
yeeld vp the keyes of the Citie ; for the more
hard the rebut is, the more hautie is the conqueft ;
the more doubtfull the fight, the more worthy the
victorie ; the more paine I take about the battery,
the more pleafure to win the bulwarke of your
breft, which if I fhould obtaine, I would count it a
more rich prize, then euer *Scipio,* or any of the nine
Worthies wonne by conqueft, and that thefe words
/ be verity, and not vanity, troth, and not trifling ;
I appeale to your good grace and fauor, minding
to be tried by your courtefie, abiding either the
fentence of confent vnto life, or deniall vnto death.

Yours, euen after death
Telegonus of *Taprobane.*

THis letter finifhed and fent vnto *Fiordefpine,* fo
troubled her patience, for that *Telegonus* was
importunate, that fhe fared like the frownes of

Bacchus, halfe mad at this secret motion, swearing reuenge, if either her selfe or her friends could performe it : and in this humor she sent him by her Page, these few lines.

✠✠✠✠✠✠✠✠✠✠✠✠✠✠✠✠✠

Fiordespine to Telegonus.

I Had scarce read thy letters before I rent them, esteeming thy papers and thy loue alike ; for as I mislike the one, so I disdaine the other. Hath ouer-much folly driuen thee into a frensie, or hath want of manners made thee impudent ? Wilt thou bragge with *Irus* the begger amongst *Penelopes* sutors, or seeke with the smoky *Cyclops* to kisse *Venus* hand ? looke on thy feete, and so let fall thy plumes : stretch not so high, vnlesse thy sleeue were longer : for *Fiordespine* scorneth so much as to looke at *Telegonus* in respect of loue, as *Iuno* did to iest with the father of the Centaures.

If I knew thy passions were as great, as thou deciphereft thy griefe, and thy thoughts as fiery as the hils in *Sycily*, I would laugh at the one, as ioying at thy sorrowes, and put oyle in the flame, as delighting to aggrauate thy miseries. / Sith then thou seeft my resolution to be so rigorous (ouer-rash youth) betake thee to thy dumpes, and fare how thou lift: for know, I mislike thy sute, and hate thy perfon, and will liue and dye thine enemy, if for no other caufe, yet for that thou haft dared to court *Fiordefpine*.

Thy mortall enemy
Fiordefpine of *Taprobane*.

AFter that *Telegonus* had read this letter, fawced with fuch peremptory difdaine, hee fell in a trance, lying in his bed as a dead carcafe : but when he was come to himfelf, hee fell into fuch extreme paffions, that his father and his friends comming into the Chamber, thought him poffeffed with fome fpirit : the Phyfician felt his pulfes, and found hee had a found body: whereupon they did coniecture it was loue : and to verifie the fame, after he had raifed himfelf vp in his bed, with a gaftly looke, he cryed nothing but *Fiordefpine* : fetching fuch greeuous grones & deepe fighes, that all the chamber fell into teares : whereupon the old Earle, hauing his haire as white as fnowe, came himfelf trudging to the Court, telling the extreme paffion of his fon, entreating *Fiordefpine* that fhe would fo much as vouchfafe to come to his houfe, onely with her prefence fomewhat to mitigate his fonnes paffions: but fuch was the pride and difdaine of my daughter, that neither the teares of the olde Earle, the intreaty of my fon, nor my command, could preuaile with her, infomuch that the old man returned comfortleffe and forrowing. Well, Telegonus lying thus diftreft by the fpace of a weeke, at laft faining himfelfe to amend, would needes walk abroad that he might be folitary, and ftumbled weake as hee was into this vale, and to this place, where fitting downe he fell into thefe paffions: Infortunate Telegonus, whofe ftars at thy natiuity were in fome curfed afpect, why didft thou not perifh at thy birth, or how did fortune frowne that / thou wert not ftifled in thy fwadling cloathes? now growne to ripe yeeres, thou feeleft more miferies than thou haft liued moments : ah loue, that labyrinth that leadeth men to worfe dangers then the Mynotaure in Greece : loue that kindleft defire, but alloweft no reward : inconftant Venus, whofe facrifices fauour of death, whofe lawes are tyrannous, whofe fauours are misfortunes ! ftrumpet as thou art; (for I difdaine to call thee goddeffe) thou and the baftard brat thy fonne, fhew your power, your deitie : reuenge my blafphemies how you can ; for how great foeuer your choller be, my calamitie cannot be more. Mercileffe women, whofe faces are lures, whofe beauties are baites, whofe lookes are nets, whofe words are charmes, and all to bring men to ruine. But of all, cruel Fiordefpine, borne of a Tyger, and nurfed of the fhee Wolues in Syria : whofe heart is full of hate, whofe thoughts are difdaine, whofe beautie is ouerlaid with pride

Let *Venus*, if fhee haue any iuftice, or *Cupid*, if he
haue the equitie of a god, make thee loue where
thou fhalt be miflikt. Alas *Telegonus*, ceafe not
with thefe praiers, the reuenge is too eafie, but cry
to the bitterneffe of thy paffions, that they quit
thy reuenge againft *Fiordefpine* : and with this his
fpeech ceafing, hee beat himfelfe againft the ground
in fuch pitifull fort, that the gods tooke compaffion,
and refolued reuenge. But while hee lay thus
perplexed, his father mift him, and taking fome of
his Gentlemen with him, fought him, and found
him in this Valley, paffionate and fpeechleffe. The
rumour of *Telegonus* diftreffe came to the Court :
whereupon, I, and my fonne, with my other two
daughters fo intreated *Fiordefpine*, that fhe granted
to go fee the Gentleman : walking therfore to
this place, here we found him accompanied with
his friends, all fignifying with teares, how they
greeued at his mifhap. *Telegonus* no fooner fawe
Fiordefpine, but turning himfelfe vpon the graffe
with a bitter looke, hee firft gazd her on the face,
then lifting vp his eyes to heauen, gaue a great
figh, as though his heart-ftrings had broke : which
/ *Fiordefpine* perceiuing, triumphing in the paffions
of her louer, fhee turned her backe and fmiled.
Scarce had fhe fram'd this fcornefull countenance,
but *Mercury* fent from the gods in a fhepherds
attire, fhooke her on the head with his Caduceus,

and turned her into this marble picture : which we amazed at, and *Telegonus* noting, turning himfelfe on his left fide, groned forth thefe words, the gods haue reuenged, and I am fatisfied : and with that hee gaue vp the ghoft.   The old Earle greeued at the death of his fonne, taking vp his body, departed : I forrowing at the Metamorphofis of my daughter, wept : but to fmall effect : for euer fince fhe hath remained, as thou feeft, a wonder to the world, and a perpetuall griefe to me.

Thus (fonne) haft thou heard the difcourfe of my daughters misfortune, which hath not been fo delightfull for thee to heare, as greeuous for me to reueale : but feeing I am entred into the dif-coueries of their ills, no fooner fhall wee haue taken our repaft, but I will fhew thee what fortuned to her fecond fifter *Eriphila*, for I knowe the nature of men is defirous of nouelties : and with that taking mee by the hand, fhe went home to her Cottage.

The second Discourse.

WEe had no sooner dined with our homely
delicates, tempring our times with prattle
of *Fiordespine*, but *Alcida* rose vp, and walked to a
Groue hard by, a place interseamed with shrubbes,
but placed between two hills, like the suppofed
entrance of hell, as there seemed that melancholy
Saturne had erected an Academie. Entring into
this Groue, so thicke as *Phœbus* was denied paſſage,
wandring awhile by many vncoth paths, at / laſt
wee came into a faire place, where was a goodly
Spring : the ſituation round, enuironed with trees :
hard by this fount, ſtood two Cedars, tall and
ſtraight, on whoſe barke was curiouſly engrauen
certaine Hierogliphicall Embleames : on the one
was carued *Mercury* throwing feathers into the
winde, and vnder was written theſe verſes.

The richeſt gift the wealthy heauen affords,
The pearle of price ſent from immortall *Ioue*,
The ſhape wherein we moſt reſemble gods,
The fire *Prometheus* ſtole from lofty ſkies :
This gift, this pearle, this ſhape, this fire is it,
Which makes vs men, bold by the name of wit.
By wit we ſearch diuine aſpect aboue,
By wit we learne what ſecrets ſcience yeelds,

By wit we fpeake, by wit the mind is rul'd,
By wit we gouerne all our actions :
Wit is the Load-ftarre of each humane thought,
Wit is the toole, by which all things are wrought.
The brighteft Iacynth hot becommeth darke,
Of little fteeme is cryftal being crackt,
Fine heads that can conceit no good, but ill,
Forge oft that breedeth ruine to themfelues :
Ripe wits abuf'd that build on bad defire,
Do burne themfelues like flyes within the fire.

On the other Cedar, was cut very cunningly
Cupid blowing bladders in the ayre : the poefie
vnder written was this.

Loue is a locke that linketh noble mindes,
Faith is the Key that fhuts the fpring of loue,
Lightneffe a wreft, that wringeth all awry,
Lightneffe a plague, that fancie cannot brooke :
Lightneffe in loue, fo bad and bafe a thing,
As foule difgrace to greateft States do bring. /

As I was reading thefe verfes, from the thicket
there came a bird flittering, of colour gray, which
houered ouer the head of *Alcida*, as though fhe
had faluted her with her wings : I maruelled at
the familiaritie of the fowle, and with that fhe
changed colours, from gray to white, and then to
redde, fo to greene : and as many fundry fhapes, as

euer *Iris* blazed in the Firmament: fo that by the
changing of hiewes, I perceiued it to be *Cameleon*:
As thus I ftood mufing at the bird, *Alcida* tooke
me by the hand, and fate downe at one of the roots
of the Cedars, bidding mee be attentiue, and fhee
would difcourfe the euill fortune of her fecond
daughter, *Eriphila*: the which I willingly confented
vnto: fhee began her tale in this manner.

The Second Hiftorie of ERIPHILA of Taprobane.

AFter that my daughter *Fiordefpine* was metamorphofed by the gods, in reuenge of her cruelty
to *Telegonus* ; time hauing rooted out fome part of
my forrowes, I beganne to folace my felfe with the
other two daughters, *Eriphila* and *Marpefia*. This
Eriphila was as wittie, as her fifter was beautifull,
fo that fhe was admired in *Taprobane*, and all the
bordering regions about, accounted (though not in
yeeres, yet in wit) a *Sibil* : beeing able to anfwere
as darke an Enigma, as the fubtilleft *Sphinx* was
able to propound : and I tell thee, fonne, as fhe
was fauoured by *Pallas*, fo *Venus* was not behind
in her fauours : for fhe was beautifull, infomuch,
that thefe gifts co-vnited, made fundrie Suters
come from fundry coafts, to bee wooers to fuch a
wily Minion.

Amongft the reft, by fortune, there arriued in
this coaft, imbarked / in a fmall Pinace, the Dukes
fonne of *Maffilia*, called *Meribates* : who comming
on fhoare for frefh water, came to fee the Court
of *Taprobane* : where being greatly welcommed by
my fonne, falling into talk with my daughter, hee
found *Eriphila* fo adorned with a fupernaturall
kinde of wit, as hee was fnared in the fweetneffe
of her anfweres : fwallowing downe the conceit of
her wifedome with fuch greedineffe, that hee lay
drunke in the remembrance of her qualities; finding feuerall delayes to make ftay in the country
couertly : caufing his Mariners to crack their
tackling, to vnrigge their Shippe in the night, that
they might haue iuft caufe to lye there the moft
part of that Summer. Loue beginning to make
this youngfter politike, caught him fo faft by the
heart, that *Mars* was neuer more feately intangled
in *Vulcans* net, nor the forerunners of *Iafon* more
fubtilly wrapped in the labyrinth, then *Meribates*
was in the fnares of fancie : for what he talked,
euen amongft the meaneft of his Mariners, was of
Eriphila : his thoughts, his mufing, his determinations, his refolutions, his dayes watchings, his night
flumbers were of the excellent wit of *Eriphila*,
infomuch that loue lodged the Nouice vnder her
Canapie, where hee breathed out thefe paffions.

Infortunate *Meribates*, whom the enuious Fates

haue fcorned to make infortunate! Haſt thou
mann'd thy felfe in a Barke to fcoure the Seas, and
in this queſt art thou like to lofe thy fences?
Soughteſt thou to abide the pleafure of *Neptune,*
and art faine to ſtand to the courtefie of loue?
Haſt thou found flames amidſt the waues? Fire in
the water, and fancy where no affection was meant?
Well now I fee, that as the Bee, that flyeth from
flowre to flowre, hauing free choyfe to choofe at
libertie, is at laſt taken by the wings, and fo fettered:
In like manner, my fancy taking the view of manie
a face, hath a reſtraint of his freedome, and is
brought into bondage with the wit of a ſtranger:
But *Meribates,* wilt thou loue fo lightly? Shall /
fancy giue thee the foile at the firſt daſh? Shall
thine eares bee the caufe of thy mifery? Wilt
thou with *Vliſſes* heare the *Syrens* fing, liſten to
their melody, and runne vnto endleſſe misfortune?

Eriphila is wife, fo was *Helena,* yet ſhee played
the wanton with *Paris*: ſhee aunfweres like the
Virgin at *Delphos,* and her words are as *Nectar.*
Rofes are fweete, yet they haue prickes: the pureſt
hunny Bee is not without his ſting: wit in a woman
is like Oyle in the flame, which either kindleth to
great vertue, or extreme vanity: Well *Meribates,*
howfoeuer it bee, wit cannot bee placed fo bad but
it is precious? What is beauty but a colour daſht
with euery breath, a flowre nipt with euery froſt, a

fauour that time and age defaceth : whereas wit
increaſeth by yeeres ; and that loue continueth
longeſt, that is taken by the eare, not by the eye :
yeeld then *Meribates*, when thou muſt needes con-
ſent ; runne when thou art called by command :
Pallas is wife, and will not bee ingratefull to her
votaries : ſay none, but *Eriphila* : for ſure, if euer
thou wilt beſtowe thy freedome, ſhee is worthy to
haue thee captiue.   If thou meaneſt to marrie, thou
canſt not haue a meeter match : yea, but how if
her heart be placed, and her mind ſettled vpon
ſome Gentleman in *Taprobane?* then were I a great
deale better to wayle at the firſt, then to weepe at
the laſt : to be content with a little pricke, then a
deepe wound ; to reſiſt loue at the brimme than
at the bottome.

   The Scorpion, if he touch neuer ſo lightly
inuenometh the whole body : the leaſt ſparke of
wilde fire will ſet an whole houſe on flame : the
Cockatrice killeth euen with his ſight : the ſting
of loue woundeth deadly : the flame of fancy ſets
on fire all the thoughts ; and the eyes of a louer
are counted incurable.

   Fearefulneſſe (*Meribates*) in loue is a vertue :
haſt thou turned ouer ſo many bookes of Philoſophy, and haſt thou not quoted *Phocas* precept
to bee fruitfull? that louers ſhould / proceede
in their ſuite, as the Crabbe, whoſe pace is

euer backward ; that though loue bee like the
Adamant which hath vertue to drawe, yet thou
fhouldeft bee fprinkled with Goates bloud, which
refifteth his operation. If the wit of fome *Pallas*
Nymphes haue inclofde thy minde, yet thou
fhouldeft take the Oyle of *Nenuphar*, that cooleth
defire : what *Meribates*, wilt thou become a precife
Pythagoras, in recounting of loue ? No, let not
the precepts of Philofophy fubie&t the will of
nature ; youth muft haue his courfe : he that will
not loue when hee is young, fhall not bee loued
when hee is olde : fay then *Meribates*, and neuer
gaine-fay, that *Eriphila* is the marke thou [doft]
fhoote at : that her furpaffing wit is the *Syren*,
whofe fong hath inchanted thee : and the *Cyrces* cup
which hath fo fotted thy fences, as either thou muft
with *Vliffes* haue a fpeedy remedie, or elfe remaine
transformed. Confider *Meribates* the caufe of thy
loue, left thou faile in the effe&ts. Is the foundation of thy fancy fixed vpon her feature ;
think with thy felfe, Beautie is but a bloffome,
whofe flowre is nipt with euery froft : it is
like the graffe in *India*, which withereth before
it fpringeth : What is more faire, yet what more
fading ? What more delightfull, yet nothing
more deadly ? What more pleafant, and yet
what is more perilous ?

Beautie may well bee compared to the bath in

Calycut : whofe ftreams flow as cleere as the floud
Padus, and whofe operation is as peftilent, as the
riuer *Ormen* : I but *Meribates*, what more cleere
then the Cryftall, and what more precious? what
more comely then cloth of *Arras*, fo what more
coftly? what creature fo beautifull as a woman,
and what fo eftimable? Is not the Diamond of
greateft dignity that is moft gliftering: and the
pearle thought moft precious, that is moft perfect
in colour?

Ariftotle faith, they cannot be counted abfolutely
happy, although they had all the vertues, if they
want beautie : yea *Apollonius* (an arch-heretike,
and a profeffed enemy againft / the facred lawes of
beauty) is driuen both by the lawes of Nature, and
nurture, to confeffe that Vertue is the more accept-
able, by how much the more it is placed in a
beautifull bodie : but what long digreffed dis-
courfe is this thou makeft of beautie, *Meribates*?
it is not vpon fuch a fickle foundation thou buildeft
thy loue : but vpon her wit, which only parteth
with death : and therefore whatfoeuer Philofophie,
or learning wils, I will confent vnto nature, for the
beft Clarkes are not the wifeft men : whatfoeuer
wifdome wills, I wil at this time giue the crimes
of beautie to my amorous paffions; for he that
makes curiofitie in loue, will fo long ftraine courtefie, that either hee will be counted a folemne

futer, or a witleffe wooer: therefore, whatfoeuer the chance be, I will caft at all.

Meribates hauing thus debated with himfelfe, refted on this refolution : that he would moderate his affection, vntill he found opportunity to dis-courfe his mind to *Eriphila* : who on the contrary fide noting the perfectiō of *Meribates*, was more enamored of his perfon and qualities, then *Phillis* of *Demophon*, or *Dido* of the falfe and vniuft *Troian*: for he was fo courteous in behauiour, fo liberall not onely of his purfe, but his courtefie, that he had wonne all their hearts in *Taprobane*.

Thefe confiderations fo tickled the mind of *Eriphila*, that fhee fell thus to debate with her felfe. What meanes (*Eriphila*) thefe ftrange and fodaine paffions: fhall thy ftayed life be compared now to the *Camelion*, that turneth her felf into the likeneffe of euery obiect? to the herbe *Phanaros*, whofe budde is fweet, and the roote bitter? to the Rauens in *Arabia*, which being young, haue a pleafant voice, but in their age a horrible crie? Wilt thou confent vnto luft, in hoping to loue? Shall *Cupid* claime thee for his captiue, who euen now wert vowed a veftall Virgine? Shall thy tender age bee more vertuous then thy ripe yeeres? What, fhall the beauty of *Meribates* inchant thy minde, or his filed fpeech bewitch thy fences? Shall the property / of a ftranger drawe thee on to affection? If thou fhouldeft hap to like him, would hee not thinke the Caftle wanted but fcaling, that yeeldeth at the firft fhot? That the bulwarke wanteth but batterie, that at the firft parley yeeldes vp the keyes? Yes, yes *Eriphila,* his beauty argues inconftancy, and his painted phrafes deceit : and if he fee thee wonne with a word, hee will thinke thee loft with the winde : he will iudge that which is lightly to be gained, is as quickly loft.

The Hawke that commeth at the firft call, will neuer proue ftedfaft on the ftand. The Niefe that will be reclaimed to the fift, at the firft fight of the lure, will bate at euery bufh : the woman that will loue at the firft looke, will neuer be charie of her choyce. Take heed *Eriphila,* the fineft fcabbard hath not euer the braueft blade ; nor the goodlieft cheft hath not the moft gorgeous treafure : the Bell with the beft found hath an iron clapper : the fading apples of *Tantalus* haue a gallant fhewe, but if they be touched, they turne to afhes : So a faire face may haue a foule mind ; fweet words, a fowre heart : yea rotten bones out of a painted fepulchre ; for all is not gold that glifters. Why, but yet the Jemme is chofen by his hiew, and the cloth by his colour : condemne not then *Eriphila,* before thou haft caufe : accufe not fo ftrictly without tryall ; fearch not fo narrowly, till thou haft occafion of doubt.

Yea, but the Mariners found at the firſt, for feare of a Rocke: the Chirurgion tainteth betimes, for his fureſt proofe: one fore-wit is worth two after: it is not good to beware when the act is done: too late commeth repentance: what is the beauty of *Meribates* that kindleth this flame? who more beautifull then *Iaſon*, yet who more falſe? for after *Medea* had yeelded, he facked the fort, and in liew of her loue, he killed her with kind-neſſe. Is it his wit? who wiſer then *Theſeus*, yet none more traiterous?

Beware *Eriphila*, I haue heard thee ſay: ſhe that marries for beautie, for euery dramme of pleaſure, ſhall haue a pound / of ſorrow: chooſe by the eare, not by the eye. *Meribates* is faire, ſo was *Paris*, and yet fickle: hee is witty, ſo was *Corſiris*, and yet wauering: No man knoweth the nature of the hearbe by the outward ſhew, but by the inward iuice; and the operation confiſts in the matter, not in the forme.

The Foxe winnes the fauour of the Lambes by play, and then deuours them: ſo perhaps *Meribates* ſhewes himſelfe in outward ſhewe a demy god: whereas who tries him inwardly, ſhall finde him but a ſolemne faint. Why, ſince his arriuall in *Taprobane*, all the Iland ſpeakes of his vertue and courteſie: but perchance hee makes a vertue of his neede, and ſo layes this baulmed hooke of fained honefty, as a luring baite to trap fome fimple Dame.

The cloth is neuer tried, vntill it come to the wearing, nor the linnen neuer fhrinkes, till it comes to the wetting : fo want of liberty to vfe his will, may make a reftraint of his nature: and though in a ftrange place hee vfe faith and honefty to make his marriage, yet fhe perhaps that fhall try him, fhal either find he neuer had them, or quite forgot them: for the nature of men (as I haue heard fay) is like the Amber-ftone, which will burne outwardly, and frieze inwardly : and like the barke of the Mirtle trees that grow in *Armenia*, that is as hot as fire in the tafte, and as colde as water in the operation.

The dogge biteth foreft when he doth not barke: the Onix is hotteft, when it lookes white : the *Syrens* meane moft mifchiefe when they fing : the Tyger then hydeth his crabbed countenance when he meaneth to take his prey : and a man doth moft diffemble when hee fpeaketh faireft. Trie then *Eriphila* ere thou truft, efpecially fince hee is a ftranger : prooue ere thou put in practife : caft the water before thou appoint the medecine : doe all things with deliberation : goe as the Snaile, faire and foftly : hafte makes wafte : the malt is euer fweeteft, where the fire is fofteft : let not wit ouercome wifedome, nor the hope of a hufband be

the hafard / of thine honeftie : caft not thy credite
on the chance of a ftranger, who perchance may
proue to thee as *Thefeus* did to *Ariadne* : wade
not too far where the foord is vnknowne: rather
bridle thy affections with reafon, and mortifie thy
mind with modefty : that as thou haft kept thy
Virginitie inuiolate without fpot, fo thy choice
may bee without blemifh : know this, it is too late
to call againe the day paft : therefore keepe the
memorie of *Meribates* as needfull, but not neceffarie:
like him, whom thou fhalt haue occafion to loue,
and loue where thou haft tried him loyall : vntill
then remaine indifferent.

When *Eriphila* had vttered thefe words, fhe
ftraight (to auoide all dumpes that folitarineffe
might breede) came to me and her fifter, and there
paffed away the day in prattle. Thus thefe two
louers paffionate, and yet fomewhat patient, for
that hope had miniftred lenitiue plaifters to their
new wounds, paffed ouer two or three daies, onely
with glances and lookes, bewraying their thoughts
with their eyes, which they could not difcouer
with their tongues: *Venus* taking pitty of her
patients, found them out fo fit occafion, that as
Eriphila with her fifter *Marpefia* were walking
alone in the garden, gathering of flowers, at that
inftant (guided by loue and fortune) *Meribates*
went into the garden to be folitarie: where ftraight

he espied his miftris walking with her fifter : now
Meribates was driuen into an extafie, with the ex-
treeme pleafure hee conceiued in the fodaine fight
of his goddeffe : infomuch, as hee ftood amazed for
feare, and neceffity found a deadly combate in the
mind of *Meribates*: he doubted if he fhould be
ouer bold, to giue offence to *Eriphila*, and fo fpill
his pottage.   But the law of neceffitie (faith *Plato*)
is fo hard, that the gods themfelues are not able to
refift it : for as the water that by nature is cold, is
made hot by the force of fire, and the ftraight tree
preffed downe groweth alwayes crooked, fo nature
is fubie&t to neceffitie, that kind cannot haue his
courfe : and yet if there be any thing which is
more forcible then neceffitie, it / is the lawe of
loue ; which fo incenfed *Meribates*, that cafting all
feare afide, he offered himfelfe to his miftreffe,
with this courteous parle.

Gentlewomen, if my prefumption do trouble
your mufes, yet the caufe of my boldneffe deferueth
pardon, fith where the offence proceedeth of loue,
there the pardon enfueth of courfe : I ftood in a
maze at the firft fight, for meethought you refembled *Pallas* and *Iuno*, departing away from
Venus, after fhee had wonne the ball : you Madam
Eriphila, like the one for wit, and *Marpefia* like
the other for maieftie : but howfoeuer (fweet faints)
you grace this Garden with your prefence, as *Diana*

doth the Groues, and honour mee, in admitting ſo
vnworthy a man into the company of ſuch excellent perſonages. *Eriphila* hearing *Meribates* in
theſe tearmes, giuing a glory to her face, by
ſtaining her cheekes with a vermillion bluſh, both
ſharply and ſhortly made this reply.

It is neuer preſumption (lord *Meribates*) that
fortune preſents by chance, and therefore no
pardon, where is no offence : our muſing was not
great, onely gathering flowres, which wee like by
the hiew but know not by the vertue : herein
reſembling louers, that aiming at the faireſt, oft
ſtumble on ſuch as are little worth : If you haue
made vs any fault, it is in giuing ſo kinde a
frumpe, with your vnlikely compariſon : I being
as vnlike to *Pallas* in wit, as *Vulcan* to *Mars* in
property: and ſhee as far different from *Iuno* in
maieſtie, as olde *Bawcis* was to *Venus* in beauty :
but you Gentlemen of *Maſſilia* haue the habite of
ieſting, and therefore ſince it is a fault of Nature,
we brooke it, and beare with it.

Meribates hearing ſo courteous and witty an
anſwere ſwilled in loue as merrily as euer *Iupiter*
did vertue : ſo that delighting to heare his miſtreſſe
prattle, hee proſecuted his talke thus.

As I am glad, Madam, that my raſhneſſe was
no occaſion of offence, ſo I am ſorrie you take
what I vttered in earneſt, / to be ſpoken in ſport :

my comparifon as I inferred it, fo by your patience
I dare maintaine it, if not able by reafons, for that
I am no Scholler, yet by loue, for that I fhall drawe
mine arguments from fancie ; which hath fet on
fire a poore ftranger's heart, that he deemes your
fweet felfe not only like *Pallas*, but *Pallas* herfelfe:
fo that had I in this humour beene Judge for
Paris in the vale, wit (not beauty) had gotten
what they ftroue for.

I but fir (quoth *Marpefia*) from whence will you
drawe your arguments to prooue mee in maieftie
like *Iuno* ? you dare not fay, from reafon, in regard
ẏ the perfons are without compare ; and from
loue if you argue, you proue your felfe double-
faced like *Ianus*, and double-hearted like *Iupiter*,
to haue two ftrings to a bowe, and two loues at
one time.

Yes Madam, quoth *Meribates*, my common
place in this Enthymema fhall bee alfo from loue,
for in affecting fo dearely your fifter, I cannot but
deeply honour you, if not in loue as my Paramour,
yet in friendly affection as her fifter.

You harpe ftill, anfwered *Eriphila*, on one
ftring, which is loue : if you be in earneft, looke
for a frowne, as I gaue you a fauour : beleeue me,
lord *Meribates*, there is nothing eafier than to fall
in loue, nor harder than to chance well ; therefore,
omitting fuch ferious matter as fancie, for that I

am vowed to *Veſta*, tell mee, will you prouide you, as me, of a Noſegay ? And if you be ſo minded, tell me, of all flowers which like you beſt ? Thoſe, Madam, that beſt fit with my preſent humour. And what bee they, quoth *Marpeſia* ? Penſes, Madam, anſwered *Meribates*, for it is a prettie flowre, and of ſundrie colours, feeding the eye with varietie, which is the chiefeſt pleaſure to the ſight : eſpecially I like it for the agnonimation, in that the word comming from *France*, ſignifies fancies. Now how I am contented with fancies, I would you could as well ſee, as I feele. / One while imagination preſents vnto me the Idea of my miſtris face, which I allow with a fancie : another while a thought of her beautie wakens my ſences, which I conforme with a fancie : ſtraight her vertue ſayes ſhee is moſt excellent, which I gratifie with a fancie : then to ſeale vp what may bee ſayd, her care and ſupernaturall wit ſayes, her conceits are diuine, which auowed with a catalogue of ſolemne oathes, I ſet downe as a maxime, with a fancie.

Thus are my thoughts fed with fancies : and to be brief, my life is lengthened out by fancies : then Madam, blame me not if I like Penſes well ; and thinke nothing, if I ſet no other flowre in my noſe-gay. And truly lord *Meribates* anſwered *Eriphila*, you and I are of one mind, I meane in choice of

flowres, but not fir, as it is called a Penfe, or as
you defcant a fancie : but as we homely Hufwiues
call it, Hearts eafe, I banifh (as with a charme)
the frownes of fortune, and the follies of loue, for
the partie that is toucht by the inconftancy of the
one, or the vanitie of the other, cannot boaft hee
meaneth hearts eafe : feeing then it breedeth fuch
reft vnto the minde, and fuch quiet to the thoughts,
we will both weare this flowre as a fauour, you as
a Penfe, but I as a Hearts eafe.

As thefe two louers were thus merrily defcanting
vpon flowres, I came into the Garden, and found
this young lord and my daughter at chat : no
whit difpleafed, in that I knew the honour of his
houfe, his great poffeffions and parentage, I winkt
at their loues, and after a little ordinary parle
called them in to dinner : where there was fuch
banding of glances and amorous lookes, betweene
Meribates and *Eriphila,* as a blinde man might
haue feene the creeples hault : well, dinner being
ended, as *Meribates* entred into the confideration
of *Eriphilaes* wit; fo fhee more impatient, as the
horfe that neuer hauing felt the fpurre, runneth
at the firft pricke; fo fhe neuer hauing felt
before the like / flame, was more hot, and leffe
wearie, than if before fhe had beene fcorched with
affection.

Now fhe called him in her thoughts beautifull,

saying ; that the fayreſt and greeneſt herbes haue the moſt ſecret operation : ſhee ſayd hee was well proportioned, and ſo the reddeſt Margarites had the moſt precious vertues : that hee was vertuous: and then ſhee called to minde the olde verſe :

Gratior eſt pulchro veniens è corpore virtus.

But when ſhee weighed his wiſe and witty arguments that he vttered in the garden, how they not onely ſauored of wit, but of mirth : then

Omnia vincit amor, & nos cedamus amori.

Shee could not but in her conſcience ſweare, that hee ſhould be the ſaint at whoſe ſhrine ſhe would offer vp her deuotion. Theſe two louers thus liuing the more happily, for that they reſted vpon hope, it pleaſed my ſonne and mee to walke abroad into a parke hard adioining to the Court, and with vs my two Daughters, and forget the ſtrangers we could not: pacing thus abroad to take the aire, when wee were in the greene meades, *Meribates* and my daughter had ſingled themſelues, and he taking time while ſhe proffered opportunity, began boldly to court her in this manner.

It is an olde ſaying (Madam) holden as an Oracle, that in many words lyeth miſtruſt, and in painted ſpeech deceit is often couered. Therefore I (ſweet miſtreſſe) whoſe acquaintance with you is fmall, and credit leffe, as beeing a ftranger, dare vfe no circumftance for feare of miftruft, neither can I tell in what refpect to bring a fufficient triall of my good will, but only that I wifh the end of my loue to be fuch, as my faith and loialtie is at this prefent, which I hope tract of time fhall trie without fpot. Thy / wit, *Eriphila*, hath bought my freedome, and thy wifedome hath made me captiue, that as he which is hurt of the fcorpion, feeketh a falue from whence he receiued the fore, fo you onely may minifter the medicine which procures the difeafe. The burning feuer is driuen out with a hot potion, the fhaking palfie with a cold drinke: loue onely is remedied by loue, and fancie muft be cured by continuall affection.

Therefore, *Eriphila*, I fpeake with teares out-wardly, and with drops of bloud inwardly, that vnleffe the mifling fhowres of your mercy mitigate the fire of my fancy, I am like to buy loue & repentance with death: but perhaps you will obiect, that the beafts which gaze at the Panther, are guilty of their own death: that the moufe taken in the trap, deferueth her chance: that a louer which hath free will, deferueth no pittie, if he fall into any amorous paffions. Can the ftraw refift the vertue of the pure Jet, or flaxe the force of the fire? can a louer withftand the brunt of beauty, or freeze if he ftand by the flame, or preuent

the lawes of nature? weigh all things equally, and
then I doubt not but to haue a iuft iudgement:
and, though fmall acquaintance may breede miftruft,
and miftruft hinders loue : yet tract of time fhall
inferre fuch tryall, as I truft fhall kindle affection.
And therefore I hope you will not put a doubt till
occafion be offered, nor call his credit in queftion,
whome neyther you haue found nor heard to be
halting: what though the Serpentine powder is
quickly kindled, and quickly out? yet the Salamander ftone once fette on fire, can neuer bee
quenched : as the fappie Myrtle tree will quickly
rotte, fo the Sethim wood will neuer be eaten with
wormes : though the Polype changeth colour, euery
houre, yet the Saphyr will cracke, before it will
confent to difloyalty. As al things are not made
of one mould, fo all men are not of one minde :
for as there hath beene a trothleffe *Iafon*, fo there
hath beene a truftie *Troylus*, and as there hath been
a diffembling *Damocles*, fo there hath beene a loyall
Lelius. And fure, / *Eriphila*, I call the gods to
witneffe, without fayning, that fith thy wit hath fo
bewitched my heart, my loyaltie and loue fhall bee
fuch, as thy honour and beautie doth merite. Sith
therefore my fancie is fuch, repay but halfe fo much
in recompence, and it fhall bee fufficient. *Eriphila*
hearing this paffionate fpeech of *Meribates*, made
him this anfwere.

Lord *Meribates*, it is hard taking the fowle when the net is defcried, and ill catching of fifh when the hooke is bare, and as impoffible to make her beleeue that will giue no credite, and to deceiue her that fpieth the fetch. When the ftring is broken, it is hard to hit the white, when a mans credite is called in queftion, it is hard to perfwade one. Blame me not (*Meribates*) if I vrge you fo ftrictly, nor thinke nothing if I fufpect you narrowly : a woman may knit a knot with her tongue, that fhee cannot vntie with all her teeth, and when the fignet is fet on, it is too late to breake the bargaine: therefore I had rather miftruft too foone then miflike too late: I had rather feare my choice, then rue my chance : for a womans heart is like the ftone in *Egypt*, that will quickely receiue a forme, but neuer change without cracking. If then I feare, thinke mee not cruell ; nor fcrupulous, if I be wife for my felfe : the Wolfe hath as fmooth a fkin as the fimple fheepe, the fowre Elder hath a fairer barke then the fweete Juniper : where the fea is calmeft, there it is deepeft, and where the greateft colour of honeftie is, there oftentimes is the moft want : for *Venus* veffels haue the lowdeft found, when they are moft emptie: and a diffembling heart hath more eloquence then a faithfull minde, for truth is euer naked : I will not, Lord *Meribates*, runne for my particular comparifon.

Thus I caft all thefe doubts, and others haue tryed them true, yet am I forced by fancy to take fome remorfe of thy paffions. *Medea* knew the beft, but yet followed the worft in choofing *Iafon* : but I hope not to finde thee fo wauering. Well, / *Meribates*, to be fhort and plaine, thou haft wonne the caftle that many haue befieged, and haft obtained that which others haue fought to gaine : it is not the fhape of thy beautie, but the hope of thy loyalty which inticeth me: not thy faire face, but thy faithfull heart : not thy parentage, but thy manners: not thy poffeffions, but thy vertues: for fhe that builds her loue vpon beauty, meanes to fancie but for a while : would God I might find thee fuch a one as I will trie myfelfe to be, for whereas thou doft proteft fuch loialtie, which fuppofe it be true yet fhall it be but counterfait refpecting mine : be thou but *Admetus*, and I will be *Alceft* : no torments, no trauell : no, only the loffe of life fhall diminifh my loue: in liew thereof remaine thou but conftant, and in pledge of my protefted good will, haue heere my heart and hand to be thine in duft and afhes.

Here (fon) maift thou iudge into what quandary *Meribates* was driuen, when he heard the anfwer of his miftris fo correfpondent to his fute : the prifoner being condemned hearing the rumor of his pardon, neuer reioiced more then *Meribates* did at this pronouncing of his happineffe. Wel, thefe louers thus agreeing, broke off from their parle for feare of fufpicion, and ioined with companie, where falling into other talke, we paft away the afternoone in many pleafant deuices. *Eriphila* and *Meribates* thus fatisfied, liuing in moft happy content, honoring no deity but *Venus*, determined as well as opportunity would minifter occafion to breake the matter to mee and her betime : but in the meane while my Sonne proclaymed for his delight, certaine Juftes and Turneyes, whither reforted all the braueft Noblemen and Gentlemen in *Taprobane*, where they performed many worthie and honourable deedes of Cheualry. The Juftes ended, my fonne bade them all to a banket : where, to grace the boord and to honour the companie, was placed my daughters, *Eriphila* and *Marpefia* : gazed on they were for their beauties, and admired for their honourable behauiour. /

Eriphila, whofe eye walked about the troope of thefe luftie Gallants, efpied a young gentleman midft the reft, called *Lucidor*, the fonne of an Efquire : a man of perfonage tall and well proportioned, of face paffing amiable, of behauiour well nurtured. This Gallant furnifhed with thefe fingular qualities, fo fet on fire *Eriphilaes* fancie, that as if fhe had drunk of the fountaine of *Ardenia*, her hot loue was turned to a cold liking. Now

her heart was fet vpon *Lucidor*, which of late was
vowed to *Meribates*, in fuch fort that her ftomake
loft the wonted appetite, to feed the eyes with the
beauty of her new louer, as that fhee feemed to
haue eaten of the herbe *Sputania*, which fhutteth
vp the ftomake for a long feafon. Yea fo impatient was her affection, as fhee could not forbeare
to giue him fuch lookes, that the Gentleman perceiued fhee was either refolued to outface him, or
elfe affected towards him. Wel, the dinner ended,
and the Gentlemen all departed, *Eriphila* getting
fecretly to her clofet, began to fall into thefe
tearmes.

Infortunate *Eriphila*, what a contrariety of
paffions breeds a confufed difcontent in thy minde?
what a warre doeft thou feele betweene the conftant refolution of a louer, and the inconftant
determination of a lecher, betweene fancie and faith,
loue and loyaltie? Wilt thou proue *Eriphila*, as
falfe as *Venus*, who for euery effeminate face hath
a new fancie? as trothleffe as *Crefida*, that changed
her thoughts with her yeeres ; as inconftant as
Helena, whofe heart had more louers, than the
Camelion colours? wilt thou vowe thy loyaltie to
one, and not proue ftedfaft to any? The Turtle
choofeth, but neuer changeth : the Lion after that
he hath entred league with his mate, doth neuer
couet a new choice : thefe haue but nature for

their guide, and yet are conſtant, thou haſt both
nature and nurture, and yet art moueable : break-
ing thine oth without compulſion, and thy faith
without conſtraint, whereas nothing is ſo hated /
as periury, and a woman hauing crackt her
loyaltie, is halfe hanged. *Ciuillia* being betrothed
to *Horatius ſecundus*, choſe rather to be rackt to
death, than to falſifie her conſtancie.

Lamia a Concubine, could by no torments bee
haled from the loue of *Ariſtogiton* : what perils
ſuffered *Cariclia* for *Theagynes?* Let theſe examples *Eriphila*, moue thee to be conſtant to
Meribates : be thou ſtedfaſt, and no doubt thou
ſhalt not finde him ſtragling. *Cauſtana*, when ſhe
came into the Court to ſweare that ſhe neuer
loued *Sudalus*, became dumbe, and after fell mad :
beware of the like rewarde, if thou commit the
like offence. Tuſh, they that would refraine from
drinke becauſe they heard *Anacreon* dyed with the
pot at his head, or that hateth an egge, becauſe
Appeyus Sanleyus dyed in eating of one, would bee
noted for perſons halfe mad : ſo if I ſhould ſtand
to my peny-worth, hauing made my market like
a foole, and may change for the better, becauſe
other in like caſe haue had ill hap, I may either
bee counted faint hearted or fooliſh. What
Eriphila, *Iupiter* laught at the periurie of louers.
Meribates is faire, but not ſecond to *Lucidor* : he

is wittie, but the other more wife : well what of
this, but how wilt thou anfwere *Meribates* ? tufh,
cannot the Cat catch mife, but fhee muft haue a
bell hanged at her eare ? he that is afraid to venter
on the Buck, for that he is wrapt in the bryers,
fhall neuer haue hunters hap : and hee that puts a
doubt in loue at euery chance fhall neuer haue
louers lucke : well, howfoeuer it be, *Lucidor* fhall
be mine, hee fhall haue my heart, and I his, or
elfe I will fit befide the faddle : and thus hauing
debated with her felfe, fhe refted perplexed, till
fhee might haue a fight of her new louer ; which
was not long: for *Lucidor* no fooner got home, but
calling to minde the amorous glances of *Eriphila*,
and noting both her beauty and her wit, although
her honour was farre beyond his parentage, yet
prefuming vpon her fauours fhowen him at the
banket, hee boldly, as loues champion, ventured
to winne what *Cupid* had / fet as a prize : fo that
he began to frequent the Court, and become a
Courtier, firft brauing it amongft the Lords, then
by degrees creeping into fauour with the Ladies,
where in time he found opportunity to parle with
Eriphila : whom for fafhion fake at the firft hee
found fomewhat ftrange, but in fhort time became
fo tractable, that there was but one heart in two
bodies ; in fo much, that not only *Meribates* and
my fonne, but all the Court faw how *Eriphila*

doted on *Lucidor* : whereat my fonne beganne to
frowne : but *Meribates* would not fee it, left his
Miftris fhould thinke him iealous, but fmothered
vp the griefe in fecrecie, and thought either time,
or the perfwafion of her friends, or his continued
affection would diffwade her from her follies.
Well, *Eriphila* had not fauored *Lucidor* long, but
there came to the Court another young Gentleman,
called *Perecius*. Who likewife was enamored of
Eriphila, and fhe of him, that fhe proued more
light of loue then fhe was wittie ; yet fhee excelled
in wit all the Virgins of *Taprobane*.

To be briefe, fo many faces, fo many fancies,
that fhee became as variable in her loues, as the
Polype in colours: which fo perplexed the minde of
Meribates, that falling into melancholy and grieuous
paffions, he exclaimed againft the inconftancie of
women, who like Fortune ftood vpon a globe,
and were winged with the feathers of fickleneffe :
yet not willing to rage too far, till hee had talked
with *Eriphila*, hee would not ftay till opportunity
would ferue, but early in a morning ftepped into
her bed chamber, where finding her betweene halfe
fleeping and waking, he faluted with great courtefie;
being refaluted againe of *Eriphila* with the like
priuate kind of familiaritie: after a few ordinary
fpeeches, *Meribates* taking *Eriphila* by the hand,
began to vtter his mind in thefe wordes.

Sweet miftreffe, I feele in my mind, a perilous and mortall conflict betweene feare and loue: by the one doubting in difcouering my mind, to purchafe your disfauour, by the other / forced to bewray what I thinke, left I perifh through my own fecrecie: hoping therefore you will take that comes from me, as from your fecond felfe; giue me leaue to fay that greeues me to repeate: How I doubt (Madame) of your conftancie: what vowes there haue paft betweene vs, what proteftations, what promifes, I referre to your owne confcience: What vnfeemly fauors you haue fhewed to *Lucidor*, what extreme fancie to *Perecius*, all *Taprobane* wonders at, with forrow, that fo witty a lady fhould proue fo light: and I efpecially, whom the caufe toucheth at the quicke, and paineth at the heart, feele more miferable paffions for your dis-loialtie, than I did receiue ioyes in hope of your conftancie. As *Meribates* was readie to haue profecuted his parle, my daughter broke off his difcourfe in this manner.

And what of this, lord *Meribates*, may not a woman looke, but fhe muft loue? are you iealous, forfooth, before the wedding? well, fuppofe I fauoured *Lucidor* and *Perecius*; *Si natura hominum fit nouitatis auida*, giue women leaue to haue more fancies than one; if not as we are louers, yet as we are women. *Venus* temple hath many entrances:

Cupid hath more arrowes than one in his quiuer, and fundry ftrings to his bowe : women haue many lookes, and fo they may haue many loues.

What, lord *Meribates*, thinke you to haue a womans whole heart? no, vnleffe you can procure *Venus* to make her blind, or fome other deity deafe; for if either fhe fee beauty or gold, or heare promifes or paffions, I thinke fhee will keepe a corner for a friend, and fo will I. But Madam, the glorious frame of the world, confifts in vnitie, for wee fee that in the firmament there is but one funne : yea, quoth *Eriphila*, but there be many ftars. The Iris or Rainbow Madam (qᵈ. he) hath but one quality. Truth anfwered my daughter, but it hath many colours : but to come to a familiar example, replyed *Meribates* : the heart hath but one ftring ; yea but, quoth *Eriphila*, it hath many thoughts, and from thefe thoughts / fpring paffions, and from paffions, not loue but loues : therefore content you, fir, for if you loue me you muft haue riuals : and fo turning her face, as in choller, to ỹ other fide of the bed, fhe bade him good morning : he paffing away out of the chamber in great melancholy, began affoon as he was alone to exclame againft the inconftancy of women : faying, they were like marigolds, whofe forme turneth round with the funne : as wauering as wethercocks, that mooue with euery winde : as fleeting as the North weſt Ilands, that flote with euery gale : wittie, but in wiles : conceited, but in inconſtancy : as brittle as glaſſe, hauing their harts fram'd of the Polipe ſtones : their faces of the nature of the Adamants, and in quality like the Jacinth, which when it feemeth moſt hot, is then as cold as Iron : carrying frownes in their foreheads, and dimples in their cheekes : hauing their eyes framed of Jette, that drawe euery beauty in a minute, and let them fall in a moment. Thus he exclaimed againſt women : but fuch was his feruent affection towards *Eriphila,* that he would neither rage againſt her openly nor fecretly, but fmothered his paſſions in filence : which growing to the extreme, brought him into a feuer, wherein lingring he dyed : but in fuch ſort, that all *Taprobane* faid, it was for the inconſtancy of *Eriphila.* Wel, his Gentlemen and mariners mourned and forrowed, in that their Pynace ſhould bring him home dead, whome they brought forth aliue : al ioyntly praying, that the gods would be reuenged on *Eriphila* : who as ſhe was then attending with me and her brother on the dead corps to the ſhippe, fuddenly before all our fights was turned into this byrd (a Camelion) : wherevpon the mariners reioyced : hoifing vp failes, and thruſting into the maine, we fcowred and returned home to the court.

Thus (Sonne) thou haſt heard the misfortune of

my two daughters, the one for her pride, the other
for her inconftancie : it is late, and the fetting of
the funne calleth us home with the Bee, to our poore
hiue : therfore we will now to / our cottage, and to
morrow at thy breakfaft I will fatisfie thee with the
hard fortune of *Marpefia* : with that I gaue the
Counteffe *Alcida* great thankes, and accompanied
my courteous Oafteffe to her cottage.

The third Difcourfe, of MARPESIA.

NO fooner was the day vp, and *Phœbus* had marched out the greateft gates of heauen, lighting the world with the fparkling wreath, circled about his head, but old *Alcida* got vp, and called me from my bedde: afhamed that old age fhould bee more early then youth, I ftart vp to waite vpon mine Oafteffe, who being readie with her ftaffe in her hand, carried me forth into the fields hard adioining to the Seafide, where wee came to a tombe, on which lay the picture of a Gentleman very artificially carued: by him hung two tables without any fimbole, embleme, impreft, or other Hierogliphicall caracter, onely there were written certaine verfes to this effect.

The Graces in their glorie neuer gaue
A rich or greater good to womankind :
That more impall's their honors with the Palme
Of high renowne, then matchleffe conftancie,
Beauty is vaine, accounted but a flowre,
Whofe painted hiew fades with the fummer funne :
Wit oft hath wracke by felfe-conceit of pride.
Riches is trafh that fortune boafteth on.
Conftant in loue who tries a womans minde,
Wealth, beautie, wit, and all in her doth find.

In / the other table were fet downe thefe verfes.

The faireſt Iem oft blemiſht with a cracke,
Loſeth his beauty and his vertue too :
The faireſt flowre nipt with the winters froſt,
In ſhew ſeemes worſer then the baſeſt weede.
Vertues are oft farre ouerſtain'd with faults :
Were ſhe as faire as Phœbe in her ſphere,
Or brighter then the paramour of Mars,
Wiſer then Pallas daughter vnto Ioue,
Of greater maieſtie then Iuno was,
More chaſte then Veſta goddeſſe of the Maides,
Of greater faith then faire Lucretia :
Be ſhe a blab, and tattles what ſhe heares,
Want to be ſecret giues farre greater ſtaines,
Then vertues glorie which in her remaines.

After I had read ouer the verſes ; *Alcida* ſayd : (ſonne) I perceiue thou doſt muſe at this tombe, ſet in ſo vncoth a place, hard by the ſteepe-downe cliffes of the Sea : eſpecially, furniſhed with Enigmaticall poſies : yet haſt thou not confidered what after thou ſhalt finde, and therefore let vs ſit downe vnder the ſhadowe of this Roſe tree, which thou ſeeſt flouriſhed in this barren place ſo faire and beautifull, and I will driue thee out of theſe doubts, by difcouering the fortune of my daughter *Marpeſia.* I deſirous to heare what the meaning of this monument ſeated ſo proſpectiue to *Neptune,*

fhould be, fate mee downe very orderly vnder the
Rofe tree, and began to fettle my felfe very attentiue to heare what old *Alcida* would fay, who
began in this manner. /

The third Hiftorie of MARPESIA
of *Taprobane*.

MY two daughters beeing thus metamorphofed,
and transformed for their follies into ftrange
fhapes : I had left mee onely my youngeft daughter
Marpefia, in face little inferiour to her eldeft fifter
Fiordefpine, for fhee was paffing beautifull : wife
fhe was, as not fecond to *Eriphila* : but other
fpeciall vertues fhe had, that made her famous
through all *Taprobane* : and as the burnt childe
dreads the fire, and other mens harmes learne vs
to beware : fo my daughter *Marpefia*, by the misfortune of *Fiordefpine*, feared to be proud, and by
the finifter chance of *Eriphila*, hated to be inconftant, infomuch, that fearing their natiuities to be
fatall, and that hers being rightly calculated would
proue as bad as the reft : Shee kept fuch a ftrict
method of her life, and manners, and fo foregarded
all her actions with vertue, that fhe thought fhee
might defpife both the fates and fortune.

Liuing thus warily, I and her brother conceiued great content in her modeſtie and vertue : thinking, though the gods had made vs infortunate by the miſhappe of the other two: yet in the fortunate ſucceſſe of *Marpeſias* life, amends ſhould bee made for the other miſhap. Perſwaded thus, it fortuned that my ſonne intertained into his ſeruice the ſon of a Gentleman, a bordering neighbour by, a youth of greater beauty then birth : for hee was of comely perſonage : of face louely, and though but meanly brought vp, as nuſled in his fathers houſe: yet his nature diſcouered that hee was hardie in his reſolution touching courage : and courteous in diſpoſition, as concerning his manners.

This / youth, called *Eurimachus*, was ſo diligent and dutifull towards his lord, ſo affable to his fellows, and ſo gentle to euery one, that hee was not onely well thought on by ſome, but generally liked and loued of all. Continuing in this method of life, hee ſo behaued himſelfe, that in recompence of his ſeruice, my ſonne promoted him not onely to higher office and ſome ſmall penſion, but admitted him into his ſecret and priuate familiarity. Liuing thus in great credit, it chanced that *Venus* ſeeing how my daughter *Marpeſia* liued careleſſe of her loues, and neuer ſent ſo much as one ſigh to *Paphos* for a ſacrifice : ſhee called *Cupid*, complaining that ſhee was atheiſt to her deitie, and one

oppofed to her principles : whereupon the boy at
his mothers becke, drewe out an inuenomed arrow,
and leuelling at *Marpefia*, hit her vnder the right
pappe, fo nigh the heart, that giuing a grone fhe
felt fhe was wounded, but how, or with what, fhe
knew not ; as one little fkilfull in any amorous
paffions : yet fhee felt thoughts vnfitting with
her wonted humor : for noting the perfon of
Eurimachus, which fhe found in property excellent,
and admiring the qualities of his minde, co-vnited
with many rare and precious vertues, which fhe
perceiued to bee extraordinarie, fhe fell to conceiue
a liking, which for the bafeneffe of his birth, fhee
paffeth ouer for a toy : but the blinded wagge,
that fuffers not his wounds to bee cured with eafie
falues, nor permitteth any lenitiue plaifters to
preuaile where hee pierceth with his arrowes, put
oyle in the flame, and fet fire to the flaxe, that
fhe felt her fancy fcarce warme, to grow to fuch a
fcalding heate, as euery veine of her heart fweet
paffions : feeling this new lord, called loue, to be
fo imperious, fhee ftooped a little, and entred into
deeper confideration of *Eurimachus* perfection, and
fo deepe by degrees, that although fhee coueted
with the Snaile to haue her pace flow, yet at length
fhe waded fo farre, that fhe was ouer her fhooes :
fo that feeling her felfe paffing into an vnknowne
forme, fhee fell into this doubtfull meditation.

What / flame is this *Marpefia*, that ouer heateth thy hart? what ftrange fire hath *Venus* fent from *Cipres*, that fcorcheth thee heere in *Taprobane*? hath *Cupids* bowe fuch ftrength ; or his arrowes fuch flight, as being loofed in heauen, hee can ftrike here vpon earth? a mighty goddeffe is *Venus*, and great is *Cupid*, that work effects of fuch ftrange operation : make not a doubt (*Marpefia*) of that is palpable: dreame not at that which thou feeft with thine eyes, nor mufe not at that which thou feeleft with thy heart : then confeffe and fay thou art in loue, and loue in thee, fo deeply, as Pumice-ftones of reafon will hardly raze out the characters. In loue? thou art young *Marpefia*; fo is *Cupid*, a very childe? a maid ; fo was *Venus* before fhee loft her Virginitie, and yet for her lightneffe, fhee was the goddeffe of loue : but with whom art thou in loue? with *Eurimachus* ! one of bafe birth, and fmall liuing ; of no credite, a meane Gentleman, and thy brothers feruant?

Confider *Marpefia*, that loue hath his reafons, and his rules to fettle fancy, and gouerne affections: honour ought not to looke lower in dignitie, nor the thoughts of Ladies gaze at worthleffe perfons : Better is it for thee to perifh in high defires, then in lowe difdaine : oppofe thy felfe to *Venus*, vnleffe her prefents be more precious : fay loue is folly, except her gifts be more rich : count rather

to dye in defpifing fo meane a choice, then liue in
liking fo vnlikely a chance : what will thy mother,
thy brother, thy friends, nay all *Taprobane* fay :
but that thou art vaine, careleffe, and amorous:
but note this *Marpefia*, loue is a league that lafteth
while life : thou art in this to feede thine eye, not
thine humour : to fatisfie the defire of thy heart,
not the confideration of their thoughts : for in
marying, either a perpetuall content, or a general
miflike is like to fall to thy felfe : what though he
be poore, yet hee is of comely perfonage : though
he be bafe of birth, yet he is wife : what hee
wanteth in gifts of fortune, hee hath in the
minde : and the defeét of honours is fupplied with
vertues.

Venus / her felfe loued *Adonis* : *Phœbe* ftooped
from heauen to kiffe a poore Shepheard : *Ænone*
loued *Paris*, as hee was a Swaine, not as the fon
of *Priamus* : loue is not alwaies companion to
dignity, nor fancy euer lodged in kings Palaces.
Then *Marpefia*, looke at *Eurimachus*, for hee is
courteous, and loue him as he is vertuous ; fupply
thou his want with thy wealth, and increafe his
credite with thy countenance : but how dare he
motion loue, that is fo low ? or enterprife to
attempt fo great an affault ? Neuer ftand in doubt
Marpefia : giue him thou but fauors, and loue and
fortune will make him bold.

Marpesia hauing thus meditated with her felfe, fought by all meanes poffible, how to make him priuy to her affeétions : fhe vfed in her falutations affable courtefie, and fomewhat more then ordinary : her lookes were full of fauours, her glances many and milde ; he vfed no exercife but fhe did com- mend, nor performed any thing, which fhee fayd not to be excellent. The young *Eurimachus* was not fuch a Nouice, but hee could efpie a pad in the ftraw, and difcerne a glowing coale, from colde cinders : hee noted her glances, her looks, her geftures, her words, examining euery particular aétion, in the depth of his thoughts, finding by the touchftone, that all tended vnto meere loue, or extreme diffimulation ; for whatfoeuer fhe did was in extremes. Well, hope put him in comfort that fhee was too vertuous to diffemble; and feare, that fhe was too honorable to loue fo bafe a man : yet fuppofing the beft, he tooke her paffions for loue, & had a defire to return a liking with affeétion : but the confideration of his parentage, of his fmall poffeffions, of her honour, his lords disfauour, and the impoffibility of his fute, was a cooling card to quench the hotteft flame that *Cupid* could fet on fire with his inchanted brand : but *Venus* had pittied the fondling, gaue him fuch precious comfortiues to incourage her champion, that he refolued to attempt, whatfoeuer his fortune were :

thus in fufpence he began to debate with himfelfe.

It / hath beene an old faying *Eurimachus*, fuckt
from his mothers teate, that it is good to looke before thou leape, and to found the Ford before thou
venter to wade, fith time paft cannot be recalled,
nor actions performed reuoked, but repented; gaze
not at ftarres, left thou ftumble at ftones : looke
not into the Lions denne, left for thy prefumption, thy fkinne be pulled ouer thine eares. In
loues thoughts are to be meafured by fortunes,
not by defires, for *Venus* tables are to be gazed at
with the eye, not to be reacht at with the hand.
In loue, *Eurimachus*? why, it fitteth not with thy
prefent eftate : fancy is to attend on high lords, not
on fuch as are feruile : it were meeter for thee to
fweate at thy labours then to figh at thy paffions:
to pleafe thy lord then to dote on thy miftreffe :
bufie then thy hands to free thy heart : bee not
idle, and *Venus* charmes are to a deafe Adder.

Cedit amor rebus, res age tutus eris.

But *Eurimachus*, *Phidias* painteth loue young,
and her garlands are made with the buds of Rofes,
not with withered flowres :   Youth holdeth the
fire, and fancy puts in the oyle ; but age carries
the colde cinders, now that heate of young yeeres
hath yeelded ; therefore if thou refufe to loue,

when wilt thou finde time to fancie? wrinkles in
the face, are fpelles againft *Cupid*, and *Venus* ftarteth
backe from white haires : then now or elfe neuer,
loue is a greater lord then thy mafter: for hee
hath deity to counteruaile his dignitie. Thou
tattleft *Eurimachus* of loue, but fay who is the
obiect : thy thoughts ayme at no leffe, nor no
lower than *Marpefia*, fifter to thy lord, a Princeffe
by birth : faire and beautifull, full of honourable
and vertuous qualities, fought by men of high
parentage ; to fay all in one word, the flowre of
Taprobane : fond foole, thinkeft thou the Kite and
the Eagle will pearch on one tree? the Lyon and the
Wolfe lye in one denne? Ladies of great worth,
looke on fuch worthleffe peafants? No, thinke
her difdaine will bee greater then thy defire : and
affure thee this, if thou prefume, fhee / will reuenge : why? is *Cupid* blind, and fhoots he not
one fhaft at random? may he not as foone hit a
Princeffe, as a Milk-maid? truth, but his arrowes
are matches : he fhoots not high with the one, and
low with the other : hee ioynes not the Moufe and
the Elephant, the Lambe and the Tiger, the Flie
and the Faulcon, nor fets not honor in any feruile
roome: yet *Omphita* the queene of the Indians loued
a Barber: *Angelica Medes*, a mercinary fouldier.
Yea *Venus* herfelfe chofe a Blacke-fmith.

Women oft refemble in their loues, the Apothe-

caries in their art : they choofe the weed for their
fhop, when they leaue the faireft flowre in the
garden: they oft refpect the perfon, more then
the parentage, and the qualities of the man, more
than his honors : feeding the eye with the fhape,
and the heart with the vertues, howfoeuer they
liue difcontent for want of riches : but build not
Eurimachus, on thefe vncertaine inftances, nor
conclude on fuch premifes, left thy foundation faile,
and thy Logike prooue not worth a lowfe : what
reafon haft thou to perfwade thee once to aime a
thought at *Marpefia*, fuch as *Venus* if fhe heard
them pleaded, would allow for Aphorifmes? if
fauors be a figne of fancie, what glances haue I
had that haue pearced deep: what looks, as dis-
couering loue: what courteous fpeeches to my face :
what praifes behind my backe? Nay, what hath
Marpefia done of late, but talke of *Eurimachus*,
and honor *Eurimachus*? what of this, young
Nouice, are not women Arch-practifers of flattery
and diffimulation? lay they not their lookes to
intrap, when they meane to keepe the fowle for
tame fooles? haue they not defire in their faces,
when they haue difdaine in their hearts? did
not *Helena* kiffe *Menelaus*, when fhee winked
at *Paris*? did not *Crefida* wring *Troylus* by the
hand, when her heart was in the tents of the
Grecians? euery looke that women lend, is not

loue : euery fmile in their face is not a pricke in
their bofome : they prefent Rofes, and beate men
with Nettles : burne perfumes, and yet ftifle them
with the blacke : fpeak faire and affable, when /
God wot, they mean' nothing leffe : If then
Eurimachus, thou knoweft their wiles, feare to
make experience of their wits ; reft thee as thou
art : let *Marpefia* vfe fauors, caft glances, praife
and difpraife how fhe lift, thinke all is wanton
diffimulation, and fo reft.

In this melancholy humour he left his loues, and
went to his labours. Loue efpying how in the
day he withftood her face with diligence, fhe caufed
Morpheus to prefent him in his fleepes with the
fhape of his Miftreffe, which recording in the
day, hee found that where fancie had pierced deepe,
there no falue would ferue to appeafe the Maladie :
that from thefe light paines, he fell into extreme
paffions. As he could take no reft, he fought
alwaies to be folitary, fo to feed his thoughts with
imaginations, that like *Cephalus*, he delighted to
walke in the Groues, and there with *Philomela* to
bewaile his loues.

Cupid pittying his plaints, fent Opportunity to
find her, who brought it fo to paffe, that as (on
a day) he walked into a place (hard adioining to
the parke, hauing his Lute in his hand, playing certaine melancholy dumpes, to mitigate his pinching

humor) *Marpefia* with one of her Gentlewomen,
being abroad in the lanes, efpied him thus folitary :
ftealing therefore behind him to heare what humor
the man was in, heard him fing to his Lute this
mornefull madrigall.

Reft thee defire, gaze not at fuch a Starre,
 Sweet fancy fleepe, loue take a nappe awhile :
My bufie thoughts that reach and rome fo farre,
 With pleafant dreames the length of time beguile.
Faire *Venus* coole my ouer-heated breft,
 And let my fancy take her wonted reft.

Cupid abroad was lated in the night :
 His wings were wet with ranging in the raine :
Harbour he fought, to me he tooke his flight,
 To drie his plumes : I heard the boy complaine, /
My doore I oped to grant him his defire,
 And rofe my felfe to make the Wagge a fire.

Looking more narrow by the fires flame,
 I fpyed his quiuer hanging at his backe :
I fear'd the child might my misfortune frame,
 I would haue gone for feare of further wracke ;
And what I drad (poore man) did me betide,
 For foorth he drew an arrow from his fide.

He pierft the quicke, that I began to ftart
 The wound was fweete, but that it was too hie,

And yet the pleafure had a pleafing fmart:

 This done, he flyes away, his wings were drie;
But left his arrow ftill within my breft,

 That now I greeue, I welcom'd fuch a gheft.

He had no fooner ended his fonet, but *Marpefia* perceiuing by the contents, that it was meant of her, ftepped to him, and draue him thus abruptly from his paffions.

If you grieue *Eurimachus* for enterteining fuch a gheft, your forrow is like the raine that came too late : to beleeue loue is fuch an vnruly tenant, that hauing his entrance vpon courtefie, he will not bee thruft out by force ; you make me call to mind the counterfait of *Paris*, when he was *Œnones* darling : for *Phidias* drew him fitting vnder a Beech tree, playing on his pipe, and yet teares dropping from his eyes, as mixing his greateft melody with paffions : but I fee the comparifon will not hold in you, for though your inftrument bee anfwerable to his, yet you want his lukewarme drops, which fheweth, though your mufike bee as good, yet your thoughts are not fo paffionate : but leauing thefe ambages, fay to me *Eurimachus* ; what may fhe bee that is your Miftreffe ?

Eurimachus amazed at the fight of his Ladie, more then *Priamus* fonne was at the view of the three goddeffes, fate / ftill like the picture of *Niobe*

turned into marble, as if fome ftrange apoplexy had
taken all his fenfes. Gaze on her face hee did:
fpeak hee could not ; in fo much that *Marpefia*
fmiling at the extremity of his loues, wakened him
out of this trance, thus:

What, cheere man, hath loue witched thy heart,
as all thy fences haue left their powers? is thy
tong tied, as thy heart is fettered, or hath the feare
of your miftris cruelty driuen you into a cold
palfie? if this be the worft, comfort your felfe,
for women will be true : and if fhee be too hard
hearted, let me but know her, and you fhall fee
how I will prattle on your behalfe : what fay you
to me, what makes you thus mute?

By this *Eurimachus* had gathered his fences
together, that rifing vp and doing reuerence to
Marpefia, he thus replyed: Madam, it is a principle
in Philofophy, that *Senfibile fenfui fuperpofitū nulla
fit fenfafio,* the colour clapt to the eye, hindreth the
fight, the flower put in the noftrill, hindreth the
fmell: and what of this Philofophical Enigma, quoth
Marpefia? I dare not madam, quoth *Eurimachus,*
infer what I would ; but to anfwere more plainly,
Endimion waking, and feeling *Phebe* grace him
with a kiffe, was not more amazed, than I at your
heauenly prefence, fearing, if not *Acteons* fall, yet
that I had committed the like fault: for at the
firft blufh, your excellency draue me into fuch a

maze, that I dreamed not of the Lady *Marpefia*, but of fome goddeffe that had folaced in thefe woods : which fuppofition made me fo mute.

You fly ftill (quoth *Marpefia*) from my demand, playing like the Lapwing, that cryeth fartheft from her neft. I afked who it was that you loued fo as to honour her with fuch a fonet.

It was, Madam, to keepe accord to my lute, not to difcouer any paffions, for all the amordelayes *Orpheus* played on his harp, were not amorous, nor euery fonet that *Arion* warbled on his inftrument, vowed vnto *Venus*. I am too young / to loue, for feare my youth be ouerbidden ; fancy being fo heauy a burden, that *Hercules* (who could on his fhoulder fuftaine the heauens) groned to beare fo weighty a lode.

If then, Madame, I ftriue aboue my ftrength, efpecially in loue, I fhall but with the Giants heape *Peleon* vpon *Offa*, paffions vpon paffions, fo long, till I be ftrooken to death with loues thundering bolt : therefore, Madame, I dare not loue.

Marpefia, who determined to found the depth of his thoughts, tooke him before hee fell to the ground, and made this reply: Truft mee *Eurimachus*, your looks, your actions, your fighes and gefture, argues no leffe than a louer : therefore feeing we are alone, none but we three, Ile haue you once in fhrift, and therefore I coniure you by your Miftreffe fauour and beautie, to tell me whether you be in loue or no.

You ftraine me fo hard, Madam, (quoth *Eurimachus*) that I am in loue, and loue fo farre in mee, as neither time nor fortune can raze out: the name of my miftreffe, Madam, pardon, for in naming her I difcouer mine owne prefumption, hauing aymed fo by the meanes of afpiring loue, as her excellency croffeth all my thoughts with difdaine: For Madam, giue me leaue to fay (making no compare) that the Graces at her birth did agree to make her abfolute: I hauing foared fo high, as the funne hath halfe melted my feathers, I feare with *Icarus* to fall into the Ocean of endleffe miferies; for be her difdaine neuer fo great, yet my defire will neuer be leffe; fcorne fhe I fhould looke fo hie, affection will not bate an ounce of his maine; but feeing the dice be in his hands, will throw at all.

But Madam, fo farre I am out of conceit to haue but one fauour at her hands, as I paffe euery day and houre in as deep perplexed eftate, as the ghofts greeued by the infernall furies: and with this, the water ftood in his eyes, which *Marpefia* not able to brooke, began to falue thus.

I wili / not *Eurimachus*, be inquifitiue of your Miftreffe name, fith you haue yeelded a reafon to conceale it, but for your loues that are lodged fo

hie, feare not man : the Blackfmith dared to couet
faire *Venus* ; the little Sparrow pecketh fometimes
wheare the Eagle taketh ftand ; and the little
Moufe feedeth, where the Elephant hath eaten
hay : loue as foone ftoopeth to vifite a poore cottage,
as a Palace : to dare, I tell thee *Eurimachus*,
in loue, is the firft principle : and *Helen* told
Paris :

Nemo fuccenfet amanti.

Thou muft then to *Paphos*, and not vfe bafhful-
neffe in *Venus* temple : facrifices ferue at her altars,
as a thing vnfit for louers ; and be fhe as high of
degree as any in *Taprobane*, court her *Eurimachus*,
and if thou miffe, it is but the hap that louers
haue. As fhee fhould haue profecuted her talke,
her brother who was ftalking to kill a Deire, came
by, and efpying them at fo priuate and familiar
chat, frowned, commanding *Eurimachus* (as halfe
in anger) to get him home : hee leauing his fport,
accompanied my daughter to the court.

These louers thus parted, were not long ere they
met, where *Eurimachus* following the precepts of
Marpefia, began very boldly to giue the affault ;
fhe very faintly, for fafhion fake, making a womans
refiftance : but the batterie was fo frefhly renewed,
that *Marpefia* yeelded, and there they plighted a
conftant promife of their loues : vowing fuch faith

and loyaltie as the troth of two louers hearts might afford.

In this happie content they liued a long while, till *Marpesia* blabbing the contract out to a gentleman of the court : it came to her brothers and her mothers eare : who taking the matter grieuously, had her strictly in examination. *Marpesia* confessed her loues, and maintained them : on the contrary / side, they perswaded with promises, and threatned with bitter speeches : but in vaine, for *Marpesia* was resolued and tolde for a flat conclusion, *Eurimachus* was the man, and none but he. Whereupon my sonne seeing no means could preuaile to remoue her affection, he thought by taking away the cause, to raze out the effects : and therfore he sent for *Eurimachus*, whom after he had nipped vp with bitter taunts, he banished from the Court.

This being grieuous to the two louers, yet the assurance of each others constancie, and the hope in time to haue the Prince reconciled, mitigated some part of their martyrdome : and *Marpesia*, to shew to the world shee was not fleeting, whatsoeuer her friends said, discouered the grief she conceiued by his absence, openly : for she went apparelled in mourning attire. Well, *Eurimachus* thus banished, went home to his father, who for feare of ỹ prince, durst not entertaine him : which vnkindnesse had doubled his griefe, that he fell almoft frantike, and began to leaue the company of men as a flat Timonift: in which humor, meeting with the Gentleman that bewraid their loues, he fought with him and flew him, and buried him fo fecretly as the care of his owne life could deuife.

Well, *Cleander* was mift: but heare of him they could not: Poftes were fent out, meffengers through all *Taprobane*, but no newes, fo that diuerfe did defcant diuerfly of his departure: fome faid he was vpon fecret difpleafure betweene him and the Prince, paffed out of the land: others, that he was flaine by theeues: fome that hee was deuoured by wild beafts. Thus debating of his abfence, he was generally lamented of all the court.

But (leauing the fuppofition of his death), againe to *Marpefia*, who taking the exile of *Eurimachus* to her heart, began to growe into great and extreme paffions, and for griefe of the minde, to bodily difeafe, that fhe fell into a Quartaine: which fo tormented her, as the Phyficians faid, ther was no hope of life, nor no art to cure her difeafe, vn/leffe her minde were at quiet: whereupon her brother fearing his fifters life, recalled home *Eurimachus*, admitted him into great fauour, and gaue free grant of his goodwill to their marriage.

Vpon this, *Marpefia* growing into a content, in

fhort time amended. After fhee had recouered her health, fhee dayly vfed the company of *Eurimachus* very priuately and familiarly, but fhe found him not the man he was before : for before he was exiled, no man more pleafant nor more merrily conceited ; now none more melancholly nor fuller of dumps, vttering farre fetcht fighes, and vncertaine anfwers, fo that it difcouered a minde greatly perplexed. *Marpefia* noting this, being on a day all alone with *Eurimachus*, in his chamber : fhee fought with faire intreaties and fweete dalliance, to wring out the caufe of his forrowes, protefting, if fhee could, euen with the hazard of her life redreffe it : if not, to participate in griefe fome part of his diftreffe.

Eurimachus, that loued her more than his life, although hee knew womens tongues were like the leaues of the Afpe tree, yet thinking her to bee wife, after a multitude of mortall fighes, hee difcourfed vnto her, how hee had flaine *Cleander*, and that the remembrance of his death bred this horror in his confcience.

Marpefia hearing this, made light of the matter, to comfort *Eurimachus*, promifing and protefting to keepe it as fecret as hitherto fhe had been conftant. But fhee no fooner was parted from her beft be-loued, but fhee was with childe of this late and dangerous newes, laboring with great paines till

fhee might vtter it to her Goffips : where we may
note, fonne (I fpeake againft my felfe) that the
clofets of womens thoughts are euer open, that the
depth of their heart hath a ftring that ftretcheth to
the tongues end, that with *Semele* they conceiue
and bring forth oft before their time : which
Marpefia tried true, for fitting one day folitarie
with a Ladie in the court, called *Celia*, fhee /
fetcht many pinching fighes : which *Celia* marking
defired her to tel her the caufe of that late conceiued grief, as to a friend, in whofe fecrefie fhe
might repofe her life. *Marpefia* made it fomewhat
coy and charie a great while, infomuch that *Celia*
began to long ; and therefore vrged her extremely.
Marpefia could keep no longer, and therefore vfing
this preamble, began to play the blabbe.

If I did not, Madam *Celia*, take you for my
fecond felfe, and thinke you to bee wife and fecret,
I would not reueale a matter of fo great im-
portance, which toucheth me as much as my life
to conceale : Women, you know, hauing any
thing in their ftomake, long while they haue dis-
courft it to fome friend : taking you therefore for
my chiefeft, and hoping all fhal be troden vnder
foote, know Madam, that *Eurimachus* hath flaine
Cleander, and that is the caufe that makes him
thus melancholy. Mary, God forbid, (quoth
Celia). It is true Madam, quoth *Marpefia*, and

therefore let whatfoeuer I haue faid be buried in this place. With that I came into [the] place, and they broke off their talke.

Celia longing to be out of the chamber, that fhee might participate this newes to her Gofips, as foone as opportunity gaue her leaue, went abroad, & meeting by chance another Gentlewoman of the Court, calling her afide, tolde her, if fhe would be fecret, and fweare not to reueale it to any one, fhe would tell her ftrange newes: the other promifing, with great proteftation, to bee as clofe as a woman could bee, *Celia* told her, how *Eurimachus* was the man that flew *Cleander*, and that her authour was *Marpefia*.

They were no fooner parted, but this newes was told to another, that before night it was through the whole court, that *Eurimachus* had flaine *Cleander* : whereupon the Prince could doe no leffe (though very loth for his fifters fake) but caufe him to be apprehended and caft into prifon : then affembling his Lords and Commons, produced / *Eurimachus*, who after ftrict examination was found guilty : the greateft witnes againft him being the confeffion of *Marpefia*. The verdict giuen vp, the prince could not but giue iudgement, which was, that within one moneth in the place where he kild *Cleander*, he fhould be beheaded. Sentence giuen, *Eurimachus* took his misfortune with patience. Newes comming to *Marpefia* of this tragicall euent, fhe fell downe in a found, and grew into bitter paffions, but in vaine.

My fonne, to fhewe how he loued *Eurimachus*, caufed a Caruer to cut out this fumptuous tombe in this forme: wherein after his death, hee refolued to burie him, fo to grace him with extraordinary honor. All things prouided, and the day of his death being come, *Eurimachus* clad all in blacke veluet, came forth, mourning in his apparell, but merrie in his countenance, as one that forrowed for the fault but was not daunted with death. After him followed my Sonne, the Earles, Lords, and Barons of the land, all in black: and I and my daughter *Marpefia*, and the ladies of the court, couered with fable vails, attending on this condemned *Eurimachus* : being come to the place, the deaths-man hauing laid the blocke, and holding the axe in his hand, *Eurimachus* before his death vttered thefe words.

Lords of *Taprobane*, here I flew *Cleander*, & here muft I offer my bloud as amends to the foule of the dead Gentleman : which I repent with more forrow then I performed the deed with furie : The caufe of his death, and my misfortune is all one : he flaine for bewraying my loues, I executed for difcouering his death : but infortunate I, to bewray fo priuate a matter to the fecrecy of a

woman: whofe hearts are full of holes, apt to
receiue but not to retaine: whofe tongues are
trumpets that fet open to the world what they
know: Foolifh is hee that commits his life into
their lappes, or tyes his thoughts in their beauties:
fuch is the nature of thefe fondlings that they
cannot / couer their owne fcapes, nor ftraine a vaile
ouer their greateft faults: their hearts are fo great,
their thoughts fo many, their wits fo fickle, and
their tongues fo flippery: the heart and the tongue
are Relatiues, and if time ferues they cannot paint
out their paffions in talke, yet they will difcouer
them with their lookes: fo that if they be not
blabbes in their tongues, they will be tatlers with
eyes: the gods haue greatly reuenged this fault
in men, letting it ouerflip in women, becaufe it is
fo common amongft that fex. *Mercurie,* for his
babbling turned *Battus* to an Index or touchftone,
whofe nature is to bewray any metal it toucheth:
and *Tantalus* for his little fecrecie in bewraying
that *Proferpina* ate a graine of Pomegranate, is
placed in hell, vp to the chin in water, with continuall thirft, and hath apples hang ouer his head,
with extreme hunger: whereof the Poet faith:

Quærit aquas in aquis, & poma fugatia captat
Tantalus: hoc ille garrula lingua dedit.

But why doe I deláy death with thefe friuolous

difcourfes of women : fuffice they are blabs? and
fo turning to the deaths-man, laying his necke on
the blocke, his head was fmitten off. The execution done ; his death was lamented, and his body
folemnly intombed as thou feeft, all exclaiming
againft my daughter *Marpefiaies* little fecrecy: who
in penance of her fault, vfed once a day to vifite
the tombe, and here to her louer['s] foule, facrifice
many fighes and teares : at length *Venus* taking
pittie of her plaints, thinking to eafe her of her
forrow, and to inflict a gentle and meek reuenge,
turned her into this Rofe tree.

As *Alcida* had vttered thefe words, there was a
fhip within kenne, whofe ftreamers hanging out,
I judged by their colours they were of *Alexandria*:
whereupon I waued them to leeward : the Mariners
(more than ordinary courteous) ftruck failes, &
fent their cockbotes a fhore : the / fhippers were
no fooner a land, but I knew them to be of *Alexandria*, and for all my misfortunes, bafely attired
as I was, the poore knaues called me to remembrance, and their reuerence done, afked if I
would to *Alexandria* : I told them it was mine
intent: whereupon, taking leaue of my old Oafteffe,
the Counteffe *Alcida*, with many thanks for my
courteous entertainment, fhee verie loth to leaue
me, went with the Mariners towards the boate.

The poore Lady, feeing her felfe alone, fell to

her wonted teares, which the gods taking pittie on,
before my face turned to a fountaine; I wondering at their deities, entered the boate, and
went to the ſhip, where welcommed and
reuerenced of the Maſter, and the
reſt, hoiſing vp all our ſayles,
we made for
ALEXANDRIA.

(∵)

XX.

MOURNING GARMENT.

1590—1616.

NOTE.

'Greene's Mourning Garment' appeared originally in 1590; but the only edition that I have been able to trace is that of 1616, for which I am again indebted to the 'Huth Library,' as before. See annotated Life in Vol. I.—G.

GREENES

Mourning Garment:

GIVEN HIM BY RE-

pentance at the Funerals

of LOVE;

which he preſents for a fauour to all
young *Gentlemen,* that wiſh to weane
themſelues from wanton deſires.

Both Pleaſant and Profitable.

By R. GREENE.

Vtriuſq. Academiæ in Artibus Magiſter.

Sero *ſed* Serio.

Aut Nvnquam vt Nvnc.

LONDON

Printed by *George Purſlowe,* dwelling at the Eaſt end of
Chriſts Church.   1616.   (4°).

To the Right
Honourable, George *Clifford,*
Earle of Cumberland :
Robert Greene, *wiſheth increaſe of all
Honourable vertues.*

WHile wantonneſſe (Right Honourable) ouerweaned the *Niniuites,* their fur-coates of biſſe
were all poliſhed with gold : But when the threat-
ning of *Ionas* made a iarre in their eares, their fineſt
ſendall was turned to ſackcloath : the exterior
habite of the *Iewes,* bewrayed their interiour hearts,
and ſuch as mourned for their ſinnes, were by
preſcript and peremptorie charge commanded to
diſcouer it in their garments.   Entring (Right
Honourable) with a reaching in-ſight into the
ſtrict regard of theſe rules, hauing my ſelfe ouerweaned with them of *Niniuie* in publiſhing ſundry
wanton Pamphlets, and ſetting forth Axiomes of
amorous Philoſophy, *Tandem aliquando* taught with
a feeling of my palpable follies, and hearing with
the eares of my heart *Ionas* crying, / *Except thou*

repent, as I haue changed the inward affectes of
my minde, fo I haue turned my wanton workes
to effectuall labours, and pulling off their vaine-
glorious titles, haue called this my *Mourning Garment*, wherein (Right Honourable) I difcouer the
forwardneffe of youth to ill, their reftleffe appetites
to amorous effects, the preiudice of wanton loue,
the difparagement that growes from prodigall
humours, the difcredite that enfues by fuch inordinate defires : and laftly, the fatall detriment that
followes the contempt of graue and aduifed counfaile. Thus (may it pleafe your Honour) haue I
made my Mourning Garment of fundry pieces ;
but yet of one colour, blacke, as bewraying the
forrow for my finnes, and haue ioyned them with
fuch a fimpathie of according feames, as they tend
altogether to the regard of vnfained repentance.
But here may your Honour bring my prefumption
in queftion, why I attempted to fhrowd it vnder
your Lordfhips patronage, as if by this I fhould
infer, that it were a perfwafiue Pamphlet to a
Patron toucht with the like paffion : which obiection
I anfwere. *Ouid*, after hee was banifhed for his
wanton papers written, *de Arte Amandi*, and of his
amorous Elegies betweene him and *Corinna*, being
amongft the barbarous *Getes*, and though a Pagan,
yet toucht with a repenting paffion of the follies of
his youth, hee fent his *Remedium Amoris*, and part

of his *Triſtibus* to *Cæſar*, not that *Auguſtus* was
forward in thoſe fancies, or that hee ſought to
reclaime the Emperor from ſuch faults ; but as
gathering by infallible coniectures, that hee which
ſeuerely puniſhed ſuch laſciuious liuers, would be
as glad / to heare of their repentant labours. Thus
(Right Honorable) you heare the reaſon of my
bold attempt, how I hope your Lordſhip will be
glad with *Auguſtus Cæſar*, to read the reformation
of a ſecond *Ouid* : pardon my Lord, inferiour by
a thouſand degrees to him in wit or learning, but
I feare halfe as fond in publiſhing amorous fancies.
And if any young Gentlemen or Schollers ſhall
weare this weede, as I doubt not many will looke
on it, and handle it, and by the vertue therof
wean themſelues from wanton deſires, and hate the
monſtrous and deformed ſhape of vice, when it is
ſhaken from vnder the vayle of pretended vertue,
let the recouery of ſuch loue-ſicke Patients, be
attributed to your Honour, whoſe Patronage
ſhrowdes it from the preiudice of contempt; and
if your Honour ſhall but looke on it, and laugh at
it, and partly like it, the end of my labours haue a
condigne counterpoiſe. In which hope I commit
your Honour to the Almighty.

Robert Greene. /

To the Gentlemen Schollers of both Vniuerſities,

increaſe of all vertuous fortunes

(*.*.*)

T was hard (courteous Loue-mates) of Learning for *Anthony* to *Captare beneuo-lentiam Senatorum*, when his owne deedes had proued him a peremptory foe to *Rome*. The *Grecians* would not heare *Antiſthenes* diſpute of the immortality of the ſoule, becauſe his former Philoſophy was to the contrary. Sodain changes of mens affeᵈcts craue great wonder, but little beliefe ; and ſuch as alter in a moment, win not credit in a moneth. Theſe premiſſes (Gentlemen) driues me into a quandary, fearing I ſhall hardly inſinuate into your fauours, with changing the titles of my Pamphlets, or make you beleeue the inward metamorphoſis of my minde, by the exterior ſhew of my workes, ſeeing I haue euer profeſſed my ſelfe Loues Philoſopher. Yet *Diogenes* of a coyner of money became a Correᵈctor of manners : and *Ariſtotle* that all his life had been an Atheift, cryed at his death, *Eris entium miferere mei* : What *Ouid* was in *Rome*, I referre to his Elegies : what he was amongft the *Getes*, I gather from his *Triftibus* : how he perfeuered in his repentant forrowes, the difcourfe of his death doth manifeft. The *Romanes* that heard his loues beleeued his penance. Then Gentlemen let me finde like fauour, if I that wholly gaue my felfe to the difcourfing of amours, bee now applyed to better labours ; thinke, though it be *Sero*, yet is it *Serio*, and though my fhowers / come in Autumne, yet thinke they fhall continue the whole yeare. Hoping you will grace me with your fauorable fufpence till my deedes proue my doctrine, I prefent you with my *Mourning Garment.* Wherein (Gentlemen) looke to fee the vanity of youth, fo perfectly anatomifed, that you may fee euery veine, mufcle and arterie of her vnbridled follies. Looke for the difcouery of wanton loue, wherewith ripe wits are fooneft inueigled, and Schollers of all men deepeft intangled. Had *Ouid* beene a Dunce, he had neuer deliuered fuch amorous precepts : had *Ariftotle* had leffe wit, he had had leffe loue, and *Hermia* had not ridden him with a fnaffle : of all flowres the Rofe fooneft withereth, the fineft Lawne hath the largeft moale, the moft orient Pearle fooneft blemifht, and the moft pregnant wit fooneft tainted with affection. Schollers haue piercing

infights, and therefore they ouerweene in their
fights, feeding their eyes with fancy, that fhould
bee peering on the principles of *Plato*: they reade
of *Venus*, and therefore count euery faire face a
goddeffe, and grow fo religious, that they almoft
forget their God : they count no Philofophy like
Loue, no Author fo good as *Ouid*, no obiect fo
good as Beauty; nor no exercife in fchooles fo
neceffary as courting of a faire woman in a
Chamber : but pleafe it you (Gentlemen) to put
on my *Mourning Garment*, and fee the effects that
grow from fuch wanton affects, you wil leaue *Ouids*
Art, & fall to his remedy, abiure *Auicen* and his
principles, and with *Horace* fit downe and dine
with his Satyres, you will think women *Mala*,
although they be to fome kinde of men *Neceffaria*,
you will hold no herefie like Loue, no infection
like Fancie, no obiect fo preiudiciall as Beautie,
and entring into the follies of your youth fore-paft,
will figh, and fay :

Semel infaniuimus omnes.

Ah Gentlemen, I wifh to you as I would to my
felfe, new Loues, not to *Venus*, but to Vertue, not
to a painted goddeffe, but to a pittifull God : and
therefore being a member of both Uniuerfities,
haue I prefumed to prefent it to the Youth of
the two famous Academies, hoping they will as

gratefully accept it, as I heartily fend it. If you enter into the depth of my conceit, and fee how I haue, onely with humanity, moralized a diuine Hiftorie, and fome odde fcoffing companion, that hath a Common-wealth of felfe-loue in his head, / fay ; euery painted cloth is the fubiect of this Pamphlet: I anfwere him with a common principle of Philofophy :

Bonum quo communis eo melius :

and if that will not ferue, let him either amend it, or elfe fit downe and blowe his fingers, till hee finde his *Memento* will ferue to fhape my Garment after a new cut. I know (Gentlemen) fooles will haue bolts, and they will fhoote them afwell at a Bufh as at a Bird, and fome will haue frumps, if it be but to call their Father whorefon : but howfo-euer, I know, *facilius eft μωμησέται quam μιμησέται,* and a dog will haue a barking tooth, though he be warned : to fuch I write not, let them be ftill vaine, but to the courteous Schollers, whom if I profite with my *Mourning Garment,* and weane them with the fight of it from their wanton defires, I haue the full defired end of my labours, in which hope refting, I commit my felfe, and my booke to your fauorable cenfures.

Yours

ROBERT GREENE. /

GREENES
MOURNING
GARMENT.

N the Citty of *Callipolis* feated in
the land of *Auilath*, compaffed
with *Gihon* and *Euphrates*, two
riuers that flowe from *Eden*, there
fometimes dwelled a man called
Rabbi Bileffi, lineally defcended from the feede of
holy *Sem*, ayming in his life to imitate his pre-
deceffors perfection, as he was allied vnto him in
Parentage. This *Rabbi Bileffi* was a man vpon
whom Fortune had powred out the *Cornucopia* of
her fauours, and prodigally had wrapt him in the
veftment of her riches, feeking as farre to exceede
Nature in excellence, as Nature had ouer-reacht
her felfe in cunning : For hee was the chiefe

Burgamafter of the whole City : aged he was,
for the Palme tree had difplayed her bloffomes on
his head, and his haires were as white as the filke
that is folde in Tyre : honour had pitcht her
pauilion in his treffes, and the tramelles of his
haire were full of reuerence : his countenance
graue, as became his yeares, and yet full of lenity ;
that as the Eagle hath talents to ftrike, and wings
to fhadow : fo his lookes carried threats to chaftife,
and fauours to incourage. This old man being
thus grac'd by Nature and fortune, hath the gifts
of the minde fo interlarded with the excellence
of all vertues, that if *Ariftotle* had been aliue, he
would haue confeft this *Rabbi* to haue attained to
the perfection / of his *fummū bonum*. Thus euery
way happy, Fortune, not content to inrich him
with thefe fauours, that he might bee the Phenix
of all felicity, gaue him by one wife two fonnes,
iffued of fuch a tree, as might difcouer the tripartite
fourme of his life.

The defcription of his eldeft Sonne.

THe eldeft, whofe name was *Sophonos*, was fo
beholding vnto Nature for the liniaments of
his body, as he could not wrong her with any
default of cunning, for fhe had fo curioufly leueld
euery lim, as thogh fhe would prefent vertue a
fubiect wherein to flourifh. His exteriour pro-

portion was not more pleafing to the eye, than
his inward perfection to the eare, refembling the
Panther in excellence of hiew, and the Syren in
harmony of vertues : young he was, for as yet the
prime of his yeeres was in the flowre, and youth
fate and bafted him Calendes in his forehead.
But as the Synamon tree looketh tawny when he
is a twigge, and the Halciones moft black when
they are moft young : fo *Sophonos* in his tender
yeeres carried graue thoughts, and in the fpring
of his youth fuch ripe fruits, as are found in the
Autumne of age : yet was he not *Morofus*, tyed to
aufterne humours, neither fo cinicall as *Diogenes*,
to miflike *Alexanders* royalty, nor fuch a *Timonift*,
but hee would familiarly conuerfe with his friends :
he counted *Cato* too feuere, and *Caffius* too fullen,
and both too fond, not laughing once a yeere with
Apollo, but holding all honeft and merry recreation neceffary, fo it were not blemifht with any
exceffe : yet as he was indued with thefe fpeciall
qualities, Nature was fpotted with fome little im-
perfections : the Phenix amongft all her golden
plumes may haue one ficke feather, and yet a
Phenix : the pureft Pome-granates may haue one
rotten kernell, and the perfecteft man is not without fome blemifh, and fo was *Sophonus* : for as he
was graue, wife, vertuous, and affable, yet hee had
that fault which / *Tully* called *defeĉtum Naturæ*,

and that was cowardize : fearefull he was of his flefh, and thought it good fleeping in a whole fkinne : hee preferd the Oliue before the Sword, and the Doue before the Eagle, peace before wars : and therefore giuing himfelfe to Marchandize, he remained at home with his father.

The defcription of the youngeft fonne.

THe youngeft, who was called *Philador*, was fo beautified with exterior fauour, that *Natura naturans*, which the Philofophers call the exquifite former of features, feemed to fet (*non vltra*) on his liniaments. When Nature had caft this curious mould, that fhe might triumph as the miftris of all perfection, fhee infufed fuch interiour and vitall fpirits into this carkafe, that it feemed repollifhed with the purity of the fenfes. For *Philador* had fo pregnant a wit, and fuch a fwift infeeing and reaching capacity, as it feemed the graces in fome Synode had poured out the plenty of their influence. Quicke it was and pleafant, full of fuch wittie *facetiæ* and affable fentences, that thofe Epithetons that *Homer* affigned to *Vliffes*, might very well haue beene afcribed to *Philador* : he was courteous to falute all, counting it commendable prodigality that grew from the Bonnet and the Tongue, alluding to this olde verfe of *Chaucer*.

Mickle grace winnes he
    That's franke of bonnet, tongue and knee.

To court amongſt the beautifull Dames of *Callipolis,* he had ſuch a ready inſinuation of pleaſant prattle, powdred with ſuch merry queſtions, ſharpe replies, ſweet taunts, and delightful ieſts, that as he was an Adamant to euerie eye, for his beauty, ſo hee was a *Syern* to euery eare for his eloquence, drawing women deſirous of his company, as *Orpheus* the *Bachanals* with his melody. Fit he was for all companies, as a man that had wit at will, his countenance at / commaund, and his thoughts in his fiſt. He could with *Cleanthes* ſtudy with a Candle, and with *Brutus* determine in the night, and yet with *Salerne* ſay :

Balnea, Vina, Venus, &c.,
    Hæc nocent oculis, ſed vigilare magis.

With *Diogenes* he would eate Coleworts, with *Ariſtippus* delicates, with *Ariſtotle* he would allow *Materia prima,* with *Moſes,* that there was no *forma* nor *priuatio,* but *fiat.* To be briefe, he could *cretizare cum Cretenſibus,* and pay ſterling where hee had receiued money that was currant : he, contrary to the diſpoſition of his brother, frequented ſuch company as was agreeable both to his yeares and his thoughts, ſpending the time as pleaſant as

his wit could deuife, and his purfe maintaine, and
would haue done more, if olde *Rabbi Bileffi* his
father had not ouerlooked him with a careful eye :
but as the Storke when hee fees his young too
forward to flye, beateth them into the neft : fo
Bileffi when he faw his fonne beginning to foare
too high with *Icarus*, hee cried to him, *Medium
tutiffimum*, with a fatherly voice, fo reclaiming him
for prouing too rauening. *Philador* feeling his
father held the reines of his liberty with a hard
hand, and that if he bated neuer fo little, he was
checkt to the fift, thought to defire that he might
trauell, and fee the world, and not be brought vp
at home like a meacock: finding therefore one
day his olde Father fitting alone in an Arbour, he
began thus :

Philadors requeft to olde Rabbi Bileffi.

Sir, quoth he, when I confider with my felfe,
what experience *Vliffes* got by trauerfing ftrange
Countries : what Aphorifmes the Philofophers
fought into, by feeking farre from home, I may
either thinke your fatherly loue too tender, that
limits me no further then your looks, or mine
owne folly great, that couet no further trauels.
Tully / faid, Euery country is a wife mans natiue
home ; & *Thales Milefius* thought, as the fun doth
compaffe the world in a day, fo a man fhould cut

through the world in his life, & buy that abroad with trauell, which at home could be purchafed with no treafure. If *Plato* had liued ftill in *Greece*, hee had neuer fetcht his Hieroglyphics from the Egyptians. If *Ariftotle* had ftill, like a Micher, been ftewed vp in *Stagyra*, he had neuer written his workes *De natura Animalium* to *Alexander* : Trauell (father) is the mother of experience ; and for euery penny of expenfe, it returnes home laden with a pound of wifedome. Men are not borne to be tyed to their cradles, nor ought wee with the Tortoife to carry our houfe vpon our backe : the Eagles no fooner fee the pennes of their young ones able to make wing, but they pull their nefts afunder, and let them fly. What? Fortune hateth meacockes, and fhutteth her hand to fuch as feare to feeke her where fhe is : here at home I deny not but I fhall haue wealth, but gotten by your labours, and lands purchafed by your trauels, fo like a Drone fhall I feede on that hony which others haue brought home vnto the Hiue : in *Callipolis* I may learne to trafficke, and to take a turne vp and downe the Exchange, I may for plea-fure take a walke about your Paftures, and either with the hound courfe the Hart, with the Hawke flye the Phefant : recreations they be, and fit for fuch as thinke no fmell good, but their Countries fmoake. But in trauelling forraine Nations, and

trauerſing the Paralels, I ſhall ſee the manners of
men, the cuſtomes of Countries, the diuerſities of
Languages, and the ſundry ſecrets the mother earth
miniſtreth : I ſhall be able at my returne, with the
Geographers, to deſcribe the ſcituation of the earth :
with Coſmographers to talke of Cities, Townes,
Seas and Riuers ; to make report what the Chaldees be in *Ægypt*, the Gymnoſophiſts in *India*, the
Burgonians in *Hetruria*, the Sophi in *Grecia*, the
Druides in *France* ; to talke as well as *Ariſtotle* of
the nature of beaſtes, as well as *Plinie* of Trees
and Plants, as / *Geſnerus* of mineralles and ſtones :
thus wit augmented by experience, ſhall make me
a generall man, fit any way to profit my Common
wealth.   Further, I ſhall haue a deep inſight into
cuſtomes of all Countries : I ſhal ſee how the
Grecians prize of learning, how they value Chiualry,
and practiſe their youth in both, ſo ſhal I taſte of
a Scholler, and ſauour of a Souldier, able, when I
returne, in peace to apply my booke, and in warre
to vſe my Launce.   Seeing then (ſir) I am in the
prime of my youth, liuing at home, onely to feede
your lookes ; let me not ſo idlely paſſe ouer the
flowre of mine age, but giue me leaue to paſſe
abroad, that I may returne home to your ioy and
my countries comfort.   Old *Rabbi Bileſſi* hearing
his ſon in this mind, began to wonder what
new deſire to ſee ſtrange Countries, had tickled

his fonnes humour, but knowing young wits were wandring, he began to reclaime him thus.

Rabbi Bileſſies anſwere to his ſonne Philador.

SOnne, quoth he, thou ſeeſt my yeares are many, and therfore my experience ſhould be much, that age hath furrowed many wrinkles in my face, wherein are hidden many actions of deepe aduice : my white haires I tel thee, haue ſeene many Winters, and further haue I trauelled then I either reaped wiſedome or profite. Sonne, as yet thou haſt not eaten bread with one tooth, nor hath the blacke Oxe trodden vpon thy foote, thou haſt onely fed on the fruits of my labours, and therefore doſt thou couet to taſte of ſtrange pleaſures : But kneweſt thou *Philador*, what a long harueſt thou ſhouldeſt reape for a little corne : What high hazards thou ſhouldeſt goe through for little amends : What large preiudice for ſmall profite, thou wouldeſt ſay, *Nolo tanti pœnitentiam emere.* Firſt, (my ſonne) note, thou art heere in thy natiue country loued of thy friends / and feared of thine enemies, here haſt thou plenty at commaund, and Fortune daunceth attendance on thy will. If thou wilt be a Scholler, thou haſt here learned men with whom to conuerſe : if a Traueller, and deſirous to know the cuſtomes & manners of men, here be Jewes, Grecians, Arabians, Indians, and men of all

nations, who may fully decipher to thee the nature of
euery climate: for the fcituation of the world, thou
haft Mappes, and maieft wander in them as farre
with thine eye as thou wouldeft repent to trauell
with thy foote. Seeing then thou maieft learne as
much in *Callipolis*, as *Vliffes* found in all his weary
& dangerous iournies, content thee with thefe
helps, and reft at home with thine olde father in
quiet: for (my fon) in trauel thou fhalt pocket vp
much difparagement of humor, which I know will
be yerkfome to thy patience : thou muft fit thine
humour to the place, and the perfon, be he neuer
fo bafe. If he wrong thee, thou muft either beare
his braue, or feele the force of his weapon, thou
fhalt be faine to content thee with the meridionall
heate that fcorcheth, and paffe through the fepten-
trionall cloudes that freeze, oft in danger of theeues,
many times of wilde beafts, and euer of flatterers.
In *Creete* thou muft learne to lye, in *Paphos* to be
a louer, in *Greece* a diffembler, thou muft bring
home pride from *Spaine*, lafciuoufneffe from *Italy*,
gluttony from *England*, and carowfing from the
Danes. Thus (my fonne) packe thee forth with
as many vertues as thou canft beare, thou fhalt
difburthen them all, and returne home with as
many vices as thou canft bring. Therefore reft
thee from that foolifh defire to trauell, and content
thee at home with thine old father in quiet. All

thefe perſwaſiue principles of the olde *Rabbi* could not diſſwade *Philador* from the intent of his trauels, but that he replyed ſo cunningly, and ſo importunately, that the olde man was faine to graunt, and bade him prouide him all things neceſſary for his iourney. *Philador* was not ſlacke in this, but with all ſpeede poſſible, did his indeuor, ſo that within ſhort time hee / had all thinges in readineſſe : at laſt the day of his departure came : and then his father bringing forth coine and treaſure great ſtore, deliuered it vnto his ſonne as his portion ; and then ſitting downe with his ſtaffe in his hand, and his handkercher at his eyes, for the olde man wept, he gaue his ſonne this farewell :

Rabbi Bileſies farewell to his ſonne PHILADOR.

NOw my ſonne, that I muſt take my leaue of thee, and ſay farewell to him that perhappes ſhall fare ill, yet before we part, marke and note theſe precepts which thy father hath bought with many yeares, and great experience.

Firſt (my ſonne) ſerue God, let him be the Author of all thy actions, pleaſe him with prayer and penance, leſt if hee frowne, hee confound all thy fortunes, and thy labours be like the droppes of raine in a ſandy ground.

Then forward, let thine owne ſafety be thy next

care, and in all thy attempts forefee the end, and
bee wife for thy felfe.

Be courteous to all, offenfiue to none, and brooke
any iniury with patience, for reuenge is preiudiciall
to a Traueller.

Be Secretary to thy felfe, and hide all thy
thoughts in thy hearts bottome, and fpeake no
more to any priuately then thou wouldeft haue
publifhed openly.

Truft not him that fmyles, for he hath a dagger
in his fleeue to kill, and if his words be like hony-
combes, hie thee from that man, for he is perillous.

Be not too prodigall, for euen they that confume
thee laugh at thee: nor too couetous, for fparing
oftentimes is difhonour.

Little talke fhewes much wifedome, but heare
what thou canft, for thou haft two eares.

Boaft / not of thy coyne, but faine want: for
the praie makes the theefe.

Be not ouercome with wine, for then thou be-
wrayeft all thy fecrets.

Ufe not dice, for they be fortunes whelpes,
which confume thy wealth, and impaire thy patience.

For women, my fonne, oh for them take heede:
they bee Adamants that drawe, Panthers that allure,
and Syrens that intice: they be glorious in fhewe
like the apples of *Tantalus*, but touch them and
they bee duft: if thou falleft into their beauties,

Philador, thou drinkeſt *Aconitum*, and ſo doeſt periſh.

Be (*Philador*) in ſecrecy like the Arabick-tree, that yeelds no gumme but in the darke night : Be like the Curlew, Phyſician to thy ſelfe, and as the Pyrite ſtone ſeems moſt hoat when it is moſt cold, ſo euer diſſemble thy thoughts to a ſtranger. Followe (*Philador*) theſe principles and feare no preiudice, but as thou goeſt out ſafe, ſo returne home without diſparagement to thy father. With this the olde man fell aweeping, and could ſpeake no more, and his ſon that had his ſpurres on his heeles, though[t] his ſaddle was full of thornes, and therfore ſhaking his brother *Sophonos* by the hand, hee tooke his leaue of his friendes : his father (old man) ſhooke his head and got him in, and away flings *Philador* as his thoughts preſent, or his future fortunes would guide him : On he paceth with his men and his foot-boyes towardes *Aſſyria*, and coaſting many Countries, he ſhewed by his expences how liberality kept his purſe ſtrings, and that he cared for money no more then for ſuch mettall as ſerued onely for ſeruile exchange : whereſoeuer he came, or with whomſoeuer he did conuerſe, he ſtil obeyed his fathers precepts, and thoſe axiomes and Economicall principles that old *Rabbi Bileſſi* deliuered to him, he obſerued with ſuch diligence, that all men ſayd, as he was witty,

ſo he was politicke, and though he was ſometimes
wanton, yet hee was alwaies chary, leſt he might
ouerſlip to bee found / faulty : beeing amongſt the
Magiſtrates of any towne, why, young *Philador*
talked of grauity, as though he did only *Catonis
lucernam olere* : hauing the lawes of countries for
the ſubieĉt of his chatt, ſomewhere he commended
Ariſtocracie, amongſt popular men *Democracie*,
amongeſt other *Oligarchia* : Thus he fitted his
humour to euery eſtate. If hee were amongſt
Schollers, then hee had *Ariſtotle* at his fingers end,
and euery phraſe ſmelled of *Cicero*, ſhewing his
witte in quirkes of Sophiſtrie, and his reading in
diſcurations of Philoſophie : if amongſt Courtiers,
why, hee could braue it out as well as the reſt :
amongſt Ladies, there hee was in his 𝔄 [ω], for he
could court them with ſuch glaunces, ſuch lookes,
ſuch louing and amorous prattle, as they thought
him oft paſſionate when he had not once ſtirred
his patience : but were they [the] fayreſt, the fineſt,
the coyeſt, the moſt vertuous, or the moſt excellent
of all : *Caueat Emptor* (quoth hee) he remembred
his fathers charge, that they were Syrens, whoſe
harmony as it was pleaſing, ſo it was preiudiciall,
and therefore he viewed euery face with a ſmile,
and gaue the fowleſt as well as the faireſt kindes
fauour, but for his loue towards thē it was like to
the breath of a man vpon ſteele, which no ſooner

lighteth on, but it leapeth off, holding women as
wantons to bee plaid with for a while, but after to
bee fhaken off as trifles. Being in this humour,
he paffed ouer many Countries, and at laft he
came into *Theffalia*, where he found the Countrie a
Champaine, yet full of faire and pleafant fprings,
and in diuers places in the vallies replenifh'd with
many pleafant groues. In this Country trauailed
Philador in the heat of Summer, when the Sunne
at the higheft fhewed the ftrength of his motion,
& paffed vp into the continent almoft a whole
day, without defcrying either towne, village, hamlet,
or houfe, fo that wearied, hee allighted and walked
afoote down a vale, where he defcryed a Shepherd
and his wife fitting, keeping flockes, hee of fheepe,
fhee of kids. *Philador* glad of this, bade his men
be of good cheare : for now (quoth he) I haue /
within ken a country Swayne, and he fhall direct
vs to fome place of reft. With that, he paced on
eafily, and feeing them fit fo nye together, and fo
louingly, he thought to fteale vpon them, to fee
what they were doing, and therefore giuing his
horfe to one of his boyes, he went afore himfelfe,
and found them fitting in this manner.

The Defcription of the Shepheard and his Wife.

I t was neere a thicky fhade,
   That broad leaues of Beech had made :

Ioyning all their tops fo nie,
That fcarce *Phœbus* in could prie,
To fee if Louers in the thicke,
Could dally with a wanton tricke.
Where fate the Swaine and his wife,
Sporting in that pleafing life,
That CORIDON commendeth fo,
All other liues to ouer-go.
He and fhe did fit and keepe
Flocks of Kids, and fouldes of fheepe:
He vpon his pipe did play,
She tuned voice vnto his lay.
And for you might her Hufwife knowe,
Voice did fing and fingers fowe:
He was young, his coat was greene,
With welts of white, feamde betweene,
Turnèd ouer with a flappe,
That breft and bofome in did wrappe:
Skirts fide and plighted free,
Seemely hanging to his knee.
A whittle with a filuer chape,
Cloke was ruffet, and the cape
Serued for a Bonnet oft,
To fhrowd him from the wet aloft.
A leather fcrip of colour red,
With a button on the head,
A bottle full of Country whigge,
By the Shepheards fide did ligge:

And in a little bufh hard by,
There the Shepheards dogge did lye,
Who while his Mafter gan to fleepe,
Well could watch both kiddes and Sheep.
The Shepheard was a frolicke Swaine,
For though his parell was but plaine,
Yet doone the Authors foothly fay,
His colour was both frefh and gay :
And in their writtes plaine difcuffe,
Fairer was not TYTIRVS,
Nor MENALCAS whom they call,
The Alderleefeft Swaine of all :
' Seeming him was his wife,
Both in line, and in life :
Faire fhe was as faire might be,
Like the Rofes on the tree :
Buxfame, blieth, and young, I weene,
Beautious, like a Summers Queene :
For her cheekes were ruddy hued,
As if Lillies were imbrued,
With drops of bloud to make the white
Pleafe the eye with more delight ;
Loue did lye within her eyes,
In ambufh for fome wanton prize :
A leefer Laffe then this had beene
CORIDON had neuer feene.
Nor was PHILLIS that faire May,
Halfe fo gawdy or fo gay :

She wore a chaplet on her head,
Her caffocke was of Scarlet red,
Long and large, as ftreight as bent,
Her middle was both fmall and gent. /
If Countrie loues fuch fweet defires gaine,
What Lady would not loue a Shepheard Swaine?

The Shepheards wife hauing thus ended her fong,
Philador ftanding by, thought to interrupt them,
and fo began to falute them thus: My friends
(quoth hee) good fortune to your felues, and welfare to your flockes, being a Stranger in this
Country, and vncouth in thefe plaines, I haue
ftraggled all this day weary and thirfty, not hauing
difcried Towne or houfe, onely your felues the firft
welcome obiects to our eyes: may I therefore of
courtefie craue your direction to fome place of reft;
I fhall for fuch kindneffe requite you with thankes.
The Shepheard ftarting vp, and feeing hee was a
Gentleman of fome calling, by his traine, put off
his bonnet and anfwered him thus: Sir, quoth hee,
you are welcome, and fuch courteous Strangers as
your felfe, haue fuch fimple Swaines at command
with your lookes, in greater matters then direction
of wayes, for to that we are by courtefie bound
to euery common Traueller. I tell you Sir, you
ftrooke too much vpon the South, and fo might
haue wandred all day, and at night haue beene

glad of a thicket, for this way there is no lodging ; but whereas, me thought, you fayd you were weary and thirfty, firft take my bottle and tafte of my drinke : fcorne it not, for we Shepheards haue heard tell, that one *Darius* a great king, being dry, was glad to fwink his fill of a Shepheards bottle : hunger needs no fauce, and thirft turnes water into wine: this we earne with our hands thrift, and this we carowfe of to eafe our hearts thirft : fpare it not Sir, theres more mault in the floore. *Philador* hearing the Shepheard in fuch a liberall kinde of phrafe, fet his bottle to his head, and dranke a hearty draught, thinking it as fauourie as euer he tafted at home in his fathers houfe: wel, he dranke and he gaue the Shepheard thankes, who ftill went forward in his prattle thus : Now that you haue quencht your thirft, for the way it is fo / hard to finde, as how charily foeuer I giue you direction, yet vnleffe by great fortune, you fhall miffe of the way ; and therefore feeing it is night, I will leaue my wife and my boy to folde the flockes, and I my felfe will guide you on to the view of a Towne. *Philador* gaue him a thoufand gramercies, and accepted his gentle proffer, and the Shepheard telling his wife where to folde, went with *Philador*, and as they paft downe the way there was a piller erected, whereupon ftood the picture of a Storke, the young one carrying the olde, and

vnder was ingrauen this motto ANTIPECHARGEIN.
Philador demanded of the Shepheard what this
picture meant? Marry fir, quoth he, it is the
reprefentation of a Tombe, for here was buried a
lufty young Shepheard, whofe name was *Merador* :
who hauing a father that was fo old as he could
not goe, was fo kinde to his olde Syre, that he
fpent all his labours to relieue his fathers wants,
nourifhing him vp with fuch fare as his flockes
could yeeld, or his penny buy ; and when the man
would couet to take the ayre, euen to this place
from his lodge would *Merador* bring him on his
fhoulders, refembling they fay herein the Storke,
who when fhe fees the Damme is fo olde fhe
cannot flye, the young takes him on his backe,
and carries him from place to place for food : and
for that *Merador* did fo to his father, after his
death they buried him here with this picture. It
was well done (quoth *Philador*) but if I be not
grieuous in queftions; what monument is that
which ftandeth on yonder hill? Our way lyes by
it (quoth the Shepheard) and then I will tell you
it. In the meane time looke you here, quoth he :
and with that he fhewed him a ftone lying vpon
the ground, whereupon was ingrauen thefe words :

Non ridet periuria Amantum Iupiter.

Here was buried a Shepheard, who in this place

forfwearing his Loue, fell mad, and after in this place flew himfelf, and was here buryed : whereupon in memorie of the fact, the Shepheards erected this monument as a terrour to the reft / to beware of the like trechery. By this, they were come to the hill where *Philador* faw a Tombe moft curiously contriued with Architecture, as it feemed fome cunning Caruer had difcouered the excellency of his workmanfhip : vpon it ftood the picture of a woman of wonderfull beauty naked, only her haire truffed vp in a caule of gold, and one legge croffing another by art, to fhadow that which Nature commands bee fecret : in her left hand fhee held her heart, whereout iffued droppes of bloud : in her right hand fhe held a pillar, whereon ftood a blacke Swan, and the olde verfe written about :

Rara Auis in terris nigro'q fimillima Cigno.

Philador feeing by the beauty of the Tombe, that it was fome monument of worth, demaunded of the Shepheard who was buryed there ? at this the Shephearde ftayd, and with a great figh, began thus : I will tell you Sir, quoth he, here was intombed the faire *Theffalonian* mayde, fo famozed in all writinges vnder the name of *Phillis* : for loue fhe dyed, and fith it is a wonder that women fhould perifh for affection, being as rare a thing as to fee a blacke Swan, they haue placed her here

holding a blacke Swan, with the poefie : and fith
we haue yet a mile and more to the place where I
meane to bring you, I will rehearfe you the courfe
of her life, and the caufe of her death : and fo the
Shepheard began thus.

The Shepheards tale.

HEre in *Theffaly* dwelled a Shepheard called
Sydaris, a man of meane Parentage, but of
good poffeffions, and many vertues, for hee was
holden the chiefe of all our Shepheards, not onely
for his wealth, but for his honeft qualities : this
Sydaris liued [fo] long without any Iffue, that he
meant to make a fifters fonne hee had his heire,
but Fortune that meant to pleafe the olde man in
his age, euen in / the winter of his yeares, gaue
him by a young wife a young daughter called
Rofamond, which, as fhe was a ioy to the olde
Shepheard at her birth, fo fhe grew in proceffe of
time vnto fuch perfection, that fhe was the onely
hearts delight that this olde man had. *Rofamond*
went with her fathers fheepe to the fielde, where
fhe was the Queene of al the Shepheards, being
generally called of them all *Diana*, as well for her
beauty as her chaftity : her fame grew fo great for
the excellency of her feature, that all the Shepheards
made a feaft at *Tempe*, to fee the beauty of *Rofamond*, where all the *Theffalonian* Virgins met

decked in the roialty of their excellency, all ſtriuing
to exceed that day in outward perfection : gallant
they were, and glorious, wanting nothing that
Art could adde to Nature, filling euery eye with
admiration ; but ſtill they expected the comming
of *Roſamond,* infomuch, that one *Alexis* a young
Shepheard, who was the Paragon of all proportions
aboue the reſt, ſayd ; that when *Roſamond* came,
ſhe could not bring more then ſhe ſhould finde :
as he ſpake theſe words, in came olde *Sydaris,* and
after him his daughter, who ſeeing ſuch a company
of bonny Laſſes, and country Swaines in their
brauery, bewrayed her modeſty with ſuch a bluſh,
that all the beholders thought that *Luna* and *Tytan*
had iuſtled in her face together for preferment :
euery eye at her preſence ſtood at gaze, as hauing
no power to draw themſelues from ſuch an heauenly
obiect ; wrapt their looks in the tramels of her
locks, and ſnared them ſo in the rareneſſe of her
face, that the men wondred, and the women hung
downe their heads, as being eclipſed with the
brightneſſe of ſo glorious a Comet. But eſpecially
Alexis : he poore Swaine, felt in him a new fire,
and ſuch vncouth flames, as were not wont to
broile in his breſt ; yet were they kindled with
ſuch delight, that the poore boy lay like the *Sala-*
mander, and though he were neuer ſo nigh the
blaze of the bauine, yet he did not *Caleſcere plus*

quam fatis. As thus all gazed on her, fo fhe glaunced her lookes on all, furueying them as curioufly, / as they noted her exactly: but at laft fhe fet downe her period on the face of *Alexis*, thinking he was the faireft, and the feateft Swaine of all the reft. Thus with lookes and chearing, and much good chat, they paffed away the day till euening came, and then they all departed: *Sydaris* home with his *Rofamond*, and euery man elfe to his cottage, all talking as they went by the way, of the beauty of *Rofamond*; efpecially *Alexis*, who the more highly commended her, by how much the more he was deeply in loue with her. The affects of his fancies were reftleffe, and his paffions peremptory, not to bee pacified, vnleffe by her perfwafiue arguments, and therefore did *Alexis* finde fundry occafions to walk into the fields of *Sydaris* to meet with *Rofamond*: oft would he faine he had loft one of his Ewes, to feeke amongft the fheep-cotes of *Sydaris*, and if Fortune fo fauoured him that he met with *Rofamond*, then his piteous lookes, his glaunces [which] were glazed with a blufh, his fighes, his filence, and euery action bewrayed the depth of his paffion: which *Rofamond* efpying, fmiled at, and pittied, and fo farre grew into the confideration of his affects, that the thoughts thereof waxed in her effectuall; for fhe began to loue *Alexis*, and none but *Alexis*, and to thinke that wanton *Paris* that wooed *Enone*, was not like to her *Alexis*: infomuch, that on a day *Alexis* meeting with her, faluted her with a blufh, and fhe abafhed; yet the Swaine emboldned by Loue, tooke her by the hand, fate downe, and there with fighes and teares bewrayed his loues: fhe with fmiles and pretty hopefull anfweres, did comfort him; yet fo, as fhee held him in a longing, and doubtful fufpence: part they did, fhe affured of her *Alexis*, he in hope of his *Rofamond*, and many of thefe meetings they had, fo fecret, that none of the Shepheards fufpected any loue between them. Yet *Alexis* on a day lying on the hill, was fayd to frame thefe verfes by *Rofamond*. |

❖❖❖❖❖❖❖❖❖❖❖❖❖❖❖❖❖❖❖❖❖❖❖❖❖❖

Hexametra ALEXIS *in laudem* ROSAMVNDI.

Oft haue I heard my liefe *Coridon* report on a loue-
day,
When bonny maides doe meete with the Swaines
in the vally by *Tempe*,
How bright eyd his *Phillis* was, how louely they
glanced,
When fro th' Aarches Eben black, flew lookes as a
lightning,

That fet a fire with piercing flames euen hearts
   adamantine :
Face Rofe hued, Cherry red, with a filuer taint like
   a Lilly.
Venus pride might abate, might abafh with a blufh
   to behold her.
Phœbus wyers compar'd to her haires vnworthy
   the prayfing.
Iunoes ftate, and *Pallas* wit difgrac'd with the
   Graces,
That grac'd her, whom poore *Coridon* did choofe
   for a loue-mate :
Ah, but had *Coridon* now feene the ftarre that
   Alexis
Likes and loues fo deare, that he melts to fighs
   when he fees her.
Did *Coridon* but fee thofe eyes, thofe amorous
   eyelids,
From whence fly holy flames of death or life in a
   moment.
Ah, did he fee that face, thofe haires that *Venus*,
   Apollo
Bafht to behold, and both difgrac'd, did grieue, that
   a creature
Should exceed in hue, compare both a god and a
   goddeffe :
Ah, had he feene my fweet Paramour the taint of
   Alexis,

Then had he fayd, *Phillis*, fit downe furpaffed in
    all points,
For there is one more faire then thou, beloued of
    Alexis.

Thefe verfes doe the Shepheards fay, *Alexis*
made by *Rofamond*, for he oft-times fung them
on his pipe, and at laft they came to the eares of
Rofamond, who tooke them paffing kindly: for
fweet words, and high prayfes are two great arguments to winne womens wils, infomuch, that *Alexis*
ftood fo high in her fauour, that no other Shepheard
could haue any good looke at her hand. At the
laft, as Fame is blab, and Beauty is like fmoake in
the ftraw, that cannot be concealed: the excellency
of *Rofamond* came to the Court, where it was fet
out in fuch curious manner, and / deciphered in fuch
quaint phrafes, that the King himfelfe coueted to
fee her perfection; and therefore vpon a day dis-
guifed himfelfe, and went to the houfe of *Sydaris*,
where, when he came, and faw the proportion of
Rofamond, hee counted Fame partiall in her prattle,
and mans tongue vnable to difcouer that wherein
the eye by viewing might furfet: hee that was
well fkilled in courting, made loue to her, and
found her fo prompt in wit, as fhe was proportioned in body: infomuch, that the King himfelfe
was in loue with her. The Noble men that were

with him, doated vpon her, and each enuied other
as iealous who fhould court her with the moft
glaunces, but all in vaine : her heart was fo fet
vpon *Alexis*, as fhe refpected King nor Keifar in
refpect of her Country Paragon, infomuch that the
King returned home with a flat denyall. This
caufed not his Noble-men to ceafe from their futes,
but they daily followed the chafe ; infomuch that
the houfe of *Sydaris* was a fecond Court: fome
offered her large poffeffions for her dowry, other
as great reuenewes, fome were Caualiers, and men
of great value. Thus euery way was fhe haunted
with braue men, that poore *Alexis* durft not come
neere the fight of the fmoake that came out of the
chimney, paft all hope of his *Rofamond*, thinking
women aymed to be fupremes, that they prize
gold before beauty, and wealth before loue : yet
he houered a farre off, while the Courtiers fell
together by the eares who fhould haue moft fauour,
infomuch that there arofe great mutinies. Whereupon the King fearing fome man-flaughter would
grow vpon thefe amorous conuents, and that *Rofamond* like a fecond *Helena* would caufe the ruine of
Theffaly, thought to preuent it thus : he appointed
a day, when all the Lords, Knights, and Gentlemen,
with the country Swaines of his land fhould meete,
and there before him take their corporall oath, to
bee content with that verdict *Rofamond* fhould fet

downe, which amongſt them all to chooſe for her
huſband, he to poſſeſſe her, and the reſt to depart
quiet. /

Upon this they were reſolued, and ſworne, and
Roſamond ſet vpon a ſcaffold, to take view of all,
the King charging her to take one, and, quoth he,
if it be my ſelfe (ſweet heart) I will not refuſe thee.
Heere *Roſamond* dying all her face with a vermillion bluſh, ſtood, and viewed all : the King in his
pompe commanded all the Realme, and aſked her
if ſhee would bee a Queene, and weare a Crowne :
but ſhee thought ouer-high deſires had often hard
fortunes, and that ſuch as reached at the toppe,
ſtumbled at the roote, that inequality in marriage
was oft enemy to Loue, that the Lion, howſoeuer
yoaked, would ouerlooke all beaſts but his phere,
and therefore the meane was a merry ſong. Beauty,
though ſhee is but a flaſh, and as ſoone as that
withers, the King is out of his bias, I muſt bee
loathed, and hee muſt haue another lemman.

Then ſhee looked lower amongſt the Lords, and
conſidered how ſweete a thing wealth was, that as
riches was the mother of pleaſure, ſo want, and
pouerty was a hatefull thing : yet quoth ſhee, all is
but traſh, I ſhall buy gold too deare, in ſubiecting
my ſelfe to ſo high a huſband : for if I anger him,
then ſhall hee obiect the baſeneſſe of my birth, the
newneſſe of my parentage, and perhaps, turne me

home into my former eftate : then the higher was
my feat, the forer fhall be my fall, and therefore
will I content me with meane defires, as I was
borne to low fortunes. Thus fhe furuaied them
all, feeing many braue youths, and lufty Caualiers,
that were there prefent for her loue. But as fhe
looked round about her, afarre off on a hil faw fhe
Alexis fit with his pipe laid downe by him, his armes
folded, as a man ouergrowne with difcontent, and
vpon his arme hung a willow-garland, as one in
extreme defpaire to be forfakē : feeing fo many
high degrees, to fnare the thoughts of his *Rofamond*,
his lookes were fuch as *Troilus* caft towards the
Greekifh tents to *Creffida*, fuing for fauour with
teares and promifing conftancy with continuall
glances : fo fate poore *Alexis*, expecting when
Rofamond fhould breathe out the / fatall cenfure
of his defpairing fortunes. *Rofamond* feeing her
louer thus paffionate, comforteth him thus. Shee
tolde the King that fhe had taken a generall view
of all the *Theffalians*, that Loue with her alluring
baites had prefented her with many fhewes of
beauty, and Fortune had there fought to inuegle
her with the enticing promifes of dignities : but
Sir, quoth fhee, my Parents are bafe, my birth
low, and my thoughts not ambitious : I am neither
touched with enuy, nor difdaine, as one that can
brooke fuperiours with honour, and inferiors with

loue. I am not Eagle-flighted, and therefore feare
to flie too nigh the Sunne: fuch as will foare with
Icarus, fall with *Phaeton*, and defires aboue Fortunes, are the forepointers of deep falls. Loue,
quoth fhe, is a queafie thing, and great Lords hold
it in their eyes, not their hearts, and can better
draw it with a penfell then a paffion. *Helena* fhal
be but a hang by, when age fits in her forehead.
Beauty is momentany, and fuch as haue onely
loue in their lookes, let their fancies flip with time,
and keepe a Calender of their affection ; that as
age drawes on, loue runs away. Seeing then high
eftates haue fuch flippery fancies, let honours and
dignities goe : *Venus* holds them needfull, but not
neceffary, and welcome the meane eftate, and the
Shepheards loues, who count it religion to obferue
affection : and therefore, feeing I muft choofe one,
and of all thefe but one, yonder fits the lord of
my loue, and that is the young Shepheard *Alexis*.
With that he ftarted vp, and the King and all the
reft of the company looked on him, and faw him
the dappereft Swaine of all *Theffalia* : being content to brooke the choice of *Rofamond*, for that
they were bound thereto by oath and promife, all
accufing Loue, that had made fo faire a creature
looke fo lowe. Well, home went the King with
his traine, and *Alexis* a proud man guarded with
the Shepheards, went toward the houfe of *Sydaris*,

where with great feafting the match was made vp.
Alexis remaining thus the poffeffor of the fayreft
Nymph of *Theffaly*, went / to his cottage, determining with himfelfe when the wedding day
fhould be. As thus he was about to refolue, it
chanced that Loue and Fortune armed themfelues
to giue poore *Rofamond* the frumpe, and that on
this manner. *Alexis* going one day abroad, met
with a Shepheards daughter called *Phillida*, a
Mayd of a homely hiew, nut-brown, but of a
witty and pleafant difpofition : with her he fell
in chat, and fhee (to tell you the truth) with her
Alexis fell in loue. In loue did *Alexis* fall with
this nut-browne *Phillida*, that he quite forgot
his faire *Rofamond*, and *Phillida* [who] perceiued
that fhe had wonne the faire Shepheard, left not
to inuegle him with her wit, till fhee had fnared
him in, that *Alexis* could not be out of her fight :
which at laft came to the eares of *Rofamond* : but
fhe incredulous, would not beleeue, nor *Alexis* confeffe it, till at laft *Sydaris* efpied it, and told it to
his daughter, wifhing her to caft off fo inconftant
a louer. But loue that was fettled in the centre
of her heart, made her paffionate, but with fuch
patience, that fhe fmothered the heate of her
forrowes, with inward conceit pining away, as a
woman forlorne : till on a day *Alexis* ouerdoating
in his fancies, ftept to the Church and married

himfelfe to *Phillida* : which news for certain brought vnto the eares of *Rofamond,* fhee caft her felfe downe on her bedde, and paffed away the whole day and night in fighs and teares : but as foone as the Sunne gaue light to the world, fhee leapt from her couch, and beganne to wander vp and downe the fieldes, mourning for the loffe of her *Alexis* : wearied at laft with tracing through the fieldes, fhee fate her downe by *Tempe,* and wrote thefe mournfull verfes. /

Hexametra ROSAMVNDAE *in dolerem amiffi* ALEXIS.

*T*Empe the Groue where darke *Hecate* doth keep
    her abiding :
Tempe the Groue where poore *Rofamond* bewails her
    Alexis,
Let not a tree nor a fhrub be greene to fhew thy
    reioycing ;
Let not a leafe once decke thy boughes and
    branches, O *Tempe,*
Let not a bird record her tunes, nor chaunt any
    fweet Notes,
But *Philomele,* let her bewayle the loffe of her
    amours,
And fill all the wood with dolefull tunes to bemone
    her :
Parched leaues fill euery Spring, fill euery Fountaine,

All the Meades in mourning weede fit them to
  lamenting.
Eccho fit and fing defpaire i' the Vallies, i' the
  Mountaines;
All *Theffaly* helpe poore *Rofamond* mournfull to
  bemone her :
For fhe's quite bereft of her loue, and left of *Alexis*:
Once was fhe liked, and once was fhe loued of
  wanton *Alexis*.
Now is fhe loathed, and now is fhe left of trothleffe
  Alexis:
Here did he clip and kiffe *Rofamond*, and vowe by
  Diana :
None fo deare to the Swaine as I, nor none fo
  beloued,
Here did he deepely fweare, and call great *Pan* for
  a witneffe,
That *Rofamond* was onely the Rofe belou'd of
  Alexis,
That *Theffaly* had not fuch an other Nymph to
  delight him :
None (quoth he) but *Venus* faire fhall haue any
  kiffes.
Not *Phillis*, were *Phillis* aliue fhould haue any
  fauours,
Nor *Galate*, *Galate* fo faire for beautious eyebrowes,
Nor *Doris* that Laffe that drewe the Swaines to
  behold her :

Not one amongſt all theſe, nor all ſhould gaine any
    graces,
But *Roſamond* alone to her ſelfe ſhould haue her
    Alexis.
Now to reuenge the periurde vowes of faithleſſe
    Alexis,
Pan, great *Pan,* that heardſt his othes, and mighty
    Diana,
You *Dryades* and watry Nymphes that ſport by the
    Fountaines:
Faire *Tempe* the gladſome groue of greateſt *Apollo,*
Shrubs, and dales, and neighbouring hils, that heard
    when he ſwore him /
Witnes all, and ſeeke to reuenge the wrongs of a
    Virgin:
Had any Swaine been lieſe to me but guilefull
    Alexis,
Had *Roſamond* twinde Myrtle boughes, or Roſe-
    mary branches,
Sweet Holihocke, or elſe Daffadill, or ſlips of a Bay
    tree,
And giuen them for a gift to any Swaine but *Alexis*:
Well had *Alexis* done t' haue left his roſe for a
    giglot.
But *Galate* nere lou'd more deare her louely *Me-*
    nalcas,
Then *Roſamond* did dearely loue her trothleſſe
    Alexis.

IX.   11

Endimion was nere beloued of his *Citherea*,
Halfe fo deare as true *Rofamond* beloued her
      Alexis:
Now feely Laffe, hie downe to the lake, hafte downe
      to the willowes,
And with thofe forfaken twigs go make thee a
      Chaplet,
Mournful fit, & figh by the fprings, by the brookes
      by the riuers,
Till thou turne for griefe, as did *Niobe* to a Marble:
Melt to teares, poure out thy plaints, let Eccho
      reclame them,
How *Rofamond* that loued fo deare is left of *Alexis*:
Now dye, dye *Rofamond*, let men ingraue o' thy
      toombe-ftone :
      Here lyes fhe that loued fo deare the youngfter Alexis,
      Once beloued, forfaken late of faithleffe Alexis :
      Yet Rofamond did dye for loue, falfe hearted Alexis.

      Thefe Verfes fhee wrote, and many dayes after
fhee did not liue, but pined away, and in moft
pittifull paffions gaue vp the ghoft : her death did
not onely grieue her father *Sydaris*, but was bruted
abroad to ỹ eares of *Alexis* ; who, when he heard
the effectual effence of her loues, and entred into
confideration of his wrongs, hee went downe vnto
the water fide, and in a fury hung himfelfe vpon
a willow tree. This tragicke newes came to the

eares of the King, who being certified the whole
truth by circumſtance, came downe, and in mourning attire lamented for the loſſe of faire *Roſamond* ;
and for that hee would haue the memorie of ſuch a
Virgine to be kept, hee erected this Toombe, and
ſet vp this Monument. /

The Shepheard had ſcarce ended his tale, but
they were within ken of a Towne, which gladded
the heart of young *Philador* : for had not this
hiſtory of *Roſamond* made the way ſomewhat ſhort,
he had been tyred long before : well, the Towne
once deſcryed, Yonder (quoth the Shepheard) Sir,
is your place of reſt : a pretty City it is, and
called *Saragunta* : good lodging you ſhall finde,
but the people within it are paſſing falſe : eſpecially
(if a plaine Country mans counſaile might auaile)
take heed of the ſigne of the Unicorne: there Sir
is a houſe of great ryot, and prodigality in youth,
it is like ruſt on yron that neuer leaues fretting till
it be conſumed : beſides, there be three Siſters, all
beautifull and witty, but of ſmall honeſty : their
eyes are hookes that draw men in, and their words
birdlime that tyes the feathers of euery ſtranger,
that none can eſcape them, for they are as dangerous as the Syrens were to *Vliſſes*. Some ſay they
are like *Circes* riches, and can turne vaine glorious
fooles into Aſſes, gluttonous fooles into Swine,
pleaſant fooles into Apes, proude fooles into Pea-

cockes : and when ſhee [they] hath [have] done,
with a great whippe, ſcourge them out at doores :
take heed maſter (quoth the Shepheard) you come
not there, vnleſſe you haue the herbe that *Vlyſſes*
had, left you returne ſomeway transformed.   Thus
Maſter, I haue brought you to the foot of the hill:
now will I take my leaue, and home to my wife,
for the ſun wil ſet ere I can get to my little cottage.
The Gentleman gaue the Swain hearty thanks,
both for his pains & his prattle, and rewarded him
well, and ſo ſent him away.   The Shepheard gone,
Philador takes his way to the City, and for that
hee had heard him tell of the three Siſters, he
went to take vp his lodging there, and ſo make
experience of the orders of the houſe, and qualities
of the women : in he rode and enquired to the
place & there alighted.   Theſe merry Minions
ſeeing ſuch a frolick Gallant come riding in,
thought that now their purſes ſhould be fild, if
his abode were lōg there, and his coffers ful of
any crownes : his boy no ſooner held his ſtyrop, /
and he lept from his horſe, but the Eldeſt of them
al, a gallant and ſtately Dame, came and ſaluted
him, and gaue him a hearty welcome, ſhewing him
her owne ſelfe ſtraight to his chamber, where hee
found all things in ſuch order, that he thought
he was not come into a common Inne, but ſome
ſtately Palace.   *Philador* ſeeing ſo faire an Hoſtis,

and fuch good lodging, fayd to himfelfe the old text :

Bonum eft nobis effe hic,

And fo thought to fet vp his reft for a weeke or two. As he was in a quandary what he fhould do, came in the fecond fifter, more braue then the firft: a woman of fuch comely perfonage, and fo fweete a countenance, that *Philador* turned his doubt to a peremptorie refolution, that there he would ftay for a while : this cunning Courtefan gaue him friendly intertainement and a welcome with a fmile, and a cup of wine to wafh downe: all which *Philador* tooke kindly, and defired her they might haue good cheare to fupper, and to promife that both fhe and her fifters would be his guefts: a little intreatie ferued, and fhe made faithful pro-mife, which indeede was perfourmed : for when fupper time came, and *Philadors* feruants had ferued vp the meate, in came (for the laft difh) the three fifters, very fumptuoufly attyred: but the youngeft exceeded them all in excellencie : vpon whom *Philador* no fooner caft his eye, but he felt himfelfe fettered. He that could [fhew] his courtefie, intertained them al as gracioufly, and welcommed them on this manner : Faire Gentlewomen (quoth he) I would by outward demonftration you could coniecture how kindly I take it, that all three

of you would vouchfafe fo friendly to come and
beare a Gentleman and a ftranger company : now
I haue no other meanes to requite you, but thankes,
and fuch fimple cheare as you haue taken paines
to prouide, but wherefoeuer I come I fhall make
report what fauourable intertainement I haue found
in this place: and giue me leaue to feate you. The
eldeft ftraying backe a little, before fhe fate, made
this reply : I am glad fir, if any waies we haue
brought you content : but / Sir, I pray you thinke
it not a common fauour that we vfe to euery
ftranger thus to beare him company, for our
cuftome is to attend below, and to be feene little
aboue ; efpecially al together in fuch equipage : if
your fortune bee better than the reft, then fay you
came in a lucky houre : but we are not fo blinde
but we can difcerne of colours, and though they
be both Cryftalline, yet difcouer a Diamond from a
Saphir, and fo Sir I will take you this night for mine
Hoaft : with that fhe and both her fifters fate down
to fupper. *Philador* feeing thefe, thought on the
three goddeffes that appeared to *Paris* in the vale
of *Ida*, and though he were paffing hungry with
long trauaile, yet had fedde his eyes with beauty
as well as hee did his ftomake with delicates, fo
that euery fenfe for fupper time was occupied.

When hee had well victualled himfelfe, and that
his belly began to be full, hee thought to try their

wittes with chat, and therefore began thus. Now Gentlewomen, do I finde the olde Prouerbe true: Better fill a mans belly then his eye, for your fauoury victuals haue ftayed my ftomake ; but mine eye reftleffe, takes fuch greedy furuey of your beauties, as I feare by long looking, he wil furfet: but I am in good hope, if I fhould fall loue-ficke, I might finde you fauourable Phyficions. It is fir (quoth the eldeft) a dangerous difeafe, and we haue little fkill in herbes, yet in what we might, we would feeke to eafe your maladie with womens medicines. I pray you, quoth *Philador*, let me afke you all a queftion without offence : you may fir (quoth the eldeft) if it be not offenfiue: & how if it be (quoth *Philador*?) Then pardon fir (q^d. fhe) if we be as lauifh to reply as you to demaund. Howfoeuer you take it (q^d. *Philador*) then this it is: I pray you faire Ladyes, are you all maides? at this they blufht, and the eldeft made anfwere they were. And fo (quoth *Philador*) long may you not continue, for feare any of you fhould dye with her Virginity, and leade Apes in hell: but it is no matter, maydes or not maides. /

Bene vixit qui bene latuit, Caute fi non Cafte.

The Cat may catch a moufe and neuer haue a bel hanged at her eare : and what needes the hand a Taber, when hee meanes to catch the Hare ?   I beleeue and hold it for a principle that you are all maides: now then let me craue fo much fauour at your hands, as to tell me if you were to chufe hufbands at your owne voluntary, and it ftood in your free election, what manner of hufbands would you chufe? I (quoth the eldeft) would haue one that were beautifull: the fecond fayd, witty : the youngeft, valiant. We haue nothing to do (quoth *Philador*) after fupper : and therefore may it pleafe you feuerally to fhew me the reafons that do induce you to this choyce. The Gentlewomen agreed to this, and the eldeft began thus.

The difcourfe of the eldeft Sifter.

I Hope Sir (quoth fhee) you expect no Rhethoricall infinuation, nor no curious *Circumquaque* to fetch my *exordium* in with figures: only you confider I am a woman, and therefore looke for no more but bare reafons without Sophiftry or eloquence. Such Philofophers generally as haue written *de fenfu*, as *Ariftotle* and other Naturalifts, or fuch Phyficions as by anatomizing haue particularly fet downe the parts of man, affirme that the fight is the moft pure, quickeft & bufieft of all the fenfes, and therfore moft curious in the choice of his object : and fo precious a fenfe it is, that nature to comfort it, made al things vpon the face of the earth green, becaufe the fight aboue all

delightes in that colour. The eye beeing the
furueyour of all exteriour obiects, pleafeth himfelfe
in thofe that are moft beautifull, and coueteth that
euery fuperficies be faire and pleafing, commending
it ftraight to the phantafie as a thing of worth.
For in flowers it alloweth with fauour of the faireft,
as the Carnation, the Rofe, the Lylly, and the
Hiacynth. In trees, the / eye liketh of the tall
Cedar, before the low Beech, and prayfeth the
ftature of the Oake, before the fmallneffe of other
plants. So in ftones, the Diamond is preferd before
the flint, the Emerauld before the marble, and
the Saphir highlier efteemed for the hue, then
the Porphuer for his hugeneffe: and fo by confe-
quence in humane creatures, loue being of al the
paffions in man the moft excellent, alotteth her
felfe to the eye, of al the parts the moft pure,
thinking that the fight will be fooneft inueagled
with the faireft: and what fairer thing can there
be then beauty? fo that loue bringing a beautifull
creature, prefents it to the eye, and that liking it
for the property, conueies the effect thereof to the
heart, and there is knit vp the fimpathy of defires.
By thefe premifes fir, then I infer that the eye is
loues Cator, and who fo pleafeth his eye contenteth
his affects: then why fhould not I choofe a beautifull hufband, whofe exquifite perfection euery way
may content my fancy? for if the eye find any

blemiſh in deformitie, ſtraight loue begins to waxe
colde, and affection to take his farewell.   A beautifull man, why he is a pearle in a womans eye, that
the lineaments of his feature, make her ſurfet with
delight, and there can be no greater content then
to enioy a beautifull and comely perſonage : and in
my opinion by ſo much the more are wel proportioned men to be loued, by how much the more
they excell the deformed.   In all things the perfection of the inward qualities is knowne by the
exteriour excellence : the Roſe being the fayreſt of
flowers, hath the moſt precious ſauour, the brighteſt
Diamond the moſt deepeſt operation, the greeneſt
herbe the moſt ſecret vertue : Nature hath euer
with a prouident foreſight harboured the moſt
excellent qualities in the moſt beautifull carkaſſe :
Diogenes had a deformed body, ſo had he a crooked
minde : *Paris* well fauoured, and full of curteſie :
Thirſites ill· ſhapen, and none (ſayth *Homer*) more
full of bad conditions : *Achilles* comely and courteous : if then ſir, the more a man be beautifull,
the more he is vertuous : /

Gnatior eſt pulchro veniens è corpore virtus.

Let mee haue for my huſband, ſuch a one as
may content mine eye with his beauty, and ſatisfie
my ſight with his proportion.

The difcourfe of the fecond Sifter.

I Cannot denie (quoth the fecond) but beauty is a precious thing, and Metaphuficall, as being diuinely infufed vpon man from aboue, but yet he that commended it moft, writ vpon [it] this diftichon.

Forma bonum fragile eft quantumque accedit ad annos,
Fit minor & fpatio carpitur ipfe fuo.

The fayreft Rofe hath his canker, the braueft branch his Caterpillers, the brighteft fun his clowde, and the greateft beauty his blemifh. *Helena* had a fkar, *Leda* a wen, *Layes* a fpot in her browe, and none fo faire but there is fome fault: but grant all thefe be graces, as *Paris* called *Helens* fkar, *Cos amoris*, yet at length fhe looking in a glaffe, figh'd to fee age triumphant in her forhead. There is none fo faire but the funne will parch, the froft nip, the leaft fickneffe will change, or the leaft exteriour preiudice blemifh, and then where is loue that grows from the pleafure of the eye? vaded, and vanifht, and turned to a cold miflike. But giue me that which is permanent, that feedeth the eare with delight, and increafeth with age, and that is wit, farre excelling beauty: for by how much the more the interiour fenfes are more precious, and the gifts of the minde more excellent then the exteriour organes and inftruments of the body, by fo much the more is wit to be preferred before

the outward proportion of lineaments: wit is a
simpathie of those perfections that growe from the
minde: and what can delight a woman more then
to haue a man full of pleasant conceits, witty
answeres, and eloquent deuices? were not the
Philosophers for their wits fellow companions to
Kings? *Ouid* that was the grand-master of loue,
wanne he / not *Corinna* more with his wit then his
beauty? yes: we finde that as the herbes are more
estimated by the inward vertue then the outward
colour, so the glories of the minde are more then
the glosses of the body: the Cedar is beautifull, yet
lesse valued then the crooked Synamond, for that
men measure the profit more then the proportion :
weeds are gathered for their operation, not for
their outward excellence, and such stones, whose
secret nature worketh most, are worth most, and so
in men, *Cicero* was not so am'able, but hee was
eloquent, and that pleased *Terentia*, *Vlisses* whom
Homer so highly commends in his *Odissea*, wounded
Circes, not with his beautie but with his wisedome,
in so much that he is called *facundus Vlisses*. How
sweet a thing is it, when euery word shal as a
harmony fall in a cadence to please the eare? euery
sillable weighed with a pleasant wit, either turned
to a graue sentence, or a pleasant iest, hauing that
salem ingenij which intangleth more then all the
curious features in the world: *Pallas* helpt *Paris*

more then *Venus*, or elſe *Helena* had ſtill remained
in *Greece*.   *Mercurie* was faine in all Amours to
be *Iupiters* meſſenger, and to witch more with his
wit, then he could do with his Deitie.   Therefore
ſeeing wiſedome is ſo pleaſing a thing, if euer I
marry, God ſend me a witty huſband.

The diſcourſe of the third Siſter.

YOu haue ſaid well, ſiſters, quoth the youngeſt,
    to haue made a good choice, both to pleaſe
the eare, and the eye, in electing wit and beauty,
as two obiects fit for ſuch excellent ſenſes : but yet
to feede my fancy, giue me a man of valour, a
Souldier, a Caualire, one that with his ſword dare
maintaine right, and reuenge wrong.   What is it
for mee to pinne a fayre meacocke and a witty
milkſop / on my ſleeue, who dare not anſwere with
their ſwords in the face of the enemy ?   Shall I
braue mine enemy with beauty, or threaten him
with wit ?   Hee will then either thinke I bring
him a faire foole, or a wiſe Coward.   Was it the
wit of *Alexander* that wonne him ſo much fame, or
his courage ?   Was it *Cæſars* penne, or his ſword
that inſtalled him Emperour ?   *Paris* got *Helena*,
but who defended her ?   *Hector*.   When the
Greekes lay before *Troy*, might not *Andromache*
ſtand on the walls, and ſee *Hector* beating *Achilles*
to his tent, with more honour then *Helena Paris*

ietting in his filkes? Yes, and therefore fhe refted her whole eftate in his proweffe, and fayd:

Tu dominus, tu vir, tu mihi frater eris.

The Oake is called *Arbor Iouis* for the ftrength, the Eagle King of Birds for his courage, the Lyon for his valor, the Diamond is efteemed for the hardneffe, and men efteemed for their magnanimity and proweffe. *Hercules* was neither famoufed for his beauty, nor his wit, but his valiant refolution made him lord of the world, and louer of faire *Deianira*. *Thefeus* was a Souldier, and therefore *Ledas* daughter firft liked him, and rewarded him with her Virginity. Tufh, *Venus* will haue *Mars* to be her Paramour. Loue careth not for Cowards: faint heart neuer wonne faire Lady: a man is the marke all wee ayme at: and who is a man without valour? Therefore a Souldier for my money, or elfe none.

Philador hearing them difcourfe fo wittily, beganne to fmile, and iumpt in with them thus. Gentlewomen, fo many heads, fo many cenfures, euery fancy liketh a fundry friend, and what is an *Antidote* to one is an *Aconiton* to another: you like a faire man, you a wife, you a valiant ; but tell mee, what if there came in a man indued with welth, who like to *Midas* could turn al to gold with a touch, fhould / hee bee thruft out for a wrangler? or might hee not rather difplace beauty, difgrace wit, and put downe valor? I fpeake this, for that I haue heard them fay ; that womens eyes are of the nature of Chrifocoll, that wherefoeuer it meeteth with gold, it mingleth with it, and their hearts like the hearbe *Aurifolium,* that if it be not rubbed with gold once a yeare, it dyeth. I know Sir, quoth the youngeft, the conclufion of this Induction, you would with thefe enigmaticall allufions prooue, that women are couetous, and care more for an ounce of giue mee then a pound of heare me. I deny it not Sir, but wealth and women would be Relatiues ; and therefore Sir, in our choyce, *Quod fub-intelligitur non deeft* : when my Sifter chofe a beautiful man, fhe meant he fhould be rich : and when the fecond fpake of wit, fhe vnderftood wealth : and thinke you me fo fimple Sir, that I would haue a beggerly Souldier? No, no Sir, whether he be beautiful, wife, or valiant, let this ftand for a principle :

Si nihil attuleris, ibis Homere foras.

Gramercy for that, fweet wench, quoth *Philador,* giue vs one cup of Claret more, *in vino veritas.* I fee women are no lyars, they will tell truth in thofe matters that require no conceited fecrecie : fo he dranke to them all : and for that it was late in the night, they all tooke their leaue of him, and went

to bedde. *Philador* once being alone, began to
commend his fortune that had brought him to
fo good a lodging, where, with three fuch witty
wenches he might make his dinners and fuppers
with pleafant chat, *philofophica conuiuia* ; but
efpecially he highly had in his thought the excellency of the youngeft, being already ouer the
fhooes in a little loue forfooth, taking but a little
fleep for his new entertained fancy. The next
morning he vp very early, and bade the Gentlewomen good morrow with a cup of Hipocras,
and after, calling the youngeft afide, where he
courted her a great / while, and at the firft found
her coy, but at the laft, they ended with fuch a
courteous clofe, that he commanded his horfes
to be put to graffe, intending for a time there to
make his refidence. The Gentlewomen feeing
the foole caught, thought to be quick Barbers,
& therefore fpared for no good cheare ; and the
more daintily they fared, the more he thanked
them, fo it might content his young Miftris, on
whofe fauour depended his whole felicity : he was
not content in gluttony to fpend his patrimony,
but fent for fuch copefmates as they pleafed, who
with their falfe dice, were oft fharers with him
of his crownes. Thus fought they euery way to
difburden him of that ftore with which he was
fo fore combred. Tufh, his purfe was well lined,

and might abide the fhaking, and therefore as yet
hee felt it not. The young Courtefan his Paramour,
thinking all too little for her felfe, beganne as
though fhe had taken care of his profite, to wifh
him, feeing he ment there to make fome aboad,
to liue with a leffe charge, and caffier fome of his
men ; which *Philador* feeing it would fpare him
fomewhat, and to pleafe his Miftris fancy, and for
his owne profit, put them all out of feruice but
one boy. The Seruingmen feeing the veine of
their young Mafter, were forry that hee tooke that
courfe of life, to bee ouer-ruled with women, but
his will ftood for a law, and though it were neuer
fo preiudiciall, yet would he be peremptory, and
therefore they brookt their difcharge with patience;
but one of them that beforetime had ferued his
father, hearing what farewell olde *Rabbi Bileffi*
gaue him, thought to take his leaue with the like
adew, and fo being folitary with his Mafter, at his
departure he told him thus :

Sir (quoth hee) I fee well, if *Vliffes* ftops not his
eares, the Syrens wil put him to fhipwracke, if he
carry not Moly about him, *Circes* will inchaunt
him, and youth if he blufh not at beauty, and carry
antidotes of wifedome againft flattery, folly will
be the next hauen hee fhall be in. I fpeake this
by experience, as feeing the Syrens of this houfe
following / your eares with harmony, that will

IX.   I 2

bring you to fplit vpon a Rocke : and here I finde
be fuch *Circes*, as will not onely transforme you,
but fo inchaunt you, that you will (at laft) buy
repentance with too deare a price. Ah Mafter,
doe you remember the precepts that your father
gaue you ; efpecially againft women, nay chiefly
againft fuch women as thefe, whofe eyes are fnares,
whofe words are charmes, whofe hands are birdlime, whofe deceit is much, whofe defires are
infatiable, whofe couetoufneffe is like the *Hidafpis*,
that the more it drinkes the more thirftie it is,
whofe confcience is like a Pomice-ftone, light and
full of holes, whofe loue is for lucre, whofe heart
is light on your perfon, whofe hand heauy on your
purfe, being Vultures that will eate men aliue?

Ah Mafter ! be not blinded with a Courtefan :
there are more maydes then Maulkin ; if you will
needs be in loue, loue one, and marry, fo fhall you
haue profite and credite ; if not, lye not here in a
confuming labyrinth : the idle life is the mother of
all mifchiefe, it fretteth as ruft doth iron, and eateth
as a worme in the wood, till all perifh. Liue not
here, Mafter, without doing fomewhat ; *Mars* himfelfe hateth to be euer on *Venus* lappe, he fcorneth
to lye at racke and manger. Confider how the
Caldes haue fet downe in their writings, that from
the firft creation of the world idleneffe was had
in hatred, and man was commanded to fatisfie his

thirſt with his hands thrift. *Adam* tilled the earth, and fedde himſelfe with his labours. *Iubal* exerciſed Muſike, and ſpent his time in practiſing the ſimpathy of ſundry ſounds. *Tubal-caine* did worke in metalles, and was a grauer in braſſe : *Noe* hauing the world before him for his inheritance yet planted Vineyards : tuſh, all the holy *Iſraelites* liued by their labours, and men hated to haue an houre idely ſpent : *Traian* numbered not that day amongſt the date of his life, which he had wholly conſumed in idleneſſe. If then this laſciuious kinde of life be ſo odious, ſhake off theſe *Calipſes*, trauell with *Vliſſes*, ſee / countries, and you ſhall, as he did, return to *Ithaca* with credite. Be a Souldier, winne honour by armes : a Courtier, winne fauour of ſome King with ſeruice : a Scholler, get to ſome Uniuerſity, and for a while apply your booke ; ſit not here, like *Sardanapalus* amongſt women, be not bewitched with *Hercules* to ſpinne by *Omphales* ſide, leaue all, yet may ye ſtoppe before you come to the bottome : but if you be ſo beſotted, that no counſaile ſhall preuaile, I am glad that I may not ſee your future misfortunes.

Although theſe words of his man draue him into a dumpe, and made him call to remembrance his fathers farewell, yet did hee ſo doate on his young Loue, that he bade his man bee iogging, and ſo went downe into the Parlour to ſhake off

melancholly with company. Thus did *Philador*
lye in the fire, and dally in the flame, and yet like
the Salamander, not feele the fire, for this is an
olde theologicall action :

Confuetudo peccandi, tollit fenfum peccati.

He counted fornication no finne, and luft, why
hee fhadowed that with loue : hee had a vaile
for euery vanity, till that he might fee day light
at euery hole.   While thus he liued in his iollity,
there fell a great dearth in the land, corne was
fcant, and the poore were oppreffed with extreame
penury ; and in fuch fort, that they dyed in the
ftreetes. *Philador* heard by the Chapmen how the
market went, and might perceiue by the cry of
the poore, what famine was fpred throughout the
whole Countrey, but hee had gold, and want
could not wring him by the finger, the blacke
Oxe could not treade on his foote, and therefore
he ftopped his eares, and prooued half mercileffe :
only his care was to fpend the day as delicioufly
as he thought the night delightful, hauing euer his
Paramor in his prefence : whofe finger was neuer
far from his purfe : tufh, all went vpon wheels,
till on a day looking into his coffers, he found a
great want, and faw that his ftore was in the
waning : whereupon hee put / away his boy, and
folde his horfes : hee had enough of himfelfe, and

too many by one. This youngfters purfe drew lowe, but as long as he let angelles flye, fo long they honoured him as a god. But as all things muft haue an end, fo at laft his coffers waxed empty, and then the poft began to bee painted with chalke. The fcore grew great, and they waxed weary of fuch a beggerly gheft. Where-vpon on a day, the eldeft of them tolde him, that either hee muft prouide money, or elfe to furnifh him of a new lodging, for there was a great dearth throughout the whole Countrey, victuals were deare, and they could not pay the Baker and the Brewer with chalke. Upon this hee went vnto his Trunke, and all his rich apparell and iewels walked to the Brokers, and for that time hee cleared the fcore. Which when hee had done, hee got him into his chamber, and fitting downe, began to call to remembrance the precepts of his olde Father : but as foone as his young Miftris was in fight, fhee banifhed all fuch thoughts out of his remem-brance.

Long it was not before he grew deeply indebted againe in the houfe, and fo farre, that he had not wherewithall to difcharge it, and then very early in the morning the three Sifters came vp into his chamber, feized of his Trunke, and that apparell that was left : yea, fo neere they went him, that they tooke his doublet that was on his backe.

Philador feeing the cruelty of his Hofteffe ; and
efpecially, how forward his Miftris was to wrong
him, rofe out of his bedde, and putting on his hofe,
(fitting on the bed fide) beganne thus.

Why (Gentlewomen) haue I been fo ill a gheft,
that I deferue fuch extremity? or fo badde a
paymafter, that fo hardly you hold Bayard in the
Stable? Are thefe the fauours that I was promifed
at my firft welcome? Are womens courtefies fuch
fharpe fhowres? Now I doe fee, although too
late, that all is not Golde that doth glifter, that
euery / Orient ftone is not a Diamond, [that] all
Drugges that are deare, are not precious, nor euery
woman that can flatter, is not faithfull. Did you
at the firft decke mee with Rofes, and now doe
you beate mee with Nettles? Did you prefent
me with Perfumes, and now do you ftifle me with
Hemlocke? Did you fay, I fhould neuer want,
and now do you wrong me, when I doe want?
Then muft I brooke it with patience, and accufe
you of periury. I haue fpent my Portion in this
houfe, my Reuenues are all fallen into your purfes,
and now for a few pence will you feeke my preiudice? Be not (and with that hee looked on the
youngeft fweet Miftris) fo cruell: if you cannot
releeue mee, yet intreat for me to your Sifters, that
they bereaue me not of my cloathes, to the difparagement of my credit : Remember the fauours

I haue fhewed you in my profperity, and requite
them with fome courtefies in my aduerfities : think
what promifes and proteftations haue paffed betweene vs. No fooner had he fpoken thefe words,
but fhe cryed out : What a beggerly knaue is this,
quoth fhe, for to challenge promifes at my hands?
and for to tell me of fauours : if thou haft fpent
thy money, thou haft had meate, and penyworths
for thy pence. Couldeft thou not (like a prodigall
patch) haue looked better into thine owne life, but
thou muft ftraine further then thy fleeue would
reach? Repentance is a whippe for fuch fooles ;
and therefore, were thy hofe off, thou fhouldeft go
in thy Shirt, vnleffe that thou doeft pay the vtter-
moft farthing. *Philador* hearing this, fetched a
very deepe figh, and fayd : Is there any griefe to a
troubled Soule? or any mifchiefe vnto the mifchiefe
of a woman? Why? infatiable are her fetches.
You haue had heere my bloud, will you haue my
heart? My liuing you haue amongft you, and
now doe you ayme at my life? Fie vpon fuch
Gripes as ceafe not to prey vpon poore *Prometheus*,
vntill they haue deuoured vp his very entrailes.

What Sifters? (quoth the youngeft) fhall wee
fuffer this / Rafcall for to raile againft vs, and bee
in our debts? Come, let vs beate him out at the
doores : with that they called vp the Seruants of
the houfe, and fo thruft him out of the Chamber,

naked as hee was, and beat him fore ; infomuch, that they did fhut him out comfortleffe and wounded. Being afhamed of himfelfe, hee durft not tarrie in the Citie where hee was knowne, but in all hafte hee got him out of the Gates, and hyed him farre from the Citie, left that hee fhould bee difcouered by fome of his acquaintance. In the meane while, the three Sifters began for to count what gaines they had gotten by their Nouice : and as they did fmile at his pelfe, fo they did laugh at his penury, and wifhed that they might haue many more fuch ghefts.

Thus were they very pleafant, whileft *Philador*, like vnto fome poore Pilgrime, wandred on ftill vpon his way, going now naked, that earft came riding with fuch pompe, and feeing himfelfe to be in the depth of miferie, that thought no frowne of Fortune could fhake him from Felicity : after that he had (in this defolate eftate) wandered a long while, being weary, hungrie, and thirftie, in the extremity of griefe, he fate him downe by a brookes fide, where hee dranke his fill, and with very forrow hee fell afleepe : and when hee awaked, and entred into due confideration of his prefent misfortune, looking vpon himfelfe, hee melted into teares, and at laft burft forth into thefe mournfull paffions.

Infortunate *Philador*, and therefore infortunate,

becaufe thou wouldeft neither be directed by
aduice, nor reclaimed by counfaile. Thy Father,
whofe yeares had reaped much experience, whofe
white haires were inftances of graue infight, whofe
age contained a multitude of reuerent aduertife-
ments, foretold thefe misfortunes, and with fore-
pointing actions, gaue thee caueats of thefe moft
bitter Croffes. / The Fawne doth choofe his foode
by the laie of the olde Bucke : the Lyon doth
teach his young whelpes : and the young Eagles
make not flight but as the olde ones do learne
them to carrie wing, yet I inftructed by my Father,
doe flye from nature as a Haggard, and refufe
nurture as one that would euer proue rauening.
Selfe-loue is a fault that followes youth, and like
the fting of the *Tarantala* fretteth inwardly before
it paineth outwardly : I thought my Fathers counfaile to bee good, but too graue for my young
yeeres : quoth I, thefe precepts are too feuere
for the Calends of my youth. What? he doth
meafure my quicke coales by his dead cinders,
and thinketh that I fhould be in the prime as he
is in the wane. No, his Aphorifmes are too farre
fetcht for me, and therefore, *Quæ fupra nos, nihil
ad nos :* What? I can fee what is good for my
felfe, and alfo preuent a preiudice if it bee imminent.

Thus did I flatter my felfe, vntill fuch time as

too late repentance hath giuen me a *Mourning Garment*. Oh now I doe plainely fee when my Father gaue vnto me precepts, hee gaue vnto me more then pence, for counfaile is more worth then coyne, but I did then lightly regard it, and therefore doe I now heauily repent it. Ah *Philador*, thou wert warned not to be prodigall, and who more riotous? Not for to ftraine aboue thy reach, and yet thou wouldeft needes beyond the Moone. Now doft thou forrow at thy loffe, and they doe fmyle that haue gained : whileft that thou haddeft Crownes crammed in thy Coffers, thou hadeft friends enow at commaundement, and wert able to take many flatterers with trencher-flyes : thou haddeft fuch as foothed thee in thy follies, and fedde vpon thy fortunes, that did ordinarily pay thee with a cappe and a knee, and that could tricke thee vp with titles of honour. But now (*Philador*) now that thou art in this extremity of want, they are all vanifhed like an empty Clowde : now that there is no wealth left they are all loft, thy Gold / is flowne, and they are fledde : Thus (poore man) fitteft thou, altogether comfortleffe and friendleffe, hauing bought witte at too deare a rate ; and only gotten this Verfe for all thy treafure :

Nullus ad amiffas ibit amicus opes.

Thus as *Philador* fate debating with himfelfe of

his former Fortunes and prefent miferie, fuch
melancholly entred into his thoughts, that hee
feared he fhould fall in defpaire : and therefore
rofe vp, and went trauelling into the Country,
paffing ouer three or foure dayes without any
foode, that hee was almoft famifhed ; till at laft
it was his good hap to meete a Citizen that had
a Farme in the country : him *Philador* humbly
faluted, and defired him of feruice: the Citizen
looking earneftly vpon him, feeing hee had a good
face, pittied the extremity of the poore young man
and anfwered him thus :

My friend (quoth hee) thou feeft there is a
generall dearth ouer the whole Countrey, and
many perifh through penurie: food is fo fcant, that
our Seruants are ready to famifh, and therefore
euery man coueteth to make his charge leffe ; yet
for that I pitty thy youth, and fauour thy perfonage, I will place thee in a Farme houfe of mine
hard by adioining, where thy labour fhall be to
feede my Swine : wherein if thou fheweft thy felfe
diligent, thy recompence fhall be the greater.
Philador glad of this, with teares in his eyes for
ioy, made this anfwere.

Mafter (quoth he) penury is a fore pinch, and
I thinke there is no fharper fting then neceffity ;
therefore, doubt not of my labour, for I will take
any paines to pleafe, and brooke any toyle to

content, and fo I befeech you to fauour me as you
fhall finde me dutifull. With that, the Citizen
tooke him into feruice, and fent him to his Farme-
houfe, where *Philador* kept the Swine, but himfelf
had very hard fare, in fo much that for extreme
hunger, he ate the hufkes with / the Hogges, and
yet had not enough to fatisfie his ftomake. Sitting
downe at laft, and feeing the Hogges feed, hauing
a hufke in his hand, he wept and blubbered out
thefe paffionate complaints.

Ah hunger, hunger, the extremeft of all extremes, now doe I fee that high defires haue
lowe fortunes : that they whofe thoughts reach
at ftarres, ftumble at ftones : that fuch as gaze at
the heauens, fall on the earth : that pride will
haue a fall, and euery fault is punifht with the
contrary. Ah *Philador*, thou that of late diddeft
fwimme in gluttony, art now pinched with penury :
thou that diddeft inuent what to eate, haft not
now any thing to eate : thine eye could not be
contented with meane cates, that now demifheth
for want of any fare : where be thy dainties, thy
exceffe, thy wines, thy delicates? all paft with
Philexenus, through thy throat, and thou left to
eate hufkes with Swine in the deepeft extremity
of hunger : ah miferable *Philador*, how art thou
Metamorphofed : where be thy coftly abyliments,
thy rich roabes, thy gorgeous attire, thy chaines

and thy rings? *Omnia vanitas,* they are fallen to the Lombard, left at the Brokers, and thou here fitteſt poore and naked, brooking this miſery as patiently as thou diddeſt ſpend thy goods riotouſly. But now *Philador,* enter into conſideration of thy hard happe, and ſee into the cauſe of thy froward Fortunes: What? ſhall I attribute it to my natiuity, and ſay the Planets did calculate as much at my birth? no, there is no neceſſitie in their influence, the ſtarres determine, but God diſpoſeth, tuſh:

Sapiens dominabitur Aſtris.

What then ſhalt thou accuſe? ah nothing but the folly of my youth, that would neither accept of aduice, nor vouchſafe of counſaile. Loue, *Philador,* loue: ah no, ſhadow not vanity / with the vale of vertue; not loue but luſt brought me to this bane: wanton affects forced me to this fall, and the pleaſure of mine eye procured theſe bitter paſſions. Beauty, ah beauty, the bane that poiſoneth worſe then the iuyce of the Baaron. Beauty, the Serpent that infecteth worſe then the Baſiliſke. Beauty, the Syren that draweth vnto death. Beauty, that leadeth youth captiue into the labyrinth, where reſteth that mercileſſe Mynotaure. But rather fond man that delighteſt in ſuch a fading flowre, in ſuch a manifeſt poyſon, in ſuch an open preiudice. The Deere knoweth Tamariſke to be deadly,

and wil not broufe on the branches, the moufe
hateth the trap, the Bee Hemlocke, the Serpent
the Oliphant: but man runneth greedily after that
which worketh his fatall difparagement. Ah *Philador*, did not thy Father forewarne thee of womens
beauty? did he not fay they were Adamants that
drew, Panthers that with their painted fkinnes doe
allure? if my fonne (quoth he thou furfetft with
their beauty, thou drinkeft Aconitum and fo doft
perifh. Tufh, but I little regarded his precepts,
but now haue I bought his axiomes with deepe
repentance: now doe I finde that their faces are
painted fepulchres, whereas their mindes are tombes
full of rotten bones and Serpents: their browes
containe like the Diamond, vertue to relieue, and
poyfon to kill, their looks are like Calends, they
can determine no certaintie, but as the leafe of the
Liquonico when it lookes moft moyft, is then moft
drye, fo when they fmyle, they imagine deceit, and
their laughters are tempered with enuy and reuenge.
Ah *Philador*, what are womens vowes? words
written in the winde : what are their promifes?
characters figured in the ayre : what are their
flatteries? figures grauen in the fnow, which are
blowne with the winde or melted with the Sunne :
what are their loues? like the paffage of a Serpent
ouer a ftone, which being once paft, can neuer be
feene.

They will promiſe mountaines, and performe Molehills, / ſay they loue with *Dido*, when they faine with *Creſida*, and follow *Demophon* with *Phillis*, when they are more ſtraggling then *Luna*: they have teares at commaund as the Crockadile to betray, and ſmyles at voluntary to bewitch : as thou haſt golde they are horſe-leeches, and will not out of thy boſome : but they hate an empty purſe, as the *Hiena* doth the ſight of a man, and will flye from thee when thou art poore, as the fowle from the Faulcon. Ah *Philador*, mighteſt thou be the laſt who were intrapt by their loue, it were well, and happy wert thou to be an inſtance to all other Gentlemen ; nay might young youth bridle their follies by thy fall, they would ere [long] ſay to themſelues

> *Fœlix quem faciunt aliena pericula cautum.*

But alas, *Philador*, *Troilus* fortunes could not make others feare the like fooliſh end. Though *Theſeus* bought *Helens* loue deare ; yet *Paris* would not bee warned, but brought her home to *Troy* : ſo thou art but one Swallow, and makeſt not Summer : and young Gentlemen will ſay, that folly will not bee euery mans fortune : but when repentance ſhall couer them with a *Mourning Garment*, then will they ſay, Had I wiſt is a little too late. But, *Philador*, why ſitſt thou here dis-

courfing againſt Loue, againſt women, againſt
beauty? Leaue them as refuze, and things too
low for thy lookes, and prouide for thy body, for
thou art here almoſt famiſhed, and ſitteſt eating
of huſkes with the Hogges, whereas the meaneſt
of thy Fathers ſeruants, his Hynd *Mercenaries*,
haue bread enough to eate, and thou ſitteſt and
feeleſt the extremity of hunger. What ſhal I do,
ſhall I home? will my Father vouchſafe of ſuch a
prodigall ſonne, who in ſo ſhort a time hath conſumed ſo large a portion? can he looke on him
with fauour that hath committed ſuch folly? or
receiue him into his houſe, that hath defpiſed his
counſaile? /

Ah, why not *Philador*? loue is more vehement
in defcent then in aſcent: Nature will plead for
me, if nurture condemne me : fathers as they haue
frownes to chaſtiſe, ſo they haue ſmyles to pardon :
aſ they can lowre, ſo they can laugh : and they are
as ready to forgiue as thou to be penitent. Then
will I home to my father, and ſay to him : Father,
I haue ſinned againſt heauen and before thee, and
am no more worthy to be called thy ſonne, make
me as one of thy hired ſeruants : with this he fell
into bitter teares, and in this refolution continued,
and taking leaue of his maſter, hyed him home
towards the land of *Hauilath* ; by the way trauerſing many Countries, and noting the manners of

men, he faw how folly had wrapt many in the
fnares of womens beauties : amongft the reft, one
day as hee lay in a thicket to fhrowde him from
the heate of the Sunne, hearing a great noyfe, hee
heard the complaint of a forfaken Louer, who
exclaimed againft the cruelty of women, that
denyed to grant loue for loue, and grew fo farre
into paffions, that pulling forth his rapier, there
he refolued both to end his loue and his life. As
hee was ready to haue fallen on his fword, *Philador*
ftept out of the thicket, and caught hold of him :
the Gentleman turning his head, and feeing fuch
a poore fnake to hinder his attempt, thought to
checke him with a frowne : but *Philador* vfed
thefe fpeeches vnto him : Sir, maruaile not that fo
meane a man hath dared to ftay you from fo bad
a deede, for to this I am compeld by manhood :
defperation is a double finne, and finall impeni-
tence hath no remiffion. There is no hap paft
hope, and therefore bewray your griefe ; perhaps,
I may perfwade with reafon, or relieue with counfaile : meafure me not by my ragges, ne eftimate
my prefent fortunes, but thinke as the fouleft
weedes haue oft the moft vertuous operation, fo
the hoode makes not the Monke, nor the apparell
the man ; but I may fooner apply a medicine for
your malady, then a feemelier Phyfician. The
Gentleman hearing fuch a fenfible induction, did

ſtraight coniecture, that whatſoeuer his preſent /
eſtate was, his nurture had beene good, and there
looking him in the face, and leaning on his rapier,
he began to diſcourſe vnto him how long time he
had been a Votarie vnto *Venus*, and a ſeruant vnto
Loue: that he was ſnared in the beauty of a young
Damſell, who the more ſhe perceiued him paſſionate,
the leſſe ſhe was pittifull, and by how much the
more hee fought to ſhew manifeſt ſignes of his
affection, by ſo much the more ſhe made little
regard of his fancy : in ſo much that wearied
with loue, and ſeeing no hope of fauour, he thought
with a momentarie death to end thoſe paſſions,
wherein ſtill to linger were worſe then any death.

At this *Philador* fell into a great laughter, and
after into theſe tearmes : What (quoth hee) art
thou ſo mad to die for loue, or ſo fond as to grieue
thy ſelfe at the frown of a woman?   I tell thee ſir
(quoth he) if thou kneweſt how Fortune fauours
thee, and how the ſtarres agree to make thee happy,
thou wouldeſt count thy ſelfe not the moſt miſerable, but the moſt fortunate of all men : ah my
friend diddeſt thou as well as I know the effects of
loue, and the wyles of women, thou wouldeſt ſay :

O me fœlicem, quantis me periculis fortuna mea eripuit!

If ſhe be faire whom thou loueſt, firſt conſider that
beauty is a flower to-day fit for the eye, to-morrow

withered and to be caſt into the furnace : that loue
which growes from ſuch a fading obieċt is momentarie, and ſubieċt to euery accident : beſides, beauty
brings with it ſuſpicion, feare, and ieloſie, ſeeing
euery mans eye will feede on a faire face, and
euery mans thought will ſeeke to be partner in thy
fancies, and how weake veſſels women be, eſpecially if they be beautifull, I referre thee to *Helena*
& *Creſſida*.   But thou ſayſt ſhe is coy : ah my
friend, womens faces are not the Chriſtals of truth,
nor their words Goſpell : what ſhe hates in outwardly, ſhe likes inwardly, and what ſhee thruſts /
away with one finger, ſhee will pull againe with
both her hands : but as long as thou fawneſt vpon
her, ſhe will be froward, but be a little abſent, and
ſhe wil wiſh thy preſence : womens thoughts are
like babies fancies, that will and will not : proffer
them meate, and they refuſe it, offer it to an other,
and they cry after it : ſo weane thou thy ſelfe from
her for a while, and frequent the companie of ſome
other as faire as ſhe, and ſo either ſhalt thou draw
her on to bee fond, or elſe by ſuch abſence, ſhake
off thine owne folly.   But ſuppoſe loue and fortune
fauour thee, that thou haſt her loue ; diddeſt thou
know what a world of woes thou doeſt enter
into by taking a wife, thou wouldeſt ſay, Fie on
loue, and farewell to women.   Be ſhe neuer ſo
faire, thou ſhalt finde faultes enow in her face

shortly to mislike : and besides, the fairest flower
hath oft the most infectious sauour ; the Cedar is
beautifull, but beares no fruit ; the Christolite of
an orient hiew, yet of a deadly operation : and so
in the fairest proportion shalt thou finde oft the
least perfection, and the sweetest face, the most
preiudiciall qualities.   Who was fairer then *Venus* ?
but such a wanton as she would neuer want one.
Clytemnestra beautifull, but a giglot.   I tell thee sir
they are sullen, and be *Morosæ*, as was *Zenia* the
wife of *Antisthenes*, or scoldes as she that ouer-
ruled *Socrates*, or froward as *Marpesia* : deceitfull,
flattering, contentious, sicke with the puffe of euery
winde, and lowring at the shew of euery storm.
These vices are incident by nature, though they
seeme neuer so vertuous by nurture.   *Penelope* had
furrowes in her brow, as well as she had dimples in
her chinne : *Artemisia* could frowne, as well as she
could smile, and *Lucrece* though she were chaste,
yet she could chide.   Sir, beleeue me, I speake it
by experience, if thou marrie one faire and dis-
honest, thou weddest thy selfe to a world of
miseries : if thou marriest one beautifull, and
neuer so vertuous, yet thinke this, thou shalt haue
a woman, and therefore in despight of Fortune, a
necessary euill. /

At this period, the passionate Gentleman put vp
his rapier into his sheath, and tolde *Philador* his

medicine had fomewhat eafed his maladie, and his counfaile mitigated the force of his defpairing paffions; infomuch, that his hot loue was waxen a little colde, and the heate of his fancie was qualified, with the lenitiue plaifters that grew from his experienc'd aduice. Therefore Sir (quoth hee) as the Date tree is not knowne by the barke, but by the bloomes: and the precious balme not by his colour, but by the operation: fo the outward fhew did not alwaies manifeft the inner man, but the effects of his vertues: and therefore not meafuring your parentage by your prefent eftate, nor your calling by your aduerfe fortune: I firft (as one that coueteth not to be vngratefull) render thankes for your Patheticall precepts, and feeing you haue kindly releeued mee with your counfaile, as *Terence* wifheth:

Re mea te adiuuabo:

I will fupply your want with my wealth, and change your fortunes with my poffeffions; fo that what I haue in treafure, fhal be parted between vs with a friendly proportion.

Philador gaue him great thankes for his courteous proffer, and tolde him that fuch vrgent hafte of his iourney called him away, as no alteration of his fortune, how beneficiall foeuer, might ftay him. My way (quoth hee) is long, & my wearineffe great: I haue many places to tread, and many

thoughts to meditate vpon : I goe laden with much
forrow, and little hope : yet defpaire I muft not,
for though my miferies be many, and my friends
few, yet doe I fay in my felfe to falue my paffion :

O paſſi grauiora ? dabit Deus his quoque finem.

Therefore Sir, if my counfaile haue done you
any comfort, or my words beene fo effectuall, as
to mitigate your / affects, think loue hath brought
me to thefe fortunes, and therefore beware of the
like follies, for he that fhunnes *Scilla*, and falls into
Caribdis, that wil accufe *Circes* for an Inchaunt-
reffe, and yet wed himfelfe to *Calipfo*, that thinks
he may fhake off fancy for a moment, and entertaine loue for a moneth, fhall tread vpon glaffe,
and worke himfelfe into a labyrinth of ouerweening
fooleries.   The Sunne waxeth low, and my Inne
is farre hence : therefore muft I leaue you : and
yet (quoth he) becaufe I fee you are willing to
learne, take this fcrowle as a prefident how to
efchew much preiudice : the only fauour that I
requeft, is, that you will be as ready to deliuer
precepts of vertue, as I haue bin to fet downe
axiomes to you : with that he gaue him a paper
folded vp, and fhaking him by the hand, bade him
farewell.   The Gentleman with great courtefie
bade him adieu, and fo they parted, *Philador*
towards his fathers, and hee towards his lodging :

yet longing to fee what was in the fcrowle, he fate
him down and vnfolded it, where he found thefe
ftrange Aphorifmes. /

The Contents of PHILADORS Scrowle.

Ouidius.

Hei mihi quod nullis Amor eſt medicabilis herbis.

Oue is a thing, I know not of what it
commeth, I know not from whence : it
groweth, but vnknowne whereof : goeth
wee know not whither, and beginneth and endeth
I knowe not which way : yet a paſſion full of
martyrdome, mifery, griefe, and difcontent, hauing
pleafures but tempered with paines, and a ſhort
delight mixed with a long repentance.

The *Hidaſpis* hath a faire ſkinne and a fweet
breath, but his ſting is fatall : gaze not too much
left thou attempt to touch and perifh.

The Crockadile weeps, but then ſhe worketh
wyles, for her teares pretend reliefe but intend
deſtruction : rue not her forrowes, left when ſhe
reioiceth thou repenteft.

The Syren fits and fings in a calme Bay, but
her feate is enuironed with rockes : beware of her
melody, for if it pleafe the eare, it pincheth the
heart.

When the Tigre hideth her clawes, then fhe menaceth for her prey : fee either her claw open, or hold her at thy Rapiers point.

The eye of a Bafilifke is as bright as a ftarre, but as preiudiciall as a thunder-bolt : whileft thou lookeft with delight, it woundeth with death : holde thine eyes from fuch obiects, left thou become an abiect.

Cyrces amongft all her potions had one moft fweete, and that turned men to Affes : tafte not of that, without before thou chaw on Moly. /

The *Hiena* will fawne on thee and fmile, but if thou follow her, fhe leades thee to a denne full of Serpents : either fhunne her flatteries, or weare the horne of a Hart that driues away infectious vermine.

There are no Hawks fooner manned then they of *India*, none eate more, and flye leffe : while fhe is full gorged, fhe keepes the fift, but keep her low, and fhe proues rauening : either be not a Falconer, or beware of fuch fowles.

Giue a Cammell ftore of prouender, and fhe will ftrike thee with her foote, beate her, and fhe will kneele till thou getteft vpon her backe : for fuch a beaft weare a cudgell, then when thou feeft her lift her heele, thou mayeft ftrike.

If thefe Aphorifmes be too enigmaticall, become a Louer, and experience will quickly fet thee downe

a comment ; but if thou canſt, find them out and
be Philoſopher to thy ſelfe.

The Gentleman read theſe obſcure principles, and
perceiued they all tended to the diſcouery of womens
qualities, wherefore he held them moſt precious :
but looking vpon the page, there he perceiued
certain verſes, which were theſe.

PHILADORS Ode that he left with the *deſpairing
Louer*.

When merry Autumne in her prime,
   Fruitfull mother of ſwift time,
Had filled *Ceres* lappe with ſtore
Of Vines and Corne, and mickle more
Such needful fruitès as do growe
From Terras boſome, here belowe ;
Tytirus did ſigh, and ſee
With hearts griefe and eyès gree,
Eyes and heart both full of woes
Where *Galate* his louer goes. /
Her mantle was vermillion red,
A gawdy Chaplet on her head :
A Chaplet that did ſhrowd the beames
That *Phœbus* on her beauty ſtreames :
For Sunne it ſelfe deſired to ſee
So faire a Nymph as was ſhee ;
For, viewing from the Eaſt to Weſt,
Faire *Galate* did like him beſt :

Her face was like to Welkins fhine,
Cryftall brookes, fuch were hir eyne :
And yet within thefe brookes were fires,
That fcorchèd youth and his defires.
Galate did much impaire
Venus honour for her faire.
For ftately ftepping, *Iunoes* pace,
By *Galate* did take difgrace :
And *Pallas* wifedome bare no prife
Where *Galate* would fhew her wife.
This gallant Girle thus paffeth by
Where *Tityrus* did fighing lye :
Sighing fore, for Loue[rs] ftraines
More then fighes from Louers vaines.
Teares in eye, thought in heart,
Thus his griefe he did impart.
Faire *Galate* but glance thine eye,
Here lyes he that here muft dye :
For loue is death, if loue not gaine
Louers falue for Louers paine.
Winters feuen and more are paft,
Since on thy face my thoughts I caft :
When *Galate* did haunt the Plaines,
And fed her fheepe amongft the Swaines :
When euery Shepheard left his flockes,
To gaze on *Galates* faire lockes.
When euery eye did ftand at gaze :
When heart and thought did both amaze, /

When heart from body would afunder,
On *Galates* faire face to wonder :
Then amongſt them all did I
Catch ſuch a wound as I muſt dye :
If *Galate* oft ſay not thus,
I loue the Shepheard *Tityrus*.
Tis loue (faire nymph) that doth [me] paine
Tytirus thy trueſt Swaine ;
True, for none more true can be,
Then ſtill to loue, and none but thee.
Say *Galate*, oft ſmile and ſay,
Twere pitty loue ſhould haue a nay :
But ſuch a word of comfort giue,
And *Tytirus* thy Loue ſhall liue :
Or with a piercing frowne reply,
I cannot loue, and then I dye;
For Louers nay, is Louers death,
And heart-breake frownes doth ſtop the breath.
Galate at this aroſe,
And with a ſmile away ſhe goes,
As one that little carde to eaſe
Tytir, pain'd with Loues diſeaſe.
At her parting, *Tytirus*
Sighed amaine, and ſayed thus :
Oh that women are ſo faire,
To trap mens eyes in their haire :
With beauteous eyes, Louers fires,
Venus ſparkes, that heates deſires :

But, oh that women haue such hearts,
Such thoughts, and such deep piercing darts,
As in the beauty of their eye,
Harbor nought but flattery :
Their teares are deawes that drop deceit,
Their faces, Calends of all sleight,
Their smiles are lures, their lookes guile,
And all their loue is but a wyle. /
Then *Tytir* leaue, leaue *Tytirus*
To loue such as scornes you thus :
And say to loue, and women both,
What I likèd, now I loath.
With that he hyed him to the flockes,
And counted loue but *Venus* mockes.

The Gentleman hauing read ouer this Ode,
held it as a treafure, and went home as free from
loue as *Tytirus* was from affection, wondering
what this poore Pilgrime should be, that had giuen
him such enigmatical precepts; and praying, that
his fortune might be anfwerable to his qualities.
Well, leauing him thus, free from his paffion,
againe to *Philador* : who wandering homewards
met with many aduentures, and saw many sights
that had made him for to wonder at the follies of
the world : at the laft he came within sight of his
fathers houfe, the which he no sooner saw but it
was such a piercing obiect to his eye, ftriking such

remorſe to his heart, that he ſate him downe and
melted into teares, thinking on the proſperity of his
former eſtate, and the miſery of his preſent fortunes : as thus hee ſate in a deepe paſſion, lifting
vp his eyes, he ſaw where his aged father was
walking in the paſtures to take the ayre : although
his aduerſe fall were a meanes to make him baſh-
full, yet the ſight of his father kindled ſo the fewel
of nature in him, that imboldned, he aroſe vp,
and went towards him in thoſe robes of diſtreſſe,
that hee was baniſhed [in] out of his Inne.   And
when he came neere, naked and poore, hee went
to his father, and falling flat vpon the ground,
ſayd : Father, I haue ſinned againſt heauen and
againſt thee, I am no more worthy to be called thy
ſonne.   Olde *Rabbi Bileſſi* looking in his viſage,
and ſeeing it was his ſonne, Nature that hath neuer
ſuch dead cinders but there be *Quædam ſcintillulæ*
certaine ſparkles of ſecret affection, began to drawe
remorſe into his face, pitty into his heart, and
teares into his / eyes, that throwing downe his
ſtaffe, hee ſtepped to his ſonne, and fell on his
'necke, weeping bitterly, and yet with ſuch an
extaſie, as the ſtorme pretended both ioy and
ſorrow, the one for his hard fortunes; the other,
for his happy recouery.   *Philador* ſeeing his father
thus paſſionate, tooke heart-a-grace, and on his
knee began thus.

✠✠✠✠✠✠✠✠✠✠✠✠✠✠✠✠✠✠✠✠✠✠✠

Philadors fubmiffion to his Father, at his returne.

I know not (Sir) what infinuation to vfe for
your fauor, fo many, and fo monftrous are the
number of my follies; nor can I plead any excufe,
the diftreffe of my prefent fortunes are fo manifeft:
onely fubmiffion muft fue to nature for a pardon,
and my repentant forrowes put in plea for fome
fatherly remorfe.   Ah the wanton defires of youth!
why they be like to the giddines of rauening
Hawkes, that bate at the fight of euery bufh:
and the prime of young age is as the flowres of
the Pine tree, that are glorious to the fight, but
vnfauoury, and without fmel.   Vanity is the mafk
wherein it marcheth, and folly is the Page that
attendeth vpon the actions of youth, fo that all
his affects are flipperneffe, and the effects full
of preiudiciall difparagement: had I regarded the
graue Aphorifmes of your aduifed counfaile or the
golden precepts deliuered from the experience of
your yeares; or the fweet actions that drop as
balm from the filuer treffes of your haire, neither
had my fall bin fuch, my diftreffe fo great, nor my
fortune fo miferable: fooles are they which fay,
bought wit is beft; efpecially, if it be rated at my
price.   Counfaile is the fweet conferue, and aduice
the pureft antidote: happy is he that is ware by

other mens harmes, and such moft miferable, that
are wife by their owne woes. /

Pifcator ictus fapit.

But hard is his hap that flies from the viper for
her fting, that hateth the Tarantala, for that hee
hath felt her venome, and infortunate is that man
that can anatomize miferie by his owne diftreffe:
Ah Father, had I reuerenced my God as I honoured
my goddeffe, and offered as many Orifons to his
deity, as I powred out paffions for her beauty: then
had I been graced with as many fauours as I am
croffed with misfortunes.   But I thought hee had
not feene my faults, and therefore went forward :
in hue I thought their faces to be Adamants, their
beauties to bee like the fpots of deuouring Panthers :
had I deemed them to be preiudiciall *Syrens*, had
I beleeued what I was foretold, *Philador* had been
leffe miferable, and more fortunate.   But I counted
their beauties metaphificall, their qualities diuine,
their   proportions   heauenly,   themfelues Angels :
I thought, as the Phenix had none but precious
feathers, as the Myrrh tree hath no Caterpillars, as
the Topas hath no operation but excellent, fo I
thought women to be fuch perfit creatures as had
nothing in them but fupernaturall.   But at laft I
found the precepts of *Rabbi Bileffi* to be authen-
ticall, that as the Sinamon tree, though it hath a

fweet barke, yet it hath bitter leaues, and the Pirite
ftone, though it haue one vertue, hath twenty
preiudiciall operations : fo women though they
were neuer fo beautifull, yet were they the painted
continents of flattery, of deceit, inconftancie, & the
very guides that leade men vnto y̆ pernicious
labyrinth of endleffe diftreffe. Had I thought
prodigality fuperfluous exceffe, my coffers had
been full of Crownes, and my heart voyd of cares :
but I counted expence the empreffe of a Gentleman, and gifts the thing that graced a traueller :
as *Traian* numbred not that day amongft the date
of his life, wherein he had not done fomething
worthy of memory, fo I did hold that *Nefanda
dies*, wherein I did / not triumph in magnificall
prodigality.　Tufh, I did thinke coyne to be called
currant *à currendo :* golde, why I held it as droffe,
and counted it the deepeft difhonour to be counted
frugall : *Parfimonia* ; why (quoth I) it is paltry,
and fparing it is the badge of a Peafant. The
Chaldes in their Hierogliphickes defcribed a Gentleman with his hand alwaies open ; meaning, that
to giue was heroicall.　And *Titus* the Emperour
fayd, Giue, if thou wilt be worthy the worlds
Monarchy : I counted *Cyancynatus* the Dictator a
foole for his frugality : I difcommended the fmal
dyet of *Caius Fabritius,* and fayd *Agathocles* was
bafe minded that dranke in earthen veffels. But

for *Lucullus*, I commended his fumptuous fare, and the prodigall thoughts of *Iulinus*.

Thus did I glory in exceffe, and thought not that meafure was a merry meane. While thus I flowed in the conceit of my folly, I had many that like trencher flyes waited vpon my perfon, more for the hope of my purfe, then for any perfect loue. And as the Doues flocke where the houfe is faire; fo where the carrion is, thither fuch hungry Eagles refort. I can beft compare them vnto empty veffels that haue loud founds, to painted fheathes that haue rufty blades, vnto glorious flowres that haue no fmell; and fo they pretend much friendfhip, and containe nothing but fuperficiall flattery. For as foone, as by drawing too oft, the Well waxed drie, that my purfe began with fo many purging glifters to waxe not onely laxatiue, but quite emptie: then thefe infinuating hang-byes flew away like vapours, and left me vnto the deep fall of my fortunes. This experience hath poore *Philador* bought with much forrow, and this wit hath hee purchafed with great repentance; infomuch, that the loathfomeneffe of my faults is more then the pleafure of my follies, and the hate of fuch vanities is greater then the defire of fuch vices: oh, then graunt pardon vnto him that is penitent, haue remorfe vpon him that groaneth vnder the burthen of his finnes: let thine eye beholde me, and thy heart pitty the extremity of my diftreffe. And if my offences be fo great that thou wilt not entertaine me as a fonne, yet make me as one of thy hyred feruants.

Rabbi Bileffi hearing the penitent paffion of his fonne, felt nature pleading for the reconciliation of fo forrowfull a pilgrimage, and therefore folding his armes about his necke, and wetting his cheeks with teares, made this fatherly reply.

❋❋❋❋❋❋❋❋❋❋❋❋❋❋❋❋❋❋❋❋❋❋❋

RABBI BILESSI *his comfortable anfwere to his fonne.*

Tell thee *Philador* (quoth he) though I haue teares in mine eyes, yet I haue ioy in my heart : thefe droppes are not fignes of forrowes, but inftances of content : I conceiue as much pleafure in thy penitence, as I reaped griefe at thy difobedience. Ah *Philador*, haddeft thou followed thy fathers counfaile, thou haddeft not tafted of this care, and my precepts funke into thy heart, thefe misfortunes had not been rewards of thy follies. But to rubbe the fore afrefh, by recounting thy offences, is but to make thee more paffionate, and me deeper perplexed. Therefore, omitting all matters that are paft, hoping thefe proteftations are not prefent forrowes, but continuall penitence, I admit thee into former fauor, forgiuing and for-

getting the follies of thy youth. With that, lifting
vp *Philador*, he imbraced him afrefh, couered him
in a new robe, but with a garment of blacke, as a
man mourning at his high faults and low fortunes,
and fo carried him home to his houfe, where hee
commanded all his feruants to make preparation
for a folemne feaft ; which was done with all
diligence. *Sophonos* being from home, and at his
returne hearing of this, had his face full of frownes,
and his heart of griefe, that fuch a prodi / gall
vnthrift fhould fo foone be reconciled, and fo
boldly entertained : infomuch, that difcontent, he
fate him down at the doore, and would not come
in. Newes was brought vnto *Rabbi Bileffi*, that
Sophonos was male content. With that, the old
man ftumbled out of the doores, and comming to
his fonne, perfwaded him to thinke nothing if
he gracioufly accepted of his penitent brother.
Sophonos with a lowring countenance made him
this anfwere.

SOPHONOS *to olde Rabbi Bileffi.*

WHY Sir (quoth he) haue I not reafon to
frowne, when I fee you fo fond, and to be
deeply difcontent, when I fee you fo diuers in your
actions? one while with *Diogenes* to exclaime
againft pride : and ftraight, with *Ariftippus* to

iet in furcoates of golde : aged thoughts fhould haue but one period, and the refolution of gray haires ought alwayes to bee peremptory : hath not *Rabbi Bileffi* inueighed againft the follies of youth? and doth he not now maintaine it in his owne fon? hath he not faid, that a prodigal man is like to a floud that ouerfloweth, which inforceth preiudice to the whole plaines? and now he welcomes him with feafting, that hath fpent all in riotous expence. What is this but to fofter folly, and to nurfe vp vice? I fpeake not this as enuying my brothers reconciliation, but that *Sophonos* hath deferued more grace, and yet hath found leffe fauor.

Ah fonne, quoth *Rabbi Bileffi*, haft thou not heard, that inexpected chances are moft welcome, that loffes recouered are moft fweete, that nature likes beft feldome feene? Ah *Sophonos*, and art thou angry then with thine olde father, for entertaining his fonne that was loft, and is found, that was dead and is aliue againe? for welcoming home of *Philador*, that returnes backe poore, but penitent, croffed / with ill fortunes, but carefull for his faults, diftreffed, but vowed to deuotion? his minde hath altered with a ftrange Metamorphofis, he hath (*Sophonos*) bought wit, and now will beware : better late then neuer : *Nunquam fero eft ad bonos mores via*. Then (my fonne) if thou bee

fonne to *Rabbi Bileſſi*, and beeſt as kind as I am
naturall ; come, and welcome home with me
thy brother *Philador*, greete him with fauours,
as I haue done with teares : be as glad to fee him
come home as thou wert forry to fee him depart,
and for thy courtefie thou fhalt haue his brotherly
loue, and my fatherly bleffing. With that *Sophonos*
was content, and his olde father carried him in :
and then *Sophonos*, as kindly as his ſtomake would
fuffer, entertained *Philador*, and then frolickly they
went to feaſting. Olde *Rabbi* reioicing at the great
change of his fons manners, in that he went forth
full of vanity, and returned home tempered with
grauity : all the company were pleafant, and a
feaſt it could not be without mufique : The Shepheards they came in with their Timbrels and
Cimballs, and plaid fuch melodie, as the Country
then required : amongſt them all, one Swaine ſtept
forth, and as they fate reuiued them with this
fong. /

The Song of the country Swaine at the returne
of PHILADOR.

He filent fhade had fhadowed euery tree,
And *Phœbus* in the weft was fhrowded
low :
Ecch hiue had home her bufie laboring Bee,
Ech bird the harbour of the night did knowe:
Euen then,
When thus
All things did from their weary labour linne,
Menalcas fate and thought him of his finne.

His head on hand, his elbowe on his knee,
And teares, like dewe, be-drencht vpon his face,
His face as fad as any Swaines might bee :
His thoughts and dumpes befitting well the place.
Euen then,
When thus
Menalcas fate in paffions all alone,
He fighed then, and thus he gan to mone.

I that fed flockes vpon *Theſſalia* plaines
And bad my lambs to feede on Daffadill,
That liued on milke and curdes, poore Shep-
    heards gaines,
And merry ſate, and pyp'd vpon a pleaſant hill.
            Euen then,
            When thus
I ſate ſecure and fear'd not fortunes ire,
Mine eyes eclipſt, faſt blinded by deſire./

Then lofty thoughts began to lift my minde,
I grudg'd and thought my fortune was too low;
A Shepheards life 'twas baſe and out of kinde,
The talleſt Cedars haue the faireſt growe.
            Euen then,
            When thus
Pride did intend the ſequell of my ruth,
Began the faults and follies of my youth.

I left the fields, and tooke me to the Towne,
Fould ſheepe who liſt, the hooke was caſt away,
Menalcas would not be a country Clowne,
Nor Shepheards weeds, but garments far more
            Euen then,   [gay.
            When thus
Aſpiring thoughts did follow after ruth,
Began the faults and follies of my youth.

My futes were filke, my talke was all of State,
I ftretcht beyond the compaffe of my fleeue,
The braueft Courtier was *Menalcas* mate,
Spend what I would, I neuer thought on griefe.
              Euen then,
              When thus
I lafht out lauifh, then began my ruth,
And then I felt the follies of my youth.

I caft mine eye on euery wanton face,
And ftraight defire did hale me on to loue:
Then Louer-like, I pray'd for *Venus* grace,
That fhe my miftris deepe affects might moue.
              Euen then,
              When thus
Loue trapt me in the fatall bands of ruth,
Began the faults and follies of my youth. /

No coft I fpar'd to pleafe my miftris eye
No time ill fpent in prefence of her fight,
Yet oft fhe frownd, and then her loue muft dye,
But when fhe fmyl'd, oh then a happy wight.
              Euen then,
              When thus
Defire did drawe me on to deeme of ruth,
Began the faults and follies of my youth.

The day in poems often did I paffe,
The night in fighs and forrowes for her grace,
And fhe is fickle as the brittle glaffe,
Held Sun-fhine fhowres within her flattering face.
   Euen then,
   When thus
I fpy'd the woes that womens loues enfueth,
I faw, and loath['d] the follies of my youth.

I noted oft that beauty was a blaze,
I faw that loue was but a heape of cares,
That fuch as ftood as Deare do at the gaze,
And fought their wealth amongft affections fnares
   Euen fuch,
   I fawe,
With hot purfuit did follow after ruth,
And foftered vp the follies of their youth.

Thus clogg'd with loue, with paffions and with
  griefe,
I faw the country life had leaft moleft,
I felt a wound and paine would haue reliefe,
And thus refolu'd I thought would fall out beft :
   Euen then,
   When thus
I felt my fenfes almoft folde to ruth,
I thought to leaue the follies of my youth. /

To flockes againe, away the wanton towne,
Fond pride auaunt, giue me the Shepheards
    hooke,
A coate of gray, Ile be a country clowne :
Mine eye fhall fcorne on beauty for to looke.
    No more,
    A doe:
Both Pride and loue, are euer pain'd with ruth,
And therefore farewell the follies of my youth.

WHen the Swaine had made an end of his
    Song, *Philador* fetcht a figh, and beeing
demanded by old *Rabbi Bileffi*, why this Sonnet
did driue him into a paffion, hee made anfwere,
that it rub'd the fcarre afrefh, and made him call
to mind how he had vainely paft ouer the prime of
his yeares, and fuffered the Caterpillers of time to
confume the bloffomes of his young thoughts.

How fweet foeuer (quoth hee) defire feemes at
the firft, it hath a moft bitter tafte at the laft :
refembling the iuice of the India apples, that are
moft precious in the mouth, and moft pernitious
in the maw. Sonne (quoth his father) leaue off
thefe dumpes, penance is enough for youths follies,
and repentance fatisfies the deepeft offences. Let
vs therefore fit our felues to the time, and be
merry, I for the recouery of thy perfon, thou for

XXI.

GREENES FAREWELL TO FOLLY.

1591.

NOTE.

'Greenes Farewell to Folly' appeared originally in 1591. For an exemplar of this edition I am under obligation to the Bodleian Library. The edition of 1617 is in the 'Huth Library.' See annotated Life in Vol. I.—G.

Greenes farewell to Folly:

SENT TO

COVRTIERS AND

Schollers as a prefident to warne them
from the vaine delights that drawes
youth on to repentance.

Sero fed ferio.

ROBERT GREENE,

Vtriufque Academiæ in Artibus magifter.

Imprinted at London by Thomas Scarlet
for T. Gubbin and T. Newman.
1591.

TO THE HONORABLE
MINDED GENTLEMAN
Robert Carey, Efquire :

Robert Greene wifheth as many good fortunes
as the honor of his thoughts doe
merite.

Auing waded (noble minded Courtier) through the cenfures of many both Honourable and worfhipfull, in cōmitting the credite of my bookes to their honorable opinions, as I haue found fome of them not onely honourably to patronize my workes, but curteouflie to paffe ouer my vnfkilfull prefumption with filence, fo generally I am indebted to all Gentlemen that with fauors haue ouerflipt my follies: Follies I tearme them, becaufe their fubiects haue bene fuperficiall, and their intents amorous, yet mixed with fuch morrall principles, that the precepts of vertue feemed to craue pardon for all / thofe vaine opinions loue fet downe in hir periods. Seeing then (worthie *Mæcenas* of letters)

my workes haue beene counted follies, and follies
the fruit of youth, many yeeres hauing bitten me
with experience, and age growing on bidding mee
Petere grauiora, to fatisfie the hope of my friends,
and to make the world priuie to my priuate refolution, I haue made a booke, called my *Farewell
to Follies :* wherein as I renounce loue for a foole,
and vanitie as a vaine too vnfit for a Gentleman,
fo I difcouer the generall abufes that are ingrafted
in the mindes of Courtiers and fchollers, with a
Co[o]lling Card of counfell, fuppreffing thofe actions
that ftraie from the golden meane of vertue.   But
(right worfhipfull) fome are fo peremptorie in
their opinions, that if *Diogenes* ftirre his ftumpes,
they will faie, it is to mocke dancers, not to be
wanton, that if the fox preach, tis to fpie which
is the fatteft goofe, not to be a ghoftly father, that
if *Greene* write his *Farewell to Follie*, tis to blind
the world with follie, the more to fhadow his owne
follie.   My reply to thefe thought-fearchers is this,
I cannot / Martinize, fweare by my faie in a pulpit,
& rap out gogs wounds in a tauerne, faine loue
when I haue no charitie, or proteft an open refolution of good, when I intend to be priuately ill, but
in all publike proteftations my wordes and my
deedes iumpe in one fimpathie, and my tongue
and my thoughts are relatiues.   But omitting thefe
digreffions (right worfhipful) to my book, which

as it is the farewell to my follies, fo it is the laft I
meane euer to publifh of fuch fuperficiall labours :
which I haue aduentured to fhroude vnder the
fhelter of your worfhippes patronage, as vnder his
wing, whofe generall loue bought with honorable
deferts, may defend it from the iniurie of euerie
enuious enemie. I can fhadowe my prefumption
with no other excufe but this, that feeking to finde
out fome one courtier, whofe vertuous actions had
made him the hope of many honours, at whofe
feete I might laie downe the follies of my youth,
& bequeath to him all the profitable fruits of my
enfuing age, finding none that either fame could
warrant me, or my own priuat fancie perfvvade
to be of more / hope then your felfe, I fet downe
my reft, and ventured boldly on your worfhips
fauour, which if as I haue found before, I obtaine
now, I fhall thinke my felfe as fortunate in getting
fo honorable a patrone for my new indeuours, as
vnhappie for blemifhing my forepaffed youth with
fuch friuolous labours. And thus hoping my
honeft refolution to do well, fhall be counte-
nanft with your worfhips curteous
acceptance, I commit you to
the Almightie.
Your worfhips in all
humble feruice,
ROBERT GREENE. /

TO THE GENTLEMEN
Students of both Vniuerſities health.

Entlemen and Studentes (my olde friendes
and companions) I preſented you alate
with my Mourning garment, howe you
cenſure of the cloth or cut I knowe not, but the
Printer hath paſt them all out of his ſhop, and
the Pedler founde them too deare for his packe,
that he was faine to bargain for the life of Tomliuclin to wrappe vp his ſweete powders in thoſe
vnſauorie papers : If my garment did any Gentleman good I am glad, if it offended none I am
proud, if good man find fault that hath his wit
in his eyes, and can checke what he cannot amend,
miſlike it, I am careles, for *Diogenes* hath taught
me, that to kicke an aſſe when he ſtrikes, were
to ſmell of the aſſe for meddling with the aſſe.
Hauing therefore Gentlemen (in my opinion)
mourned long enough for the miſdeedes of my
youth, leaſt I ſhould ſeeme too Phariſaicall in my
faſtes, or like our deare Engliſh breethren that
meaſure their praiers by the houre glaſſe, fall a
ſleepe in preaching of repentance. I haue nowe left

of the intent, and am come to the effect, and after
my mourning prefent you with my Farewell to
follies, an vltimum vale to al youthful vanities:
wifhing al Gentlemen as wel Courtiers as Schollers,
to take view of thofe blemifhes that difhonor youth
with the quaint fhew of pleafant delights. What
a glorious fhew would the Spring prefent if the
beautie of hir floures were not nipt with the froftes?
how would Autumne boaft of hir fruites, if fhe
were not difguifed with the fall of the leafe, and
how would the vertues of youth fhine (polifhed
with the ripe conceit of wit) if they were not
eclipfed with the cloudes of vanity. Then fweete
companions and louemates of learning, looke into
my Farewel, and you fhall find the poifons which
infect young yeares, and turning but the leafe
reade the Antidotes to preuent the force of fuch
deadly confections. Lay open my life in your
thought and beware by my loffe, fcorne not in your
age what you haue learned in your Accidence,
though ftale yet as fure as check, *Felix quem faciunt
aliena pericula cautum.* Such wags as haue bene
wantons with me, and haue marched in the Mercers booke to pleafe their Miftris eye with their
brauerie, that as the frolike phrafe is haue made
the tauerne to fweat with riotous expences, that
haue fpent their wits in courting of their fweete-
hearts, and emptied their purfes by being too

prodigall, let them at laſt looke backe to the follies
of / their youth, and with me ſay farewell vnto all
ſuch vanities.   But thoſe young nouices that haue
not yet loſt the maidenhead of their innocency, nor
haue heard the melody of ſuch alluring Syrens, let
them read that they may loth, and that ſeeing into
the depth of their follie, they may the more deteſt
that whoſe poyſoned ſweeteneſſe they neuer taſted.
Thus generally I woulde wiſh all to beware by me
to ſay with me farewell to follie.   Then ſhould
I glorie that my ſeede ſowne with ſo much good
will, ſhoulde yeeld a harueſt of ſo great aduantage.
But by your leaue Gentlemen, ſome ouer curious
will carpe and ſay that if I were not beyond, I
would not be ſo bold to teach my betters their
dutie, and to ſhew them the Sunne that haue
brighter eyes than my ſelfe, well *Diogenes* tolde
Alexander of his follie and yet he was not a King.
Others will flout and ouer read euerie line with
a frumpe, and ſay tis ſcuruie, when they themſelues
are ſuch ſcabd Iades that they are like to dye of
the fazion, but if they come to write or publiſh
anie thing in print, it is either diſtild out of ballets
or borrowed of Theologicall poets, which for
their calling and grauitie, being loth to haue anie
prophane phãphlets paſſe vnder their hand, get
ſome other *Batillus* to ſet his name to their verſes:
Thus is the aſſe made proud by this vnder hande

brokerie. And he that can not write true Englifhe
without the helpe of Clearkes of parifh Churches,
will needes make him felfe the father of interludes.
O tis a iollie matter when a man hath a familiar
ftile and can endite a whole yeare and neuer be
beholding to art? but to bring Scripture to proue
any thing he fayes, and kill it dead with the text
in a trifling fubiect of loue, I tell you is no fmall
peece of cunning. As for example two louers on
the ftage arguing one an other of vnkindneffe, his
Miftris runnes ouer him with this canonicall fentence, A mans confcience is a thoufand witneffes,
and hir knight againe excufeth him felfe with that
faying of the Apoftle, Loue couereth the multitude
of finnes. I thinke this was but fimple abufing
of the Scripture. In charitie be it fpoken I am
perfwaded the fexten of Saint Giles without
Creeplegate, would haue beene afhamed of fuch
blafphemous Rhetoricke. But not to dwell in the
imperfection of thefe dunces, or trouble you with a
long commentarie of fuch witleffe cockescombes,
Gentlemen I humbly intreat pardon for my felfe,
that you will fauour my farewell and take the
prefentation of my booke to your iudiciall infights
in good part, which courtefie if I find at your
hands as I little dout of it, I fhall reft yours as
euer I haue done.

Robert Greene. /

Greene his farewell to Follie.

Hen the ftate of *Italie* was peftered with the mutinous factions of the Guelphes and Ghibellines, fo that the common wealth groned vnder the burden of their feditious tumults, and the Church infected with fundrie fchifmaticall opinions, was ftained with that blemifh of diffention. *Florence*, a citie greatly molefted with this ciuill controuerfie, in fted of palmes that prefented peace, was ftored with armour that denounced warres, the ftréets that were a mart for the trafficke of merchants, ferued for a place wherein to martiall fouldiers, the Senate went not in roabes of purple to challenge reuerence, but in coates of ftéele to maintaine their fafetie: age, honour nor religion bare no priuiledge in their foreheads, but the nobilitie with ambition and the commons with enuie, fo diffented in their feuerall thoughts, that

the particular ruine of the Citie, and the generall
fubuerfion of the weale publique was daily expected.
Yet amidft thefe broiles the houfe of the *Farneze*
fo behaued them felues with fuch equal proportion,
that they were neither friends to the Guelphs nor
foes to the Ghibellins, but with an indifferent
poife of affectiõs, countermanded the factious
mutiny of thofe two mortall enimies. The chiefe
of thefe was *Ieronimo Farneze*, a noble man, honorable for his parentage, and honoured for his vertue,
one that in his youth armed his / actions with
proweffe, and in his age made a proofe of his life
by wifdome, who difcouering the miferie of time
by experience, founde that fweeter was the deaw
that dropt from peace, than the fhowers that
powred downe from wars, that the garland of
Mercurie was more precious than the helmet of
Mars, that quiet and content fooner refted vnder
the marble altar of *Pallas*, than vnder the filuer
targets of *Bellona*, not that the noble man thought
it difhonorable to be martiall, but that he counted
it prodigall to be factious : to auoide therefore all
fufpition that might enfue by his refidence in fo
troublefome a Citie, fetting his houfehold affaires
in fome good order, accompanied with his wife,
three daughters, and foure young Gentlemen,
allied vnto him by affinitie, hee departed from
Florence, feated himfelfe in a farme of his about

fixe miles diftant from *Vienna* : the eldeft of his daughters was named *Margaret*, the feconde *Fraunces*, the youngeft *Katherine*, all which as ioyning in a fympathie of their parents propagation, were beholding to Nature for beauty, to Fortune for wealth, and to the Gods for wifedome and vertue : the young Gentlemen were thefe, Seignior *Peratio*, feignior *Bernardine*, feignior *Cofimo*, and meffieur *Benedetto*, all as I faid before, allied to *Farneze* by affinitie, and therfore honorable, and directing the courfe of their liues after his compaffe, and therefore vertuous. Thefe thus affociated both in nature and nourture, accompanied the olde Countie to his houfe, where arryuing they found a Grange place by fcituation melancholie, as feated in the middeft of a thicket, fitter for one giuen to metaphufi[c]al contemplation than for fuch yong Gentlemen, as defired fooner to daunce with *Venus*, than to dreame with *Saturne*, whofe thoughts aimed not at the ftoicke content of *Pythagoras*, but at an exteriour conceite of honeft pleafure, which contrarie to their expectation in fuch a centurie or Countrie cottage, / they founde : for *Ieronimo Farneze* féeing the picture of difcontent fhadowed in their foreheads, conceiuing this frowarde humour to come, for that the place of their abode was fo folempnely feated, beganne at the enteraunce into the bafe Court to vfe thefe words.

Gentlemen, the learned and wife worldlinges whome experience and wifedome hath priuiledged to cenfure rightly of the due expence of time, haue thought with the Phifition, that as the ftomacke hath his orifice ftrengthened as well with the iuyce of bitter wormwood as with the fap of fwéete liquerice : fo the minde oft fteppeth as foone to content by beeing paffionate as pleafant, defire hangs not alwaies on the héeles of delight, man hath his time to meditate, and holy writ tels vs, that as we haue a daie for mirth, fo we haue a daie to mourne ; *Salomon* whofe content paffed al proportion of meafure, counted all things vanitie that ftooped to the centre of the earth, *Alexander* amidft al ŷ Embaffadors at *Babylon*, ftole thrée dayes to bée folitarie, *Philip* woulde bée put in remembrance of his mortalitie : and we Gentlemen, that haue liued pleafantlie at *Florence* wearing out time with vanitie, may now refine our fenfes dulled with the taft of fundrie vaine obiects, and for a wéeke or two betake our felues to this folitarie place, wherein I thinke to finde no other pleafure but a fwéete meditation and friendly conference of the vaine fuppofe of fuch as thinke none Philofophers but Epicures, and none religious but Atheifts. Thus Gentlemen, I appoint your penaunce, and therefore fhew me your opinion by your countenance. Seignior *Peratio* who was

nephew to *Ieronimo*, made aunfwere for the reft
and faide, they were all content : wherewith the
olde Countie leading the waie, entered the houfe,
where finding all thinges in a readines they went
to dinner: the frefh air had procured a good
appetite, that little talke paft till they had ended
their repaft: dinner / being done, counting it
Phificke to fit a while, the olde Counteffe fpying
on the finger of feignior *Cofimo* a ring with a
deaths head ingrauen, circled with this pofie,
Greffus ad vitam, demanded whether hee adorde
the fignet for profit or pleafure: feignior *Cofimo*
fpeaking in truth as his confcience wild him, tolde
her that it was a fauour which a Gentlewoman
had beftowed vpon him, and that onely he wore
it for her fake.   Then, quoth the counteffe, tis a
whetftone to fharp fancie : if it be madam quoth
Cofimo, I am not fo olde but I may loue : nor fo
young fir, quoth fhee, but that you may learne by
that to leaue fuch folly as loue : no doubt nature
works nothing vaine, the Lapidarie cuts not a
ftone, but it hath fome vertue : men weare not
iems only to pleafe the fight, but to be defenfiues
by their fecret operatiõs againft perils, & fo feignior
Cofimo wold I haue you vfe the gentlewomans
fauour, not for a whetftone to further folly, but
for a cooling card to inordinate vanities.   *Themifto-*
cles wore in his fhield the picture of a ftorke, his

motto *Antipelargein*, for that he would not be
ftained with ingratitude. *Socrates* had but one
toie in his houfe, and that was the counterfait of
patience, for that he had a fhrew to his wife :
By your leaue madame (quoth *Cofimo*) had not
Socrates coūterfait alfo a fentēce: yes anfwered
Farneze, but my wife plaies like the Prieft that
at his *Eleuatio* left out his *Memento*, the motto
was this, *Neque hæc fufficit*, meaning patience was
as good a medicine to cure a wafpifh woman of
fullenes as an ants egge in firop for him that is
troubled with the Sciatica.　The Gentlemen laught
at the drie frumpe of *Farneze*, and the Counteffe
for that fhe had talkt of patience, tooke it for a
prefident, and profecuted her intent in this maner.
Ieft howe you pleafe Gentlemen, ftill I faie that
well cannot be gainfayd how the image of death
figured in *Cofimos* ring, fhould be a glaffe whereby
to direct his actions, that the pagans who builde
their bliffe in the / fwéete conceit of Fame, vfed
the picture of death as a reftraint to all forward
follies.　*Alexander* when he named himfelfe the
fon of *Iupiter*, was reuoked from herefie by the
fight of a dead mans fcull that *Califtenes* prefented
to him in a cafket. *Auguftus Cæfar* fet on the
dore of his banketting houfe the fcalpe of a dead
man, leaft extremitie fhould turne delight to vice:
fo feignior *Cofimo*, vfe you your miftres fauor as

a benefit to profit the minde, not as a toy to pleafe
fancie. *Cofimo* was driuen into a dump with this
fodain infinuation of the counteffe, as in déed he
ftood like the picture of filence, whereat *Bernardin*
fmiling made the counteffe,this anfwere.

I cannot denie madame, but you fay well, yet
your cenfure is a little too peremptorie, neither
can I gainfay but fuch a refolution would do well
in age, whofe fappe fhronke from ỹ branches,
côforts the water, but affoords no bloffoms: your
hairs being filuer had a fômons vnto death, &
therefore to be armed with deuotion: our yeres
growen & budding forth a reftles defire to plefure,
which if we fhould cut off with a continuall remembrance of death, we fhould preuent time &
metamorphofe our felues by conceit into a contrary fhape: the Aftronomer by long ftaring at
the ftars forgets the globe at his féet: fo fearefull
was *Phaeton* of the figne in the zodiaock, that
he forgat his courfe: & fo would you haue the
delight of youth dafht with the fight of a death
head, ỹ laying afide al recreation, we fhould fall
to be flat Saturnifts. By this doctrine madam,
you would erect again the Academie of the ftoicks,
& make young men either *apathoi* to liue without
paffions, or els fo holy to die without fin: the
gentlemen were glad that *Bernardino* had made
fuch an anfwere, & *Farneze* to draw them farther

into talke, told his wife ẙ he thought ſhe was
driuen to a *non plus* : no ſir (qd ſhe) but the gentleman miſtakes me, for I meane not to haue him
ſo holy as to liue without ſinne, but ſo honeſt as
to liue without follies, which our Florentins/ſhrowd
vnder the ſhadowe of youth, that in déede are
meére enemies to the glorie of youth. *Meſſieur
Benedetto* interrupted the counteſſe, as one amongſt
al the companie moſt giuen to follie, for he was
a fine courtier and was thus quicke in his replie.
I remember madame that *Phocion* carped at all
men that went ſhod, becauſe he him ſelfe was
euer barefoot. *Antiſthenes* admitted no gueſt but
Geometritians. None ſupt with *Caſſius* but ſuch
as neuer laught, and they which feéle your humour
muſt (though not in yeres yet in action) be as
old as you, or elſe they are fondlings. But they
which ſtood at *Diogenes* tubbe came as well to
laugh as to learne, and we that heare you, may
ſooner fall a ſléepe than follow your doctrine, for
I perceiue vnder this worde folly, you abridge
young gentlemen of euerie laudable pleaſure and
delight, allowing mirth in no meaſure, vnleſſe
pourd out after your proportion : As to hunt,
to hauke, to daunce, to loue, to go cleanly, or
whatſoeuer elſe that contenteth youth his folly.
And thus by an induction you conclude *omnia
vanitas*. The Lady *Katherin* hearing hir mother

fo fharply fhaken vp by meffieur *Benedetto*, pro-
tecting hir boldneffe with a modeft blufhe made
this anfwere : And fir quoth fhe, they which
laught at *Diogenes* perhaps were as foolifhe as
he was cynicall : & might with *Alexander* whatfoeuer they brought take a frumpe for a farewell :
my mother fets not downe peremptorie precepts
to difallow of honeft recreation, but neceffary
perfwafion to difwade men from vanitie : fhe
feekes not with *Tullie* to frame an Orator in
conceipt, with *Plato* to build a common wealth
vpon fuppofes, nor with *Baldeffar* to figure out
a courtier in impoffibilities : but feeing the wings
of youth trickt vp with follies plumes, feekes to
perfwade him with *Icarus* from foaring to high.
And I pray you, qd *Benedetto*, what terme you
follies, womens fancies? no fir, quoth fhe, mens
fauours. *Sylenus* affe neuer fawe a wine bottle
but he would winch, / and you cannot beare the
name of folly but you muft frowne: not that
you miflike of it in thought, but that deckt in
your *pontificalibus* a man may fhape *&* *cetera* by
your fhadow: *Benedetto* let not this bitter blow
fall to the ground but told hir hir Latine was
verie bad and worft placft: for *&* *cetera* was no
word of art for a foole, but in déede he did remember Parrats fpake not what they thinke, but
what they are taught : And fo, quoth *Cofimo*,

you make a bare exchange with Ladie *Katherine*
for a foole to deliuer a popingay, but in déede
to take hir parte in this, we Florentines, nay more
generallie, we Italians ouer wife in our owne conceipt, ftand fo much vppon wit that follie treading
vppon our héeles bids vs oft looke backe vnto
repentance: Seignior *Farneze* taking time by the
forehead iumpt in with *Cofimo*, and faid that not
onely Italians but other nations whatfoeuer were
faultie in that imagination, and that follie was
as common as loue, and loue fo common that he
was not a gentleman that was not in loue : and
by this argument, quoth *Cofimo*, you conclude all
gentlemen both fooles and louers : I reafon not
anfwered *Farneze a coniugatis*, but féeing that we
are thus farre entered into the Anatomie of follies,
let vs fpende this afternoone in difcourfing of the
fondneffe of fuch our countriemen, as ouergrowne
with felfe loue drownes themfelues in that follie
which all the world giues vnto vs as due : I meane
pride, which feignier *Peratio* for that I knowe you
alwaies to haue borne the profeffion of a fcholler,
I commit vnto your charge : Not to me fir, quoth
Peratio, I pray you kéepe decorum, let the Ladie
Katherine difcourfe of that which beft beféemeth
hir fexe : for if we may giue credit to men verie
fkilfull and excellent in Chronographie, the firft
patterne of pride came from *Eua* the moother of

women and the miftreffe of that faulte : You
miftake the matter, quoth the Ladie *Katherine,*
Eua was obedient / and fimple, following nothing
but what hir hufbande forefhewed and foretaught
hir. Let vs leaue women, quoth *Farneze,* and
priuiledge them a little to be proud, onely *Signor*
Peratio touch you the follie of our Italians, and we
will be filent auditours to your good philofophie :
The gentlemen fetled them felues in filence,
which gaue a proofe to *Peratio* that they agréed
to *Farnezes* requeft, and therefore he began his
talke in this manner.

Although gentlemen it hath pleafed the Countie
to giue me in charge the difcourfe of fuch a
weightie matter as the difcouery of pride, yet I
knowe my fufficiencie fo farre vnable to performe
his requeft, as of force I muft craue pardon if
either my cenfures be too rafhe or verdi£t offenfiue : refting therefore in hope of your courteous
patience, thus to the purpofe. The learned clerkes
whofe experience may auouche their fayings for
Oracles, affirme this folly to difcend by courfe of
propogation, as naturally inferted into the minde
of man *ab ipfis incunabilis,* fetting downe by
phyficall reafons that pride doth poffeffe the inward
fenfes of infants as *fenfum cõmunem & Phantezian*
before any exterior obie£t can delude the fence
with vanitie, which *Plato* confidering in his *Timæo*

calleth it *Anthropomafia*, the fcourge of man, as a
vice fo déepely bred by the bone, as it will hardly
be rooted out of the flefh, alluding the reafon that
his maifter *Ariftotle* did for the heart which liuing
firft dieth laft: fo pride entring at the cradle endeth
in the graue. *Scipio Affricanus* the great, whofe
triumphes had filled the ftréetes of *Rome* with
trophes, being demãded why the ftate of *Rome*
began to ruinate, what made him forfake the
fenate, why he liued folitarie from the ciuill
gouernement, why he tafted not the fruites of his
foregotten glories? anfwered to all thefe demands
briefely, for that *Rome* waxeth proude, meaning
that pride as ill befitteth a crowne as a cottage: /
what ouerthrewe the houfe of the *Tarquins* but
pride, what wrought the confufion at *Babel* but
the pride of *Nemroth*? Pride ouerthrew the
pompe of *Alexander*, and had not pride hatched
ambition the Romanes had neuer bewailde the
death of *Pompey*: to repeat a catalogue of infinit
examples were friuolous: and therefore leauing this
generall difcouerie let vs come to a more particular difcourfe of this follie. Our Florentins which
profeffe themfelues to be fouldiers, are wedded to
this vaine, as men fhadowing the verie fubftance
of pride with the two colours of fame and honour:
for what attempts they féeke to atchieue by
martiall proweffe, what exploites they perfourme

in warres, what daies and nightes they fpende in
watching either to preuent or preiudice the enemie,
ftill claime the finall caufe of thofe actions to be
fame or honour. But who heareth the fundry and
feuerall brauados our martialiftes make of their
ftrange encounters? how cunningly they ordred
their fquadrons? how couragioufly they incountered
the enemie? how ftoutly they affaied the pufh of
the pike? how ftrongly they bare the fhocke of the
horffe? what lances they brake? what maffacres
they made? what ftratagemes they perfourmed?
what citties they both affaulted and facked, fhall
finde this report to taft of felfe loue, and thefe
warlike endeuours to fauour as much of pride as
either of fame or honour. But grant their allega-
tions true, they couet to be famous and honourable,
yet fhall we finde the end of thefe vertuous
imaginatiõs, to be touched a little with the ftaine
of this follie : for the defire of fame aimed with
afpiring thoughts foreth fo high, that feeking with
Phaeton to rule aloft, his very prefcription draweth
them in a felfe conceipt of their owne glories.
Had not *Haniball* founde pride in the hope of
fame, he had neuer / fcaled the *Alpes* to befiege
Capua. Had not *Alexander* béene proude in the
glorie of his victories and conqueftes, he had neuer
fighed that there was but one worlde to fubdue.
Hercules was proude of his labours, *Hector* of his

combats with the Grecians, and to be fhort, the meaneft fouldiour getting either fame or honor by fundrie hardy and happy attempts, glories fo much in the glorious reward of his indeuor that willingly he paffes his proportion, and commeth within the compaffe of this follie.

Seignior *Bernardino*, who all his life time, had profeffed him felfe a foldiour, feeing *Peratio* fo peremptorily to appech his profeffion of pride, made this anfwer. I can not thinke, feignior *Peratio* but your natiuitie being rightly calculated, hath *Mercurie* fo predominant, as we may cenfure without offence, that you are farre more bookifh than wife, efpecially in martiall affaires, whofe honourable conceit I fée is fo farre beyonde the reache of your capacity, that in gazing at a ftarre you ftumble at a ftone, and in aiming particularly at a fouldiour, you generally load him with the fault of the whole worlde: are you fo fimple your felfe as to account euerie humour that fitteth man with delight to be pride, that the defire of fame and honour is nothing elfe but felfe loue? Then fir, let me fay, that *Mineruas* owle was proude, for pirking vnder hir golden target, and that *Apelles* boies aimed at felfe loue for grinding colours for their maifters fhadowes. But it did not preiudice the valour of *Themiftocles* to be called coward at the mouth of *Ariftot*, becaufe the foole was a

fidler, and knewe fcarfe a fpeare from a fpigot,
neither may fouldiours take offence to be thought
proude at your handes, which neuer faw battell
but in your booke, and yet I can not deny but
there be fuch fantaftick martialists / as you talke
of, whofe tongues are more hardie than their
hands, and dare fooner fcale the heauens with a
braue than anger a man with a blow: fuch feignior
Peratio as Thrafonically countenance themfelues
w̄ the title of a fouldior, comprehend you within
the cōpaffe of folly : but thefe perfonages which in
defenfe of their country and defpight of the enemy,
féeke after fame and honour, and glorie in the
gaine of fuch a golden benefit, let them triumphe
in their conquefts, & delight themfelues in recounting thofe fauours which fame hath beftowed vpon
them for their warlike indeuours. But fir, in this
difcourfe of pride you are partiall & play like
Diogenes, who carping at the beggery of *Antifthenes,*
neuer marked the patch on his owne cloake.
Sylenus would oft inuey againft drunckennes with
a bottle of wine in his hande. *Therfites* appeached
Menalcas of deformitie, him felfe being moft
il fauoured : and you fir, induce a fouldiour as
prologue to your comedie of pride, whereas you
fchollers ought to be formoft in the fcene, for he
that maketh but a ftep into the vniuerfitie of
Padua, where the youth of *Florence* chiefely

flourifhe, and with a déepe infight marketh the
nature of our Mercurialifts, fhall find as fit a
harbour for pride vnder a fchollers cap as vnder
a fouldiours helmet, and that as great felfe loue
lurketh in a fide gowne, as in a fhort armour.
Tell me good feignior *Peratio*, is not *Mercurie* as
arrogant as *Mars* is prefumptuous? The one is
figured with wings as bewraying his afpiring
thoughtes, the other pictured in armes, as import-
ing a refolution. Turne they not ouer manie
leaues? Reade they not large volumes? Confume
they not long time? Apply they not their wits
and willes? Some in Aftronomy to gaze at the
ftarres, fome in Phyficke to fearch out the nature
of fimples, other in the Mathematiks / to worke
out metaphyficall experimentes, euerie a particu-
laritie in euerie art: fpending all his life to haue
the worlde giue a plauditie of their ftudies. Is
not this, feignior *Peratio*, a tickling humour of
felfe loue, that may bring fchollers within the
compaffe of pride? *Tullie* gadded the ftréetes of
Rome, that the people might call him *pater patriæ*.
Demoftenes tooke fuch a conceit of his eloquence,
that he walked vp & downe *Athens* to haue the
citizens fay, *hic eft ille Demoftenes*. *Plato* was fo
proude that he fcarfe thought King *Dionyfius* his
fellowe, and not onely in learning, but in life and
apparell fo neate, that *Diogenes* féeing a braue

curfier richly decked with golden trappers, demanded of him when hee was in *Cumæo,* as taking
the horffe for one of *Platoes* difciples : and I thinke
ye fchollers of *Padua* haue fo long read *Platoes*
workes, that ye taft of *Platoes* vanities, I mene not
of his philofophy, but of his follies : for now he
peareth no touch in *Padua* that can not as well
praue it with *Plato* as reafon with *Plato,* that couet
as well to imitate *Ariftotle* in the fumptuoufnes
of his apparell as the fubtilneffe of his arguments,
that hath not a tailer as well to picture out his
lineaments, as a Stationer to furnifh out his librarie :
therefore feignior *Peratio* looke to your owne laft,
meafure not the length of an other mans foot by
your owne fhoe, but ioine the fouldier and fcholler
in one fillogifme, and then the premifes equall,
conclude how you lift. Seignior *Farneze* and the
reft fmiled at the fharpe reply of *Bernardino,* and
among the reft meffieur *Benedetto* galled *Peratio*
with this gléeke. By my faith gentlemen feignior
Bernardino, in my opinion hath done well not onely
in his defence of a fouldier, but in his Satyricall
inuectiue againft fchollers, wrefting *argumentum*
coniunctum againft *Peratio* him felfe : I hope fir you /
are a batchelor, and therefore this kinde of phrafe
giues the leffe offence. *Peratio* thought to pufh
him with the pike, as hee had hit him with the
launce, refembling the fall of *Hector,* who while he

vnarmde *Patroclus* was vnhorſed himſelfe : *Peratio*
ſomewhat cholerike, & not well able to brooke the
frump of *Benedetto*, was thus rough with him :
maſſe courtier I am glad you kéepe ſo good a
decorum, as to let the lightnes of your head &
lauiſhnes of your follies ſo well to agree in *eode*
tertio : you take *Bernardinos* part, but when the
gentleman ran ſo mery a deſcant on the pride of
ſchollers, had he by hap but glancſt at the gaudineſſe
of your apparell, he had ſpoken farre more reuer-
ently of ſchollers than he did : for you Florentine
Courtiers, nay to be flat, we Florentine Gentlemen,
to bring my ſelfe within the ſame predicament,
diſcouer our ſelues to be the verie anatomies of
pride : for he that marketh our follies in being
paſſing humorous for the choiſe of apparell, ſhall
finde *Ouids* confuſed *chaos* to affoorde a multitude
of defuſed inuentions.   It was obieded to *Cæſar*
for a fault in his youth that he euer vſed to go
vntruſt, and we count it a glorie, by a careleſſe
cloathing of our ſelues, to be counted malcontent.
Sardanapalus was thruſt from his empire, for that
he was a little effeminate, and we ſtriue to be
counted womanish, by kéeping of beautie, by
curling the haire, by wearing plumes of fethers in
our hands, which in warres our anceſtors wore on
their heads, they feared of men, we to be fauoured
of women.   *Alexander* fell in hate of his Macedons,

being the monarch of the whole world for wearing
a Perfian roabe imbroidered with gold, and we
Florentines that are fcarfe maifters of one towne,
fo decke our felues in coftly attire, fo rich and fo
rare, that did the Macedons liue and fée our
follies, / they would grant *Alexander* to weare his
robe without enuy as a priuiledge : yea now a daies
Time hath brought pride to fuch perfection in
Italie, that we are almoft as fantafticke as the
Englifh Gentleman that is painted naked with a
paire of fhéeres in his hande, as not being refolued
after what fafhion to haue his coat cut. In truth,
quoth *Farneze*, to digreffe a little from your
matter, I haue féene an Englifh Gentleman fo
defufed in his futes, his doublet being for the
weare of *Caftile*, his hofe for *Venice*, his hat for
France, his cloake for *Germanie*, that he féemed
no way to be an Englifhman but by the face.
And quoth *Peratio*, to this are we Florentines
almoft grown : for we muft haue our courtefies fo
cringed, our conges deliuered with fuch a long
accent, our fpéeches fo affected, as comparing our
conditions with the liues of our anceftors, we féeme
fo farre to differ from their former eftate, that did
Ouid liue, he woulde make a fecond Metamorphofis of our eftates. Now maffe *Benedetto*, are
not you and the fcholler fellowe comperes in
follies ? Hath not pride taught the one as large

principles as the other? Are not Courtiers as
proude of their coates as we of our bookes? Nay
Gentlemen, not fouldiours, fchollers and courtiers
onely, but all other eftates whatfoeuer are com-
prifed within the compaffe of our inquifition, and
may verie well and rightly be appeached of this
folly.

But feignior *Peratio*, quoth the olde Counteffe,
what doe you thinke euerie one proud that weareth
coftly apparell? No Madam, quoth *Peratio*,
neither doe I thinke but verie beggers haue their
pride, and therefore appoint the feat of this folly
in the heart, not in the habit: for as the coule
makes not the monck, nor the gray wéede the
frier, fo fumptuous attire, procureth not alwaies
prefumption, neither doeth pride / euer harbour in
filkes: pride looketh as lowe as the cottage, and
pouertie hath his conceit tainted with felfe loue.
Crates was more proud of his fcrip and wallet, than
Creffus of all his wealth. *Plato* had fuch an infight
into the péeuifh pride of *Diogenes*, that he durft
boldly fay, *Calco fuperbiâ Diogenis*. The begger
Irus that hanted the pallace of *Penelope*, would
take his eafe in his Inne as well as the péeres of
Ithaca. Thoughts are not meafured by exteriour
effects, but by inward affectes. Roabes made not
Agathocles leaue to drinke in earthen veffels, but
ragges fhrowded a proude mind in *Eubulus*, that

prefumd to call him the fonne of a potter : tis as bad a confequent to call a king proud for his treafure, as a begger humble for his want, and therefore in my opinion, from the king to the begger, no eftate is frée from this follie. But pride as the predominant qualitie in euerie fexe, degrée and age challengeth in euerie ones mind fome fpecial and particular prerogatiue. To confirme which, Gentlemen if you will giue me leaue, I will rehearfe you a pleafaunt hiftorie. The Countie and the reft of the Gentlemen and Ladies, defirous to heare *Peratios* tale, fetled themfelues to filence, and he beganne in this manner.

The Tale of Peratio.

WHile the citie of *Buda* remayned frée from the inuafion of the Turk and was one of the chief promontories of Chriftendom, there reigned as king *Iohannes Vadiflaus*, a man fo posfeffed with happines in the prime of his youth, as it féemd / the ftarres in his natiuitie had confpired to make him fortunate. By parentage royally and rightly difcended from the ancient kings of *Hungaria*, by birth fole king and monarch of all the Tranfalpine regions, nature had fo curioufly performed his charge in the lineaments of his bodie, & the planets by happie afpeéts fo carefully inriched his mind with fundrie gifts : as it was in

queſtion which of all theſe might chalenge by right
the ſupremacie. But as the pureſt chriſtall hath
his ſtrakes, the cléereſt ſkie his cloudes, the fineſt
die his ſtaine : ſo *Vadiſlaus* amidſt all theſe golden
legacies bequeathed to him by nature, Fortune and
the gods, had yet a blemiſh darkened all his other
glories with diſgrace.   For his minde was ſo puffed
vp with a diſdainefull kinde of pride, that he
purchaſed not onely a ſpeciall enuie of his nobilitie,
but a generall hate of his commons : ſeated thus
by his owne conceipt in a ſecure content, although
in verie déede daylie ſtanding upon thornes : for
that the liues of kings pinched with enuie are as
brittle as glaſſe, he thought Fortune had beene
tied to his thoughtes in a ſtring, and that the forehead of time had bene furrowed with no wrinckles,
that kings might commande the heauens, and that
ſuch monarchs as he might attempt with *Xerxes* to
tie the Occean in fetters : but experience taught
him that the counterfet of Fortune, was like the
picture of *Ianus*, double faced, in the one preſenting
flatterie, in the other ſpight : that time had two
wings, the one plumd with the feather of a doue
to foreſhew peace, the other with the pennes of
an eagle to denounce warres, that kings might
determine but God diſpoſe : that a ſcepter was no
warrant to priuiledge them from misfortune, that
euerie bliſſe hath his bane, that euerie pleaſure

hath his paine, and euerie dram of delight counter-
poifed with / a whole tunne of miferie. But in
the bloffoms of his youth, when felfe loue tickled
him forwarde to ouerweene of his owne eftate,
confideration, the enemie of vntimely attempts,
had not trode on his héele, but taking the raines
of libertie in his handes, he ranne with *Phaeton*
headlong into his owne misfortune. For on a
day, as oft he defired to delight his fenfes with
the fragrant verdure of the meades, intending to be
folitarie, for he hated difport, in that he fcorned
any of his nobility fhoulde beare him companie,
he paffed fecretly out at a pofterne gate, onely
accompanied with one of his nobles, whom amongft
all the reft he admitted into priuat familiaritie :
an Earle he was, and called *Selydes*, and went to a
groue hard adioyning to the pallace, where in an
arbour that nature, without the helpe of art, had
moft curioufly wrought, he paffed away parte of the
day in melancholy meditation : at laft tickled with
a déepe conceit of his owne happineffe, commanding his noble man a part, he beganne thus to footh
him felfe in his owne follies. Haft thou not heard
Vadiflaus, nay doeft thou not know, that kings are
gods, and why gods, becaufe they are kings, that
a crowne contayneth a worlde of pleafures, and
Fortune euer commeth at the fight of a fcepter, that
the maieftie of a prince is like the lightning from

the Eaft, and the threates of a king like the noyfe
of thunder? What fayeft thou *Vadiflaus*, are
kings goddes? Why doeft thou fo muche abafe
thy felfe? kings are more than goddes, for *Iupiter*
for all his Deitie was glad to reigne a pettie king
in *Créete*, *Saturne* fued for the Diademe of *Italie*,
both goddes, if Poets fay true, and yet both inferiour vnto thée in crowne and kingdome. The
Tranfalpine Regions that border vppon the *Rheine*
are thine, thou art fole king in all thofe dominions./
The ftarres feares to croffe thée with any contrary
afpeét, the temple of peace opens hir gates at thy
prefence: riche thou art, featured thou art, feared
thou art, happy thou art, conclude all that may bée
fayd either of honour, fauour, or fortune, a king
thou art *Vadiflaus*: yea, fo furely feated in the
Monarchye, as did the heauens oppofe themfelues
againft thy profperitie and happineffe, their fpight
were in vaine to determine thy ruine and ouerthrow. Therefore *Vadiflaus* bring not contempt
to fuch a royall dignitie by too muche familiaritie:
difdayne in a king is the figure of maieftie, tis
glorious for princes to let their fubieéts feare at
the thoght of their Soueraigne, fo then *Vadiflaus*,
let this cenfure bée ratified, and from henfe foorth
vfe thy nobilitie as neceffarie members to perfourme
thy commande, but for companions, none *Vadiflaus*,
but kinges. At this he fwelled, and being droncke

with the dregges of his owne folly, defirous to bée
foothed in this imagination, he called vnto him the
Countie *Selydes*, vnto whome hee vttered thefe
wordes.

Thou féeft *Selydes*, I am a king, to be feared of
men, becaufe honoured of the goddes, tell me
fréely without flatterie, what doeft thou thinke
either of me or my gouernement? The Countie
who all his life time had bene a courtier, and yet
neuer learned nor loued with *Ariftippus* to be
Dionyfius fpaniell, craued pardon of the king:
which granted, he framed his talke in this manner.

I can not deny (mighty foueraigne) but kings
are gods, in that they ought to refemble their
Deities in gouernement and vertue, but yet as the
faireft Cedar hath his water boughes, the richeft
Marguerite hir fault, and the fwéeteft rofe his
prickle: fo in a crowne / is hidden far more care
than content, for one moment of perfect eafe a
whole moneth of difquiet thoughtes, that were the
perils apparant that are hid in a Diademe, hardly
would ambition boaft in fuch triumphes: the gold
of *Tholoffe* gliftered and yet it was fatall, *Seianus*
horfe was faire to the eye yet vnluckie, a fcepter
befet with ftones is beautiful but dangerous: kings
(my liege) are men and therefore fubiect to miffe,
mortall and therefore bondflaues vnto Fortune,
and yet the title of a crowne oft puffeth vp their

mindes fo with pride, as forgetting themfelues,
they fuddenly prooue infortunate. *Polycrates* fo
fwelled in the conceit of his happineffe, as hee
thought the heauens coulde not countermand his
profperitie, yet experience taught him that Time
and Fortune ftoode on a gloabe and therefore
mutable, that the calmeft fea hath his ftormes,
and the higheft fteps to felicitie, the déepeft fall
to misfortune : for the beginning of his youth was
not fo profperous, as the ende of his age was
tragicall. *Nero* was proud, and therefore tyrannous, for the one is a confequent to the other, and
fo by pride loft both life and Lordfhip : kings
(my liege) haue found this by experiēce, & haue
feared to make proofe of it by triall : fo that
Philip had a boy to put him in minde of his
mortalitie. *Alexander* woulde bee called the fonne
of *Iupiter*, but *Califtenes* made him denie fuch
arrogancie in *Babylon*. *Crefus* was proude of his
pelfe, but *Solon* pulde downe his plumes by
preferring *Byton* before him in happineffe : kings
heads are not impalled with fame, for that they
are kings, but becaufe they are vertuous. *Auguftus
Cæfar* was not famous for his Empire but for his
clemencie. *Seuerus* was not chronicled for his
treafure but for his iuftice. *Antonius Pius* / had
not his picture plaft in the Capitoll, becaufe of his
fcepter, but for he was mercifull : So my Lorde to

your queftion, I thinke your maieftie a king in déede with large dominions, and honoured with royall titles of dignitie, and it fitteth not a fubiect to miflike of his princes gouernement : onely this I conclude, and this hartely I wifh, that your highneffe may liue fauoured of the goddes, and loued and honoured of men. He that brufeth the Oliue trée with hard iron, fetcheth out no oyle but water, and he that pricketh a proude heart with perfwafions, draweth out onely hate and enuie. For *Vadiflaus* fo grudged at the friendly aduertifementes of the Countie *Selides,* that choaking his choler with filence, he made no replie, but went home to the palace : where, for the receit of a fifhe, thinking to repay a fcorpion, he whetted his thoughtes onely on reuenge. And Fortune, who ftill thought to fauour him in his follies, foothed him with fucceffe in his enuie, that raysing him to the higheft fphere of felfe conceit, fhe might throw him downe to the loweft center of difpaire : for manie dayes had not paft before, by fome finifter meanes, he had wrought fo with the reft of his nobilitie, that the Countie was founde faultie by falfe witneffe in a penall ftatute, that his goodes were confifcated vnto the kings vfe, his bodie exiled into *Germanie,* and his onelye daughter, for one and but one hee had, as a diftreffed virgine was refte at once both of parentes and patrimonie. The Countie

arming his thoughtes with pacience, againſt the
deſpight of Fortune, counting it good counſayle to
make a vertue of neceſſitie, left his daughter in
ſteade of a dowrie to inriche hir marriage, fatherlye /
doctrine to increaſe her manners: for giuing hir
coyne that enuie had reft, leauing hir aduiſe and
counſayle that experience had taught, counting it
more happineſſe to haue his daughter prooue wiſe
than wealthie, as preferring the giftes of the mind
farre before the goodes of Fortune, parting thus
from his onelye childe, from his fréendes and from
his Countrye hee coulde not but ſorrowe, and yet
in ſuch meaſure, as diſpaire coulde take no aduaun-
tage of his paſſions. The Ladye, as made of a
more tender complexion, let looſe the fountaynes
of hir teares, and hauing taken hir farewell of hir
father lamented his caſe, as farre as the rech of
hir eye could kéepe the Barke within ken, and
after the ſhippe was out of ſight, and ſhée left
alone and comfortleſſe on the ſhoare, ſhée beganne
after this manner to complayne with hir ſelfe.

Diſtreſſed and ſorrowfull _Mæſia_, for ſo was hir
name, where ſhalt thou beginne to recount thy
gréefes, or make an ende of thy diſpayring ſorrowes : the prime of youth, which to others is
a ſummer of good happe, being to thee a froſtie
winter of misfortune? Nowe doeth experience
teache thée for trueth, which earſt thou accountedſt

for a fable, that the priuiledge of honour is fealed
with the fignet of time, that the higheft degrées
haue not the fureft feates, that nobilitie is no
warrant againft mifhappe, that the higheft cedars
are blafted with lightning, when the lower fhrub
waues not with the wind, fmall brookes bubble
foorth filent ftreames, when greater feas are troubled
with tempeftes: enuie yea enuie, the verie caterpiller
of content, fpareth the touche of a cottage, when
he endeuours the ruine of a pal/lace, he fcorneth
a begger when he ftricketh a king, and vouchfafeth
not to checke pouertie, when hee giueth honour
the mate. Then *Mæfia*, what reafon haft thou
to bewayle thy prefent fall, and not rather to ioy
at thy future hap? accufe not fates or Fortune as
thy foes, when their defpight redounded not to
thy loffe, but thy libertie, whilome thou wert
honourable, and therefore fearefull, now thou art
poore, and therefore fecure : alate reftleffe, feare
of mifhappe difquieted thy fléepes in a pallace,
nowe a quiet content fhall afoorde thée fwéete
flumbers in a cottage : there didft thou figh in
filkes, heere mayeft thou fing in ruffet, there
nobilitie was counterpoyfed with care, here
pouertie is inriched with quiet. Then *Mæfia*,
chaunge thy affeétions with thy fortunes, liue as
though thou wert borne poore, and hope as one
affured to dye riche: for there is no greater

honour than quiet, nor no greater treasure than
content. But alas my father, mine aged father:
Scarfe had fhee vttered thefe wordes, but griefe
prefented fuche a heape of diftreffed thoughts,
that either the heart muft burft by fmoothering
fuch fcalding forrowes, or elfe the tongue and
eyes refolue vnto playntes and teares. Ah des-
pightfull and iniurious Fortune, quoth fhée, well
did *Zeuxes* paint thée blinde, and yet without a
vale, as hauing thine eyes not couered with a
lawne, but darkened with defpight: the froft
nippeth the budde when he fpareth the root,
the goddes flue the brattes of *Iocafta* but fpared
Oedipus, the wrinckles of age fhoulde be war-
rauntes of weale, the filuer haires fhould bee
pledges of peace. But fynde or furie as thou art,
thou haft threatned my father with a contrarye /
malice, in the cradle giuing him fwéete fyrops, at
the graue prefenting him with bitter potions, in
the prime of his youth bring[ing] him a fléepe with
honour, in the ende of his dayes difquieting his
thoughtes with pouertie. Silence *Mæfia*, leaft
Fortune hearing thy complaynts, ioy in hir owne
fpight, and triumphe in thy forrowes : the fwéeteft
falue of mifhappe is pacience, and no greater
reuenge can be offered Fortune, than to reft
content in miferie : teares are no cures for diftreffe,
neither can thy prefent plaintes pleafure thy abfent

father: then *Mæſia* comfort thy ſelfe, and what
time thou ſhouldeſt beſtowe on diſcourſing thy
misfortunes, ſpende in oriſons to the goddes, to
redreſſe thy fathers cares and reuenge his iniuries:
and vppon this reſolution ſhe reſted, and for that
ſhe would kéepe a *decorum*, as well in hir attire
as in hir actions, ſhe put off hir rich roabes and
put on homely ragges, transforming hir thoughtes
with hir apparell, trauelled from the court into
the countrie: where ſéeking for ſeruice, ſhe had
not paſſed long, before ſhe met with a welthy
farmers ſonne, who handſomely deckt vp in his
holy day hoſe, was going very mannerly to be
foreman in a Morice dãce, and as néere as I can
geſſe thus he was apparelled : he was a tall ſlender
youth, cleane made with a good indifferent face,
hauing on his head a ſtrawne hat ſtéeple wiſe,
bound about with a band of blue buckram: he
had on his fathers beſt tawnye worſted iacket :
for that this daies exploit ſtood vpon his credit :
he was in a pair of hoſe of red kerſie, cloſe truſt
with a point afore, his mother had lent him a newe
muffler for a napkin, & that was tied to his girdle
for looſing: he had a paire of harueſt gloues on his
hands as ſhewing good huſbãdry, & a pen & inck-
horn at his backe: for the young man was a little
bookiſh, his pompes were a little too heauie, being
trimmed ſtart-vps made of a paire of boote legges,

tied before with two white leather thongs: thus handſomely arrayed, for this was his ſonday ſute, he met the Ladie *Mæſia*, and ſeeing hir ſo faire and well formed, farre paſſing their countrie maides in proportion, and nothing differing in apparell, he ſtoode halfe amazed as a man that had ſeene a creature beyond his countrie conceit, and in déede ſhe was paſſing faire, for this I remember was hir deſcription.

Hir ſtature and hir ſhape was paſſing tall,
Diana like, when longſt the lawnes ſhe goes :
A ſtately pace like Iuno *when ſhe braued,*
The queene of heauen fore Paris *in the vale :*
A front beſet with loue and maieſtie,
A face like louely Venus *when ſhe bluſht*
A ſeely ſhepherd ſhoulde be beauties iudge :
A lip ſweete rubie red, gracd with delight,
Hir eies two ſparkling ſtarres in winter night,
When chilling froſt doth cleere the azurd ſkie :
Hir haires in treſſes twind with threds of ſilke,
Hoong wauing downe like Phœbus *in his prime:*
Hir breaſts as white as thoſe two ſnowie ſwannes
That drawes to Paphos Cupids *ſmiling dame :*
A foote like Thetis *when ſhe tript the ſands,*
To ſteale Neptunus *fauour with her ſteps :*
In fine, a peece deſpight of beauty framd,
To ſee what natures cunning could affoord.

Thus I haue hearde the Ladie defcribed, and this hir rare forme droue this countrie youth into this maruelous admiration: at laft *Mæfia* feeing the poore fellowe in a maze, after falutations done as countrie like as fhe could, and yet too courtly for / his calling, fhe enquired of him if hee knew anie good and honeft houfe, where fhe might be entertained into feruice. The young man who all this while had ftarde her in the face, told her that fhe came in pudding time, for his mother wanted a maide, and if fhée could take anie paines no doubt fhe fhould find a houfe fit for her purpofe. And (quoth hee) I haue fuch good hope that you will proue well, that although this daie I fhoulde haue bene fore-man in a may-game, yet I will rather marre the plaie then your market, and fo will tourne backe to leade you the waie to our houfe. *Mæfia* gaue him thankes, and together they went to his Fathers, where after the young fpringall had talked a while with his mother, for he was his fathers eldeft fonne, the good wife had fuch liking of the maide, that fhee gaue her an earneft penny to ferue her for a yéere, and fo hired her before the Conftable. *Mæfia* beeing thus honeftly plaft, by her good behauiour grewe into fuch fauour with all the houfe, that the olde fooles began to thinke her a fit match for their eldeft fonne, and in this hope vfed her meruailous well. But leauing her

to her Countrie content, at laſt to *Vadiſlaus*, who
hauing nowe glutted enuie with reuenge in banniſh-
ing the good Earle, pearked ſo highe with *Danidas*
Parrat, that at the laſt hee fell to the grounde: For
pride had taught him this principle, that princes
wils ware lawes, and that the thoughts of kings
could not erre : diſdaine and contempt, two monſters
of nature, had ſo ſotted his mind with ſelfe loue,
that as his aƈtions grew to be inſolent, ſo his
gouernment began to be tyrannous, commanding
as fancie wild him to affeƈt, not as iuſtice wiſht
him to affoord : he ſought not with *Auguſtus* to
be called *Clemens*, but with *Tarquin* to glorie in
the title of *Superbus* : alluding the diſtike which
Virgil wrote in the praiſe of *Cæſar* to him/ſelfe,
Diuiſum imperium cum Ioue Cæſar habet. He
would not with *Phillip* bee called martiall, but
with *Alexander* be honored as the ſonne of *Ammon*:
hee ſought not to ſit in his throne with a braunch
of palme, to gouerne with peace, but vſed a ſwoorde
as a ſcepter to rule with conſtraint. Long hee dyd
not continue in this life, but that hee grewe in
mortall hate with his ſubieƈtes : the poore commons
grudged and groned vnder the burden of his
crueltie, the Nobilitie beganne to conſider with
themſelues, that more did the ſtate of *Rome* ruinate
in one yeere vnder the gouerment of the Emperour *Calygula*, than it proſpered in manie vnder

the vertuous regiment of *Traian*, that more blos-
fomes die the firft nippe in a morning, than the
heate of the Sunne can reuiue in a whole daie, and
more harme doeth the pride of a king in a moment,
than good pollicie can reftore in a moneth : where-
vpon they determined to forewarne him of his
follies, and to perfwade him from that courfe of
life, which woulde in time bring the commonwealth
to mifchiefe, and him felfe to misfortune : finding
fit time and opportunitie with a generall confent
they beganne to diffwade him from his prefumption, but *Vadiflaus* who brookt not to be countermanded by anie of his nobles, returnde them this
fcornfull anfwere.

My Lords, as the Sunne is fet in the heauens, fo
kings are feated vppon earth : the one too glorious
an obiect for euerie eie to gaze at, the other too
full of maieftie for anie man to controule. The
woulfe had his fkin pulled ouer his ears for
prying into the lions den : the actions of Princes
are like the pearles of *Arabia*, the one too coftly
for euerie marchant to prife, the other too honourable for euerie bafe perfon to cenfure of. Dare
the proudeft birde beare wing againft the / Eagle ?
Is not the print of a lyons clawe a feale of his
fafetie, and the verie title, nay the verie thought of
a king, a warrant of his bliffe ? Take héede my
Lordes, let the preiudice of others bee a prefident

for you to beware: me thinke the Countie *Selydes* mifhap might warne you from preffing too much on my fauour. *Seneca* by grudging at *Neros* bliffe procured his owne bane. *Califtenes* checking the thoughts of *Alexander* wrought his owne ouerthrowe. Kings muft not be controuled for that they are Kings, and therefore from henceforth doome not of my doinges leaft. And with that he flung from them in a rage, as one aiming at reuenge, if heereafter they miflikt of his gouernment. The nobles whome difdaine had armed to defpaire, beganne to murmure at the kings wicked refolution, and [refolued] either to frée the commonwealth from miferie, or by attempting fuch an enterprife to procure their owne mifhap: amongeft them all *Rodento*, a nobleman more bolde then the reft burft forth into thefe paffions.

My Lordes and worthie Peeres of *Buda*, feared for your valour, and famous for your victories, let not the priuate will of one man bee the ruine of fuch a mightie kingdome: kings are Gods, then let them gouerne like Gods, or giue vs leaue to account them worfe then men : let the examples of other nations tie vs to the confideration of our prefent eftate. The Athenians preferred the weale of their Countrie before the pride of *Alcibiades*, *Cæfar* was flaine in the Senate for his pride, *Hannibal* twice exiled *Carthage* for his prefumption,

Dyonifius banifhed out of *Scycily* for his infolencie : Crownes (my Lordes) are no plackardes of wicked - neffe, Securitie waiteth not anie longer vpon a Scepter than it is fwayde with equitie, a Diademe is no longer glorious then it is / decked with vertue, fo ỹ occafion prefents vs a double proffer, either by foothing ỹ king in his pride to fuffer the com- monwealth to perifh, or by rooting out fuch a prince, to faue both our felues and the kingdome from preiudice : now my Lords the ballance is poifed, choofe which part you pleafe. *Rodento* hauing fet their harts on fire with thefe wordes, they all confented to recall Countie *Selides* from banifhment, and if at the fecond perfwafion the king would not take a better courfe, to make him fole monarch of *Buda* : they wer not flack in their purpofed intent, but difpatcht letters fecretlie by a fpéedie Poft into *Germanie* : which the Countie *Selides* receiuing, fufpected at the firft a further mifchiefe, but at laft throughly fatisfied by the meffenger of their faithful intent, he cut ouer with as much fpéed as might be, & fecretly in the night came to the houfe of *Rodento*, where being honourablie intertained, the next daie all the nobles affembled, and there in counfaile tolde the Countie *Selides* how in requitall of his exile they meant either to fet him in his former eftate, or elfe to inrich him with the benefit of a crowne. The

County was vnwilling to grant to their requeſts,
yet at laſt ſéeing deniall could not preuaile, he
conſented, and all ioyntly went together to the
Court: where they founde the king walking
according to his wonted manner in his accuſtomed
melancholie: who ſcarce ſaluting his Lordes with
a good looke, yet ſtraight had eſpied the Countie
Selides: at whoſe ſight with a face inflamed with
cholar, and eies ſparkling hate, hée demanded why
the Countie Selides was reuoked from exile, how
he durſt preſume ſo nigh to approch his preſence,
or which of his Lords was ſo hardie as to admit
him into their company? Rodento ſpeaking for
the reſt made anſwere, that as the Countie Selides
was baniſhed without cauſe, ſo he might lawfully
returne with / out pardon, that offences meaſured
with enuie, were to be ſalued without entreatie,
& therfore did no more then they all preſent were
readie to iuſtifie: and further, whereas his maieſtie
was ſo ſotted in ſelfe conceit that he held his will
as a lawe, and made a metamorphoſis of a monarchie into a flat gouernment of tyrannie : they
were come to perſwade his highneſſe from ſuch
folly, wherein if he reſolued to perſiſt, they were
determined not onely to depriue him of his crown
and kingdome, but before his face to celebrate
the coronation of Selides. Vadiſlaus hearing this
peremptorie reſolution of his Lordes, was nothing

difmaide, but with a countenance ouer fhadowed with difdaine, tolde them hee feared not their braues : for quoth he, the trecherous attempt of a fubiect cannot difmaie the princely courage of a king. When the flaues of *Scythia* rebelled againft their Lordes, they were not fubdued with weapons, but with whips. *Cirus* punifhed traitors, not with the axe to infer death, but with a fooles coate to procure perpetuall fhame : therefore my lords I charge you vpon your allegeance take holde of that outlawe *Selides*, put him in prifon till he heare farther of my pleafure, and for your owne partes fubmit your felues and craue pardon. The noble men plaide like the deafe Addar that heareth not the forcerers charme, neither could they bee dif-fwaded from their intent by the threates of a king, but following their purpofe, prefently depofed him of all regal dignitie, and celebrated the coronation of *Selides* : who feated in the regall throne, had no fooner the fcepter in his hand, but enuie beganne to grow in his heart, and reuenge haled him on to feale vp his comicall fucceffe with tragicall forrow, for he commanded *Vadiflaus* to be pulled out of his roabes and put into rags, in ftead of a crowne to giue him a fcrip, for a fcepter a palmers / ftaffe, making generall proclamation that none of what degrée fo euer, fhoulde allowe him anie main-tenance, but that his inheritance fhoulde be the

IX. 18

wide fields, and his reuenues nought elſe but
charitie. *Vadiſlaus* thus at one time depoſed and
metamorphoſed from a king to a begger, was now
diſdayned of thoſe whome before he did ſcorne,
and laught at by ſuch as before hee did enuie : the
nobilitie ſhakt him off as a refuſe, the commons
vſed him as a bad companion, both ioyntly forgat
he had ben their king, and ſmoothly ſmiled at his
misfortune. *Vadiſlaus* as a man in a trance, being
paſt a little from his pallace, ſeeing the place which
whilome was the ſubiect of pleaſure, now the obiect
of diſcontent, that wher he did command as a king,
he was controlled as an abiect, he fel into theſe
diſtreſſed paſſions.

Is youth the wealth of nature, to be wracked
with euerie flawe ? Is honour the priuiledge of
nobilitie, ſubiect to euerie fall ? Hath maieſtie
that makes vs fellow partners with the Gods in
dignitie, no warrant to graunt a ſympathy of their
deities, that as we are equal in highnes, ſo we may
be immortal in happines ? Why doeſt thou enter
Vadiſlaus into ſuch friuolous queſtions, when thy
preſent misfortune telles thée kings are but men,
and therefore the verie ſubiects of Fortune ? Ah
vnhappie man, hadſt thou confeſſed as much as
proofe ſets thee downe for a principle, the ouer-
flowing gale of ſelfe loue had neuer brought thy
barke perforce to ſo bad an harbour. Hadſt thou

gouerned like a God in equitie, thou hadſt ſtil
ruled like a God in honour : but pride perſwading
thée a crowne had made thée more than a man,
hath now induced time to aſſure thée, that thou
art the worſt of all men. Kings ſeats are like the
rooms that *Egiſtus* made for ſtraungers, wherein
beeing placed, the eare was de / lighted with
melodie, the eie with ſundrie ſhewes of content,
the ſmelling with ſwéet ſauors : but to counteruaile
theſe pleaſures, ouer their heads hung naked
ſwoordes in ſlender fillets of ſilke, which procured
more feare than the reſt did delight : maieſtie is
lyke the triple ſtring of a Lute, which let too lowe
maketh badde muſicke, and ſtretched too high,
either craketh or ſetteth all out of tune. Fortunes
fauours reſemble the prickes of a Porcupine, that
careleſlie gazed at, pleaſeth the eie and the touch,
but narrowly handled, both hurteth the ſight and
the ſenſe. Ah *Vadiſlaus*, had conſideration foretaught thée theſe vntimelie principles, thou hadſt
neither found the ſeats of kings vnſure, maieſtie
out of time, nor fortune but as ſhée is to all men
inconſtant. But pride, what ſayeſt thou of pride
Vadiſlaus? Was it not lawfull for thée to be
prouder then all men, that wert higher in dignitie
then all men? Might not a crown yeeld to thée a
ſelfe conceit in thy actions? What diddeſt thou
béeing king that beſeemed not a king? Diſdaine

I tell thée is the glorie of a Scepter, and in that ftill bee refolute : beeft thou neuer fo poore in eftate, bée ftill a Prince in thought : parentage is without the compaffe of Fortune, the Gods may difpofe of welth, but not of birth : imagine thy palmers bonnet a princes diadem, thinke thy ftaffe a fcepter, thy graie wéeds coftly attire : imaginations are as fwéete as actions : and feeing thou canft not bée a king ouer nobilitie, bée yet a king ouer beggers : holde pouertie as a flaue, by thinking thy want ftore, and ftill difdayne all that art defpifed of all : *Dionifius* was for the fame braue minde exiled out of his kingdome, but hée kept a fchool in *Corinth*, and there although hee were not a prince ouer men, yet hée was a king ouer boies, and the force of his imagination foothed him in a princely content. /

Tufh *Vadiflaus*, neuer fhrinke at this fhot, now thou art more thē a king, for thou art a monarch both ouer fates and fortune, and yet this priuiledge is left thée, that none in *Buda* can challenge, thou maieft boafte thou haft bene a king, and whofoeuer giues thée for almes, neuer yéeld him thankes, for hée beftowes but what once was thine : *Vadiflaus* arming him felfe thus with a defperate kinde of patience, paffed poorely difguifed and defpifed through his owne Countrie. And *Selides* fafely feated in the kingdome, after hée had fet the

affaires of the weale publike in good order, tooke
all his care to know where his daughter was
beftowed, but hearing no newes where fhée was
harboured, made generall proclamation through all
his dominions, that who fo could tell newes what
was become of the ladie *Mæſia* the kings daughter,
fhould be greatly aduanced in calling, and haue a
thoufand crownes for his paines. The Farmers
fonne happened to bée with his mothers butter at
the market when this proclamation was made, and
comming home, tolde it in fecret for great newes,
how that the king was depofed from his crowne,
& *Selides* created in his place, and that whofoeuer
could tel where *Mæſia* was fhould be well rewarded
for his labour. The old Farmer nodding his head
at thefe newes, made anfwere: you may fée fonne,
quoth he, what it is to bée a great man: I tell you
the gaie coates of kings couers much care, as they
haue many pleafures, fo they haue mickle perils:
the plowman hath more eafe then a king: for the
one troubles but his bodie with exercife, the other
difquiets his minde with waightie affaires: I warrant
thée wife, we haue as much health with féeding
on the browne loafe, as a Prince hath with all
his delicates, and I fteale more fwéete naps in the
chimney corner in a wéeke, then (God faue his
maieftie) the King doth / quiet fléepes in his beds
of doune in a whole moneth. Oft haue I heard

my Father faie (and I tell thée our predeceffours
were no fooles) that a hufbandman plowed out of
the ground three things, wealth, health, and quiet,
which (quoth hee) is more worth then a kinges
ranfome : but tis no matter, let not vs meddle
with kings affaires, but if the councell haue thought
it good to put downe *Vadiflaus*, he may thank his
own pride, which fonne learne of me, is the root
of all mifchiefes, and if they haue crowned *Selides*,
wée fée a goodly example, he that humbleth himfelfe fhall be exalted : but I would I could tel
where the kings daughter were, for he that reaps
fauour and wealth gets a double benefite. *Mæfia*
who heard thefe newes of her Fathers preferment,
fmiled in her owne conceit, that fortune had made
fo fharpe and fhort a reuenge, and that now after
many miferies paft ouer with patience, fhée might
not onlie faie *Dabit Deus his quoque finem,* but *Hæc
olim mæminiffe iuuabit.* The remembrance of honor
tainted her chéekes with a purple die at the fight
of hir prefent drudgerie, the hope of dignity tickled
hir mind with a fodaine ioy, to thinke what a
metamorphofis fhould happen at her pleafure, but
when fhe called to minde the Countrie fayings of
her olde maifter, and fawe by proofe how fickle
fortune was in her fauors, and had confidered what
mifhap laie in maieftie, and what a fecure life it
was to liue poore, fhe found dignitie ouerfhadowed

with danger, wheras pouertie flept quietly at his plough beame. Honour wilde her to bewraie what fhe was, quiet perfwaded her that content was a kingdome. Perplexed thus ẘ fundrie thoughts, after her houfe was handfomely and hufwifely dreaft vp, fhe toke her fpinning wheele to the doore, and there fetting her felfe folitarily in the fhade, fhe had not drawen forth thrée or foure threddes, but *Vadiflaus* in his / beggers roabes came to the doore, and féeing fo neate a Countrie wench at her whéele, without anie falutations, after his cynicall manner began to gaze on her beautie. The maide taking him for no other but fome ftout begger, as Countrie maides vfe to folace themfelues, began to carroll out a fong to this effect.

Sweet are the thoughts that fauour of content,
  the quiet mind is richer then a crowne :
Svveet are the nights in careleffe flumber fpent,
  the poore eftate fcornes fortunes angrie frovvne :
Such fvveet cõtent, fuch mindes, fuch fleep, fuch blis
  Beggers inioy, when Princes oft do mis.

The homely houfe that harbors quiet reft,
  the cottage that affoords no pride, nor care :
The meane that grees with Countrie muſick beft,
  the fweet confort of mirth and muficks fare :

Obſcured life ſets downe a type of blis,
a minde content both crowne and kingdome is.

The ſong of *Mæſia* ſomewhat touched the minde
of *Vadiſlaus*, that meruailing what pretie muſition
this ſhould be that had ſo ſwéete a voice and ſo
pithie a dittie, he began to interrupt her melodie
in this ſorte. Faire maide, for ſo I may tearme
you beſt, in that I giue thée but thy due to ſaie
thou art beautifull, and allow thée a fauour in
thinking thou art honeſt, tel me, is this Country
cottage thy fathers houſe? and if it be thy birth
is ſo baſe, & thy bringing vp ſo bad, how hap
thou haſt found diſquiet with dignity, and care
containd in a crowne? Haſt thou ſeene the
court, and ſo ſpeakeſt by experience, or learnd
this dittie as a ſong of courſe, and ſo hitteſt the
crow by hap? *Mæſia* hearing the begger ſo in-
quiſitiue, eſpecially placing his wordes in / ſuch
a commanding phraſe, thinking him to be no
other then his ragges did report, ſhooke him vp
thus ſharply. Tis for beggers (quoth ſhee) whome
fortune hath tied to the curteſie of others, to craue
almes with treaties, not to demand queſtions with
inquiſition, for as they haue no other plackard
than pouertie, ſo their charter is ſubmiſſion and
lowlines: whatſoeuer my tongue contained, ſtep
thou not farther than thy ſcrip: thou art meane

inough, therefore quiet inough : no almes would
do thée more good than a queſtion : and therefore
ſtaie while my thredde is drawen, and thou ſhalt
haue my deuotion. *Vadiſlaus* whoſe pride was
not changed with his apparell, told her ẏ the
vertue of the trée was not diſcerned by the outward barke, but by the inward ſap, that the
Lapidarie might be deceiued in colours, that
roabes made not kings, nor rags beggers, that
Appollo beeing a God, metamorphoſed himſelfe,
not into a prince, but to a ſhepheard, that *Mercurie*
for his pleaſure tooke the forme of a cowehearde,
to try the tabling of *Bacchus* : outward ſhewes are
not inward effeⅽts, and therfore ſhe might miſtake
him, and though his cloathing diſcouered pouertie,
his calling might be honourable. *Mæſia* hearing
ſo well ordered an anſwer to come from ſuch a
diſordered perſon, began to note more narrowly the
lineaments of his face, & at laſt perceiued it was the
quondam king *Vadiſlaus*, but ſtill diſſembling what
both ſhe thought and knew, made him this anſwere :
Friend, if I haue ſhot awrie blame the marke that I
aimed at, and not my cenſure by outward ſhow, for
we Countrie maids are ſo homely brought vp, that
wée count none kings but what weare crownes,
and all beggers that carrie ſcrippes and craue
almes, if your degrée be aboue your ſhewe, it was
youre owne faulte, and not my folly that made

mée so foolifhe : my / fong I hope what fo ere ye
be, hath giuē none offence : if thou haft bene rich,
it tells thée what difquiet is in dignitie, and that
the cottage affoords more quiet then a kingdome :
if thou wert neuer but as thou art, then maift
thou fée what content is in pouertie, and learne
that the obfcure life conteineth ỹ greateft bliffe :
kings are men, and therefore fubiect to mifhap :
Fortune is blinde, and muft either miffe of her aime,
or fhoote at a great marke, her boltes flie not fo
lowe as beggerie, when honour is pierced with
euerie blow : and therefore *Marcus Curcius* that
had thrice bene dictator, and as many times
triumphed, hidde himfelfe in a poore farme to be
frée from the iniurie of fortune. *Vadiflaus* driuen
into a paffion with this parle, afked her why fhe
told him of the ftratagems of kings, féeing her felfe
was a begger : for that, quoth *Mæfia*, thou didft
fcorne euen now to be ,counted a begger : nay
quoth *Vadiflaus* for that thou knoweft, or at the
leaft doeft fufpect that I am a king : *Mæfia* tolde
him fhe had fmall reafon to make fuch a furmife,
but defired that fhe might know if hée were
Vadiflaus, that of late was depofed : I am quoth
he, the fame, I tel thée maide, euerie waie the fame,
for mifhap hath no whit altered my minde. Then
(quoth *Mæfia*) hath fortune done ill, to ioyne in
thée both pouertie and pride, for either hath

Report a blifter on her tongue, or thy fall did
infue of difdainfull infolencie: thy fault hath bene
alwaies the fall of princes, the ruine of ftates, and
the vtter fubuerfion of kingdomes: *Dyoclefian* the
Romane was fo proude, that he called himfelfe
brother to the Sunne, and was the firft that euer
made edict to haue the feete of Emperours kift,
in figne of feruill fubmiffion: his end was madneffe: the pride of *Pompey* was his ouerthrow:
the defire of kingly title caufed *Cæfar* to die in
the fenate houfe: / but thy harueft is out of the
graffe, and my councell commeth now, as a fhower
of raine doeth when the corne is ripe: yet féeing
you are fallen into pouertie, let mee aduife thée
how to beare it with patience. Want is not a
depriuation of vertue, but a releafe of care and
trouble. *Epamynondas* was not called halfe a God,
no[r] *Lycurgus* a fauiour, becaufe they abounded in
wealth and were flaues to their paffions, but becaufe they were Princes, and yet content with
pouertie: then let their liues be a marke whereby
to direct your actions, that as you are fallen from
dignitie by default, fo you may liue in pouertie
with patience, & fo die a more honorable begger
then thou diddeft liue a king, and if thou meruaile
who it is that giues thée fuch friendly councell,
know I am the daughter of *Selydes*, who driuen by
thy iniuftice to this diftreffe, although my father

now a king, yet I find fuch content in pouertie,
as I little haft to exchange this life with dignitie.

Vadiſlaus carefully marking the weight of euery
word, efpecially proceeding from her whom he
had iniured, bluſhed at the fight of her patience,
and yet as a man whom defpaire had hardned on
to miſhappe, nothing relented at her perfwaſions,
but in a melancholy furie flong from the doore
without faying one worde, or bidding her farewell.
Mæſia noting ſtill the peruerfe ſtomacke in the
man, fayde to her felfe, What folly is there greater
than Pride, which neyther age nor pouertie can
extinguiſh ? What afterwarde became of *Vadiſlaus*,
the Annales of *Buda* makes not mention, but onely
of this, that he died poore, and yet proude. For
Mæſia pittying her fathers forrowes that he made
for her abfence, more for his content than for anie
delight in dignitie, ſhortly after ſhee forfooke the
Countrie and went to the court. /

Peratio hauing ended his tale, the whole companie commended his difcourfe, and efpecially the
old counteffe, who not onely gaue him praife as
a laurell for his labours, but thanks, as due to him
by deferts, faying, that in déede pride was one
of thofe finnes which nature had fram'd without
change, that Fortune was a miſtreffe ouer other
paffions, and Time had a medicine for other

maladies, onely pride and the gout hath his fimi-
litude in effects, that they were incurable. Wel
madam, quoth *Bernardino*, *Peratio* hath done well,
but praie God he refemble not the rich Bifhop of
Cullen, that preaching againft couetoufnes, had a
poore mans leafe to pawne in his handes, which
hee vfed as an inftrument to act againft vfurie : he
is a fcoller madam, and therefore within the
compaffe of his owne conclufions, for we fee thofe
Vniuerfitie men ouercome themfelues deeply in
this folly, infomuch that not content to be proude
at home, they feeke by trauell to hunt after vanity.
As I cannot, quoth *Peratio*, excufe my felf, fo
I will not accufe all generally, becaufe the premifes
are too peremptorie that inferre fuch cenfurers, but
no doubt, fchollers are men, and therefore fubiect
to this fault. And fo be courtiers, quoth Ladie
Katherine, for you may fmell their pride by their
perfumes. Tis well qd. *Benedetto*, that feignior
Farneze hath made an exception of women, other-
wife *Peratio* had neuer made an ende of his
difcourfe. *Peratio* taking hold of Lady *Katherines*
talke, thought to croffe *Benedetto* ouer the thumbs,
and therefore made this reply. Truth it is, that
Tully writ to *Atticus*, that the conqueft of *Afia* had
brought fiue notable follies into the Citie of *Rome*,
to make glorious fepulchres, to weare rings of
gold, to vfe fpice in meats, to alay wine with fugar,

and to carrie about fwéet perfumes and fmels.
Thefe meffieur *Benedetto*, *Tully* countes follies and /
ỹ vfe as fauours : he thought them preiudiciall,
and ye courtiers count them as neceffary, and
therefore argue how you lift, I will haue you within
the compaffe of my difcourfe. I can fmile, quoth
the Ladie *Katherine*, to fée how meffieur *Benedetto*
thinking to wring water out of a ftone, hath
ftumbled on a flint, which ftriking too hard hath
brought fire. Yet (quoth *Cofimo*) his lucke was
good, for hee burnt but his owne clothes. Seignior
Farneze hearing thefe drie blowes, broke off their
talke at this time by commanding one of his mẽ
to couer for fupper, which done, fitting down with
his guefts about him, euerie one plied his téeth
more than his tongue, *Benedetto* excepted, who
was fo chafed in conceit at the Lady *Katherine*,
that his thoughts onely were emploied after dinner
how to be reuenged, which indéed he performed
in this forte.

The fecond difcourfe of Folly.

AFter *Farneze* & the reft had fatisfied their
ftomacks with meat, & their minds with
mirth, *Cofimo* féeing *Benedetto* fo paffionate, began
to whet him on to pratle in this maner. Maffe
courtier, qd. he, to drawe you out of your dũps
with a demãd, I pray you anfwer me to this

queſtiõ : why do ỹ painters in figuring forth the
counterfet of loue, draw her blind, & couered with
a vale, when as we ſee that in nothing there is
a déeper inſight than in loue : *Benedetto* ſéeing
Coſimo put forth this queſtiõ only to moue talke,
told him, that if he had ſpent but as many idle
houres about ỹ ſubſtance of affeċtion, as he had
done daies about the quiddities of fãcy, he would
willingly haue anſwered his demand : but ſéeing
twere for a ſouldier to teach *Orpheus* how to handle
his harpe, hée would aunſwere him as *Zeuxis* did
king *Perſius*, who deſiring him to ſhewe how he
coulde drawe the piċture of enuie, preſently brought
him a looking Glaſſe wherein *Perſius* / perceiuing
his owne phiſnomie bluſht : And yet for al this,
qd. *Bernardino,* ſeignior *Coſimo* doth not change
countenance, and yet we all know him to be a
louer : and therefore, quoth the Ladie *Frances,*
within the compaſſe of folly, for this I remember
that *Anacrion* ſaieth, *Cupid* was depriued of his
ſight, not by nature but by iniurie, for the Gods
ſummoning a parliament, whereat appeared all
the heauenly deities, *Cupid* by hap, or rather by
fatall preſence of the deſtinies, met with Folly,
who ſurcharged with ouerwéening paſſions, began
to diſpute of their ſeuerall powers : the boy not
able to brooke compariſons, bent his bow, and
was ready to diſcharge an arrowe againſt Follie,

but fhée being readier furnifhed with wepons,
neither regarding his youth, beautie, nor deitie,
fcratched out his eies, in requital wherof fhe was
by the Gods appointed his guide. Then by this,
quoth *Peratio*, there is no loue without folly.
That I denie, anfwered the Ladie *Frances*, for
true and perfeƈt loue is beyonde the deitie of
Cupid, and therefore without the compaffe of
follie. But fuch loue as you yong Gentlemen
vfe, that hath as great a confufion of paffions, as
Ouids chaos had of fimples, is that which I meane,
in truth it is luft, but fhadowed with the name of
loue which rightly *Euripides* calleth a furie. I am
gladde, quoth *Farneze*, that we are entered into
the difcourfe of loue, for I will inioyne this nights
worke to bée about the difcouerie of the verie
fubftance of luft, which drowned in voluptuous
pleafures, haleth on the minde to the foule deformed finne of lecherie, a fault that we Italians
greatly offend in, and yet the cuftome of finne
hath fo taken awaie the feeling of the offence,
that wee fhame not oft times to glorie in the fault.
And for that feignior *Cofimo* I haue knowen you
amongeft all the reft to bee moft amorous, though
I muft needes / confeffe alwaies honeftly, yet for
that you haue béene acquainted with fuch paffions,
I commit the charge vnto your hands. *Cofimo*
féeing the company fmile, in that the Countie had

tied him to fuch a tafke, willingly would haue
furrendered vp his right into an other mans handes,
but fearing to difpleafe *Farneze*, and by fhrincking,
to difcouer where his fhoe wroong him, arming
him felfe with patience, feemed very content: and
therefore began to frame his fpeech in this manner.
Although (Gentlemen) *Hiparchon* coulde play on
his flute, yet he was not to difpute of Muficke, in
that hee knewe more by the practife of his finger,
than by fkill of the concordes. *Epheftion* coulde
handle *Bucephalus*, but not ride *Bucephalus*. *Mene-
cas* the Macedonian was a very good fimpler, but
knewe not how to confect a potion, as one aiming
at the vertue of the hearbe, not at the qualitie of
the difeafe : fo although I haue, as a nouice, gazed
at the temple of *Venus*, yet I am not able to difcourfe of the Deitie of *Cupid*: tis no confequent,
that by feeling a fewe paffions, I fhould be able to
fet downe principles, or that a fparke of fancy
fhould kindle a whole flame of wanton affections,
yet that I be not accufed to be more fcrupulous
than courteous, I will fay what I haue heard and
read of this follie. The Cyriniake Philofophers,
as *Ariftippus*, *Metrodorus* and *Epicurus*, who
founded their *fummum bonum* in pleafure, to
fhadow their brutifhe principles with fome fhewe
of reafon, drew, as *Phidias* did ouer his deformed
pictures, courteines of filke, that the outward vale

might countenance the imperfection of his art,
placing the fubftance of pleafure vnder the fimple
fuperficies of vertue, couering an inuenomed hooke
with a faire baite, and like *Ianus* prefenting a
double face, the foremoft of flatterie, the hind-
moft of forrow.   *Hercules* meeting / vice and
vertue, found the one gorgeoufly tricked vp in
ornamentes of gold, the other courfely attired
in fimple clothing, vertue bare faced wering in
forehead the counterfait of trueth, vice valed with
a mafke to couer the deformitie of hir vifage,
wherein appeared the ftaynes of pleafure, as the
infection of leprofie, which *Plutarke* noting, being
demanded what pleafure was: aunfwered, a fwéete
ftep to repentaunce, alludinge vnto the cenfure of
Phocion, who wrote of the picture of *Venus* this
fentence : *Ex vino Venus ex venere ruina & mors.*
But féeing my charge is not to fpeak generally
of pleafure, but of that follie which claiming the
name of pleafure, moft befotteth the fences of all
other obiectes with deceit, I meane luft, which the
better to bring in credit, is honoured with the
title of loue, I muft confeffe my felfe herein to be
of *Ariftotles* opinion, who being demanded by
Alexander the great, what loue was, anfwered, a
metamorphofis of mens bodies and foules into
contrarie fhapes : for after that the impreffion of
luft, inueigled by the fading obiect of beautie, hath

crept in at the eye and poffeffed the heart, we
wholy deliuer our felues, as flaues to fenfualitie,
forgetting our God for the gaine of a goddeffe,
whofe altars fauours of ftincking perfumes, and
whofe temple is not perfumed with rofes, but
infected with hemblocke : they which facrifice vnto
Vefta offer vp incenfe with fire, they which ftande
at the fhrine of *Venus* offer vp bladders onely filled
with winde, the one reprefenting the pureneffe of
chaftitie, the other the lightneffe of affection : you
fay true, quoth the Ladie *Frances*, *Venus* coffers
are alwaies emptie, and therefore giuing great
founde, hir garments imbroidered with feathers,
as noting inconftancie : for he that marketh the
confufed eftate of you Florentines, / who couet to
be counted louers, fhall finde howe vnder that
one folly you heape together a maffe of mifchie-
uous enormities : for the Gentleman, that drawne
by a voluptuous defire of immoderate affections,
feekes to glut his outward fences with delight, firft
layeth his platforme by pride, feeking to allure
a chaft eye with the fumptuous fhewe of apparell,
vnder that mafke to entife the minde vnto vanitie,
others by an eloquent phrafe of fpeeche to tickle
the eare with a pleafing harmonie of well placed
words : well placed in congruitie, though ill con-
ftrued in fence : fome by Muficke to inueigle the
minde with melodie, not fparing to fpende parte

of the night vnder his miftreffes window, by fuch
paines to procure hir difhonour and his owne misfortune. Thefe (Gentlemen) be fruites of your
loues, if I tearme it the beft way, and yet follies
in that they preiudice both purfe and perfon : the
fame baite is flatterie, which giueth the foreft
batterie to the bulworke of their chaftitie, for
when they fée the minde armed with vertue, hard
to be wonne, and like the Diamonde to refufe the
force of the file, then they apply their wittes and
wils to worke their owne .woe, penning downe
ditties, fongs, fonnets, madrigals, and fuche like,
fhadowed ouer with the penfell of flatterie, where
from the fictions of poets they fetche the type and
figure of their fayned affection : firft, decyphering
hir beautie to bée more than fuperlatiue, comparing
hir face vnto *Venus*, hir haire vnto golde, hir eyes
vnto ftarres : naye more, refembling hir chaftitie
vnto *Diana*, when they féeke onely to make hir as
common as *Lais* : then howe hir feature hath fired
their fancie, howe hir fight hath befotted their
fences, howe beautie hath bewitched them : paynt-
ing out their paffions as *Appelles* did puppettes for
children, which inwardly / framed of claye, were
outwaredlye trickt vppe with frefhe colours, they
plunge in paine, they waile in woe, they turne
the reftleffe ftone with *Syfyphus*, and alleage the
tormentes of *Tantalus*, what griefe, what payne,

what forrow, what fighs, what teares, what plaintes,
what paffions, what tortures, what death is it not
they indure till they optaine their miftreffe fauour,
which got, infamie concludeth the tragedie with
repentance : fo that I allow thofe pleafing poems
of *Guazzo*, which begin : *Chi fpinto d'amore*, thus
englifhed.

He that appaled with luft would faile in haft to
*   Corinthum,*
There to be taught in Layis fchoole to feeke for a
*   miftreffe,*
Is to be traind in Venus troupe and changd to the
*   purpofe :*
Rage imbraced but reafon quite thruft out as an exile,
Pleafure a paine reft, tournd to be care, and mirth as a
*   madneffe :*
Firie mindes inflamd with a looke, inraged as Alecto :
Quaint in aray, fighs fetcht from farre and teares,
*   marie, fained :*
Pen ficke, fore, depe plungd in paine, not a place but
*   his hart whole.*
Daies in griefe and nights confumed to thinke on a
*   goddeffe,*
Broken fleeps, fwete dreams, but fhort fro the night to
*   the morning :*
Venus dafht, his miftreffe face as bright as Apollo,
Helena ftaind, the golden ball wrong giuen by the fheep-
*   heard.*

Haires of gold, eyes twinckling ſtarres, hir lips to be
  rubies,
Teeth of pearle, hir breſts like ſnow, hir cheekes to be
  roſes.
Sugar candie ſhe is, as I geſſe, fro the waiſt to the
  kneeſtead,
Nought is amiſſe, no fault were found if ſoule were
  amended,
All were bliſſe if ſuch fond luſt led not to repentance.

So that of theſe verſes I conclude, that ſuch
young Gentlemen as tickled with luſt, ſeeke to
pleaſe their ſenſes with ſuch pernicious delights,
may iuſtly come within the compaſſe of this folly :
may (quoth the Ladie *Margarite*)? let the ſelfe
ſame predicament comprehende ſuch fantaſtike
poets, as ſpende their times in penning downe
pamphlets of loue, who with *Ouid* ſeeke to nouriſh
vice in *Rome* by ſetting downe *Artem amandi*, and
giuing diſhoneſt precepts of luſt and leacherie,
corrupting youth with the expence of time, vpon /
ſuch friuolous fables : and therefore deſerue by
Auguſtus to be baniſhed from ſo ciuill a countrie
as *Italie*, amongeſt the barbarous *Getes* to liue in
exile.

Stay there, quoth meſſieur *Benedetto*, your com-
miſſion is too large, and your cenſures too Satyricall,
we read not that any woman was euer Stoicke or

Cynicke, either to be fo ftrict in paffions, or bitter
in inuectiues, and to write of loue, not to fauour
the follie but to condemne the fault : and therefore Madam, either be more partiall or more
particular. Thefe glances (quoth *Farneze*) are
nothing to the purpofe, and therefore feignior
Cofimo to your charge : I knowe fir, anfwered
Cofimo, that Madam *Frances* hath faid well, in
painting out the phantafticke defcription of a louer,
yet hath fhe béene fauourable in figuring out their
follies : for this loue or rather luft endeth not,
till it tafteth of the very dregges of adulterous
lechery, a folly, nay a finne fo in hate with God
and contempt with man, as *Seleucus* forbad it to
be named amongft the *Locrians*. The end of
concupifcence is *luxuria*, fayeth *Socrates* in his
difputation with *Euthydemus*, frō whom floweth,
as from a fea of wickednes, inceft, murther, poifon,
violēce, fubuerfiō of kingdoms and infinit other
impieties. *Ariftotle* being demanded what adulterie was, made anfwer, a curious inquiry after
an other mans loue, and being defired to penne
downe the effects, wrote thefe or fuch like wordes.
He that féeketh by a plaufible fhadow of flattery
to feduce a minde from chaftity to adulterie, finneth
againft the law of nature in defrauding a man of
his due, his honour and reputation, fpoiling him
of a moft pretious iewell, which is the lofs of his

wiues loue and frendſhip : for as the ſeethim trée
being cut or pearted with braſſe, ſtraight periſheth,
ſo the league of marriage violated by adultery
extinguiſheth loue, and leaueth be / hind at the
moſt, nought but the painted vale of flatterie :
the peace of the houſe is changed into diſcorde,
diſſention in ſtead of laurell preſenteth a ſword,
and content ſléepeth not with *Mercuries* melodie,
but waketh with *Aleƈtos* diſquiet : the face that in
forme being honeſt, reſembleth the ſunne in
beautie, ſtained with adulterie, bluſheth to ſée the
ſame as guiltie of hir owne deformitie : credit hath
ſuffered ſhipwracke and fame as ſpotted with the
foyle of diſhonour, all theſe hatefull diſcommodities
inſuing by the voluptuous deſire of ſuch young
Gentlemen, as wedded to vanitie, glory in the title
of this folly.   I maruel then, quoth *Peratio*, what
woman (theſe effeƈts conſidered) will liſten vnto
the melody of ſuch Syrens, whoſe allurementes
perſwades them to ſuche misfortunes, or howe they
can thinke that man to loue them, which by fulfil-
ling his momentary luſt, procureth their perpetuall
diſcredit, and ſubuerſion both of ſoule and bodie.
Know you not (quoth *Benedetto*) the reaſon of
that, are not the thoughts of women like the
inhabitants of *Scyrum*, which knowing that the
ſauour of Dates is deadly vnto their complexion, yet
neuer ceaſe till they dye with Dates in their mouthes.

You miſtate it, quoth the Lady *Frances*, it is becauſe men conſume them ſelues into teares with the Crocodile, till they haue gotten their pray, and then they neither reſpect their honour nor honeſtie. Howſoeuer it bee, quoth *Coſimo*, I haue not to deale with women, but for our Florentines, I know none more addicted vnto this folly, which to conclude, hath bene ſo odious amongſt our anceſtaurs, that it hath béene chaſtned with ſeuere puniſhmentes. *Alexander* greatly blamed *Caſſander*, becauſe hee offered but to kiſſe a minſtrels mayde. *Auguſtus Cæſar* made the lawe *Iulia*, which permitted the father to / kill the daughter for adulterie. *Cato* baniſhed a Senator for kiſſing his wife in his daughters preſence. *Marcus Antonius Carcalla* was baniſhed his Empire for luſt, with infinite other, whoſe miſeries, mishappes, and misfortunes were innumerable onely for this folly, as *Tarquinus Superbus* for *Lucrece*, *Appius Claudius* for *Virginia*, *Iulius Cæſar* for *Cleopatra*, *Iohn* Countie *Armiake* for his owne ſiſter, *Anthonie Venereus* duke of *Venice* for his Secretaries wife, *Abuſahid* king of *Fez* for the wife of *Coſimo de Cheri*, as *Leon* in his deſcription of *Affrike* ſetteth downe : but amongeſt all theſe Gentles, an hiſtorie at large for the confirmation of this my diſcourſe.

THE TALE OF
Cofimo.

Hile *Ninus* the fonne of *Belus* raigned as Soueraigne ouer the dominions of *Egypt*, and kept his Court Royall in *Babylon*, there dwelled in the fuburbes of the Citie a poore labouring man called *Mænon*, who was more honeſt than wealthye, and yet fufficiently rich, for that hee liued contente amongeſt his neighbours: this poore man accounted his poffeſſions large enough, as long as hee enioyed and poffeſſed his grounde in quiet, imitating *Cyncynatus* in his labours, who founde health of bodie and quiet of mind the chiefeſt treaſure, by tilling his fielde with continual toyle. But as content had fatisfied his thoghts in / this, fo *Mænon* was as greatly fauoured of Fortune, for he had a wife of the fame degrée and parentage, fo beautifull, as there was none fo faire in *Babylon*, fo honeſt, as there was none more vertuous, fo courteous, that there was not one in the whole city who did not both loue and like of *Semyramis* the wife of *Mænon*, for fo was hir name: infomuch that *Ninus* defired to haue a fight of hir beauty, and

in difguifed apparell, went to the poore mans houfe,
where feeing fuch a heauenly faint about hir
homely hufwifery, fitter (as he thought) to be a
paramour for a prince, than a wife for a fubiect,
fighed and forrowed that fhe was not in his power
to commande : yet fauouring hir in that fhe was
honeft, as fancying hir for that fhe was beautifull,
he departed with refolution to be maifter of his
owne affections, and not to depriue the poore man
of fo great good. After he was returned to the
palace and was folitarie by him felfe, the *Idea*
of hir perfection reprefenting a humane fhape of
a heauenly creature, fo affaulted his minde with
fundry paffions, that giuing the raines of libertie
to his wanton appetites, he fell into thefe tearmes.
Vnhappy *Ninus*, and therefore vnhappy becaufe a
king and fubiect to fenfuality, fhall the middle of
thy yeares bee woorfe than the prime of thy
youth, fhall loue conquer that Fortune could neuer
fubdue, fhall the heate of affection fearche that in
the frute that it coulde neuer hurt in the budde,
fhalt thou gouerne a kingdome and canft not
fubdue thine owne paffions? Peace *Ninus*, name
not fo much as loue, race out fancy with filence,
and let the continency of other kings be prefidents
for thée to direct thy courfe aright. *Alexander*
made a conqueft of his thoughts, when the beauty
of *Darius* wife bad him battell. *Cyrus* abftained

from the fight of *Panthea*, becaufe he would not
be intemperate. *Pom / pey* would not fpeak to the
wife of *Demetrius* his frée man for that fhée was
faire : and what of this *Ninus*? Yet had *Alexander*
concubines, *Cyrus* a lemman, and *Pompey* was not
fo chaft, but he liked *Phrinia*, and fo maift thou
make a choice of *Semyramis* : fhée is poore and
vnfit for a king : I, but fhe is faire, and fit for none
but a king : loue filleth not the hand with pelfe,
but the eie with pleafure : fhée is honeft: truth, but
thou art a monarch, and the waight of a fcepter is
able to breake the ftrongeft chaftitie : but that is
more *Nynus*, fhée is another mans wife: but hir
hufbande is thy fubiecte, whom thou maieft command, and hee dare not but obey : haue not
beggers their affectiõs as wel as kings? may not
Semyramis? nay doth fhe not loue poore *Mænon*
better than euer fhee will like *Nynus*? yea, for
crownes are as farre from *Cupid* as cottages,
princes haue no more priuiledge ouer fancie than
peafants : yet *Nynus* feare not, loue and fortune
fauoureth not cowards, command *Semyramis*, nay,
conftraine *Semyramis* to loue thée, and vppon this
refolue, for kings muft haue power both ouer
men and loue. *Nynus* refting vpon this refolution,
determined to trie the mind of *Semyramis* how
fhee was affected towards her hufband, and therefore difpatcht a Letter to her to this effect.

It may féeme ftrange *Semyramis*, that the monarch of *Egypt* fhould write to the wife of a poore labourer, féeing the proportion of our degrées are fo far vnequall, but if it bee confidered that kinges are but men, and therfore fubiect to paffions, fooner fhalt thou haue caufe to forrow for my griefes, than mufe at my writings. Did my defire aime at a kingdome, I wold attempt to fatisfie defire with my fword? Did enuie crie for content, then coulde I ftep to reuenge : were my thoughts as infatiate as *Midas*, the worlde is a / ftorehoufe of treafures : thefe defires are to be fatisfied with friends or fortune, but the reftleffe forrow that fo pincheth my minde with difquiet, onely refteth in thy power to appeafe. It is *Semyramis* the deitie of beutie, which is priuiledged farre aboue dignitie, that Gods haue obeyed, and men cannot refift : the fight of thy perfection entered at the eie, the report of thy vertues tickling the eare, and both ioyntly affaulting the heart with fharp and furious alarums, haue fo fnared my minde, as naught pleafeth the eies that is not thy obiect, and nothing contenteth the eare but *Semyramis*. Séeing then the Egyptian monarch, who hath triumphed ouer all the nations of the South and Eaft climate, with many bloudie conqueftes, is by them brought as a captiue, feruile to thy beautie & his owne paffions, boaft that loue

hath lotted thée fuch a victory, and be not ingrate-
ful to the Gods, by denying me that I deferue,
fauour. But perhaps thou wilt obiect thou art
married, and therefore tyed to poore *Mænon*, (for
loue hath taught me thy hufbands name) that
honeftie beareth bloffoms as wel in a cottage, as in
the court, that vertue harboreth as foone with
beggers as princes, that fame or infamie can ftoup
as low as they can fore high, that report and enuie
foonner ftingeth want than plentie : this *Semyramis*
I confeffe, but yet the picture of the eagle placed
ouer the temple of *Venus*, feared the faulcon for
offending her doues. *Damætus* popiniay pearched
vnder a dragon of braffe to auoide the vultures
tyrannies : difhonour touches not the vefture of
a king, and the concubines of princes purchafe
renowme, not infamie : *Mænon* is poore, and will
ioy to haue fuch a riuall as *Nynus* : the want of
Semyramis darkens the glorie of her beautie, which
the loue of a king fhall inrich with ornamentes.
Then *Semyramis* pittie his plaintes, who is thy
foueraigne / and might command, and yet defirous
to be thy paramour, féekes a conqueft, not by
conftraint, but by intreaties : in graunting which
thou climbeft to dignitie, and fleepeft at the foote
of a fcepter : honour and quiet entertaines thée with
delight : and to thefe thou addeft thy friends preferment and thy hufbands welfare : if as thou art

poore, thou art proud, and felfe conceit armes thée
with difdaine, confider that the counterfait of kings
cannot bee drawen without the fhadowes of duetie,
and that the pill that purgeth the cholar of a
prince is reuenge.   This thinke, and farewell.

Nynus Monarch of Egypt.

He committed this Letter to the charge of one
of his Secretaries, whom he made priuy to the
contents, who poafting in haft to the houfe of
Semyramis, found her bringing one of her babes
afléepe with a fong.   The Secretarie delighted with
the pleafing harmonie of her voice, ftood a little
liftning to her melodie, at laft ftepped into the
houfe: at whofe prefence the poore woman amazed,
for that her cottage was not accuftomed to fuch
guefts, fhe blufht, which gaue fuch a glory to her
former beautie, and such a prefident of her inward
vertue, that the Secretarie enuied the happie
placing of his foueraines paffions : yet after her
homely fafhiõ fhe intertained him, greatly fearing
when he deliuered her. the Letters, ỹ they had
bin fome warrant to apprehend her hufband for
fome fault, but by the fuperfcription fhe perceiued
they were directed to hir : hauing fet before ỹ
fecretarie a meffe of creame to bufie him, fhe ftept
afide to read the contents, which whẽ fhe perceiued
and wel noted the effects, not onely alluring with

promiſes, but perſwading with threats, ſhe burſt into
teares, curſing that daie where[in] ẙ king had / a
ſight of her face as diſmall and infortunate, falling
at laſt from teares into theſe feareful complaints :
Are the deſtinies (poore *Semyramis*) fore-pointers
of good or ill, ſo inequall allotters of miſhappe,
that ſome they bleſſe with daily fauours, and others
they croſſe with continuall hard fortunes? Had
the fates no proportion in their cenſures? coulde
it not ſuffice thou wert poore, but thou muſt be
miſerable? cannot enuie paint the picture of
content at thy cottage dore, but ſhe muſt grudge?
is there no ſhrub ſo low, but it is ſubiect to the
winde: no woman ſo poore if ſhee bee faire, but
ſome blaſing her beautie aimeth at her chaſtitie?
Then *Semyramis* be patient but reſolute, rather
chooſe deſpite and ſorrow than diſgrace and infamie. Is labour an enemie to loue, howe then
ſhoulde affection touch mée who am neuer idle?
therefore fond foole, doth loue enuie thée, becauſe
thou art not idle, but by labour ſheweſt thy ſelfe
a recreant to his law. But yet *Semyramis* conſider
who it is that perſwades thée to loue, *Nynus* a
king, a monarch, and thy ſoueraigne: one whoſe
maieſtie may ſhadowe thy miſſe, and whoſe verie
name may warrant thée from the preiudice of
enuie: if thou offend, dignitie counteruailes the
fault, and fame dare not but honour the concu-

bines of kings. For fhame *Semyramis*, footh not thy felfe in fuch follies : are not kings feates obiects for euerie eie to gafe at? Are not their actions cenfured by euerie bafe perfon? As the pyramides are markes for the fea, fo their doings are notes for the world : Doth not fame build in the foreheads of princes? yes *Semyramis*, kings faults though they are paffed ouer with feare, yet they are iudged of with murmure : the greater the dignitie, the greater the offence : fhame followeth vice euerie where, and adulterie, if lawes were not partiall, deferueth punifhment as well in a king as in a begger. *Mænon* is poore but thy hufband, in louing him thou pleafeft the Gods. *Nynus* is rich and a monarch, in contenting him thou difhonoureft thy felfe and difcontenteft the heauens: hath *Babylon* counted thée faire, fo thou art ftil by referuing thy beautie? hath *Babylon* counted thée honeft? fo remaine ftill by preferuing thy chaftitie : be not more charie ouer thy beautie than ouer thine honeftie, for many knowe thée by fame that neuer fawe thy face. Then *Semyramis*, aunfwere the kings paffions with denial : but alas he threatneth reuenge : fwéeter it is to die with credit thã liue with infamy. Then why ftaieft thou thus fondly debating with thy felfe? reply as one that preferreth fame before life, and with that fhe ftept to a ftandifh, and taking paper wrote a Letter to this effect.

IX. 20

Kings are Gods, not that they are immortall, but
for they are vertuous : Princes haue no priuiledge
to do ill, Fame is not partial in her trumpe : the
chiefeft treafure is not golde, but honour : to
conquere a kingdome is a fauour of fortune, to
fubdue affection is a gift from the Gods : loue in
kings is princely, but luft is pernitious : kinges
therefore weare crownes, becaufe they fhould be
iuft : iuftice giue[s] euerie one his due : *Semiramis*
is *Mænons* wife, and therfore his inheritance : the
Gods threaten Princes as well as poore men : hot
loue is foone colde : the eie is variable, inconftant
and infatiate : Adulterie is odious, though graced
with a fcepter, beutie is a flipperie good, Princes
concubines prife honour too deare, in felling the
precious iewell of honeftie for golde : death is a
farre more fwéete than difcredite, fame to bee
preferred before friendes. *Nynus* is a king, whofe
feate is fure fanctuarie for the oppreffed : *Semiramis*
is poore, yet honeft, loue of *Mænon* in her youth,
and loyall to / him in hir age, refolued rather to
dye than be proued vnchaft : fubiects pray for
their foueraignes, wifhing they may liue princely
and dye vertuous.

Semyramis the faithfull wife of poore Mænon.

This confufed *chaos* of principles being written
and fealed vp, fhe deliuered it to the Secretarie

who courteoufly taking his leaue hied in haft to
the Court, where the king carefully expecting his
comming, receiuing the letter, vnript the feales :
where in ftead of an amorous reply, he found
nothing but a heape of philofophicall axiomes, and
yet his doom anfwered to the full : the pithie
fentences of *Semyramis* whome by hir penne he
found to be poore, honeft, beautifull, and wife, did
not take ỹ effect, which poore foule fhe aimed at,
for in ftead of cooling his defires with good coun-
fayle, fhe inflamed his mind with a deeper affection:
for where before he onely was allured with hir
beautie, nowe he was entifed with hir wifedome.
Pallas gaue him a déeper wounde than *Venus*, and
the inwarde vertues were more forcible than the
outwarde fhadowes : fo that he perfifted in his
paffions, and began to confider with him felfe, that
the meanes to procure his content, was onely the
fimplicitie of *Mænon*, with whome he woulde make
an exchange rather than be fruftrate of his defire :
an exchange (I meane) for *Ninus* being a widower
had one onely childe, which was a daughter, about
the age of fixteene yeares : hir he determined to
giue in marriage vnto *Mænon*, rather than he would
not enioy *Semyramis*, thinking that the feare of his
difpleafure, the burthen of his owne pouertie, the
hope of preferrement, the tickling conceit of
dignity, would force the poore vaffall to looke

twife on his faire wife before he refufed fuche a
proffer: think / ing this pretence to bee his beft
pollicie, hee refolued prefentlye to put it in
execution : and therefore foorthwith commanded
a Purfuiuant to fetche *Mænon* vnto the Court : who
comming with commiffion vnto the poore mans
houfe, founde him and his wife at dinner: to
whome, after he had declared the fumme of his
meffage, he departed, willing him with as much
fpéede as might be to repaire vnto the Court.
Mænon although amazed with this newes, yet for
that his confcience was cléere feared not, but with
as much haft as was poffible, made him felfe readie
to goe. *Semyramis* diffembled the matter, fetcht
hir hufbande forth his newe hofe, and his beft
iacket, thinking to fpunge him vp after the clean-
lieft fafhion, that *Ninus* might fée fhe had caufe
to loue and like fo proper a man : fetting hir
hufbande therefore foorth in print, he tooke his
waye vnto the Court, where at the gate the
Secretarie awayted to bring him into prefence :
whither no fooner hee was entered, but the king
takinge the poore man afide, began to common
with him in this manner.

Mænon for the Soueraigne to make a long dis-
courfe vnto the fubiect were friuolous, féeing as
the one for his maieftie is priuiledged to commande
and conftrayne, fo the other by obedience is tyed

to obeye : therefore omitting all needelesse pream-
bles, thus to the purpose : *Mænon* thou art poore,
and yet a Lorde ouer Fortune, for that I heare
thou art content, for it is not richesse to haue
much, but to desire little, yet to thy want thou
hast such a fauour graunted thée by the Destinies,
as euerie waie may counteruaile thy pouertie, I
meane the possession of thy wife *Semyramis*, whome
mine eye can witnesse to be passing faire and
beautifull : / enuie, that grudged at thy happinesse,
and loue that frowned at my libertie, ioyning their
forces together, haue so disquieted my minde with
sundrie passions, as onely it lies in thy power to
mittigate the cause of my martyrdome, for know
Mænon, I am in loue with thy wife : a censure I
knowe, which will bee hard for thee to digest, and
yet to be borne with more patience, for that thou
hast a king and thy soueraigne to bee thy riuall :
her *Mænon* I craue of thée to bee my concubine,
which if thou grant not, thinke as nowe thou hast
pouertie with quiet, so then thou shalt haue both
content & dignitie. The poore man who thought
by the kings spéeches that his wife had bene con-
senting to this pretence, framed the king this
answere.

I knowe right mightie soueraigne, that Princes
may command, where poore men cannot intreate,
that the title of a king is a writ of priuiledge in

the court of Loue, that chaftitie is of fmall force to
refift, where wealth and dignitie ioyned in league,
are armed to affault : kings are warranted to command, and fubiects to obey, therefore if *Semiramis*
be content to grant the intereft of her affections
into your maiefties hands, I am refolued to redeliuer
vp my fee fimple with patience. No *Mænon*, qd.
Ninus, as thy wife is faire, fo fhe is honeft, and
therefore where I cannot command I wil then
conftraine, I meane, that thou force her to loue me.
Mænon grieuing at the wordes of the king, made
this replie. If my wife, mightie *Ninus* bee contented to preferre a cottage before a crowne, and
the perfon of a poore labourer before the loue of a
Prince, let me not (good my Lord) be fo vnnaturall
as to refolue vppon fuch a villanie, as the very
beafts abhore to commit : the lion killeth the
lyoneffe beeing taken in adulterie, the fwanne
killeth her make for fufpition of the fame fault,
and fhall I whom reafon willeth to be / charie
of my choife, force my wife perforce to fuch a
folly : pardon my liege, neuer fhall the loyaltie of
my wife be reuenged with fuch treachery : rather
had I fuffer death than be appeached of fuche
difcourtefie. *Ninus* hearing the poore man fo
refolute, thought there was no adder fo deafe, but
had his charme, no bird fo fickle but had hir call,
no man fo obftinat but by fome meanes might be

reclaimed, therfore he made him this anfwer. *Mænnon* be not fo fonde as to preferre fancie before life, nor fo infolent as to refufe the fauour of a king, for the affection of an inconftant woman : though I meane to depriue thee of a prefent ioy, fo I meane to counteruaile it with a greater bliffe : for the exchange of *Semyramis*, I meane to giue thée my daughter *Sarencida* in marriage, fo of a fubiect to make thée a fonne and my equall, fo that nothing fhall be different betwixt vs but a crowne and a kingdom : for a poore wife thou fhalt haue a rich princeffe, from pouertie thou fhalt rife to honour, from a begger to a duke : confider with thyfelfe then *Mænon*, how I fauour thée, which might poffeffe my defire by thy death, and yet féeke it at thy handes by intreatie and preferrement : take time now by the forehead, fhe is bald behinde, and in letting hir turne hir backe, thou bidft fare well to oportunity : if thou refufe dignitie, my daughter and the fauour of a foueraigne, hope not to liue nor inioy thy wife : for this cenfure holde for an oracle, *Ninus* before night will enioy the loue of *Semyramis*. This feuere refolution of the king droue poore *Mænon* into a thoufand fundry paffions, for he confidered with him felfe *Semyramis* was a woman, and in the middle of hir age, and though fhe were beautifull fhe was but a woman, and had hir equals : he knew that *Sarencida*

was honourable, of royall parentage, the daughter
of a king, beautifull, young, / and riche: he felt
pouertie to be the fifter of diftreffe, and that there
was no greater woe than want: dignitie prefented
to his imagination the glory that deaws from
honour, the fwéete content that preferrement
afoordes, and howe princely a thing it was to be
the fonne in law to a king: thefe vnacquainted
thoughts fore troubled the minde of the poore
man, but when he called to remembrance the conftancie of *Semyramis*, how the motion of fuche a
mightie monarch, was in vaine to mitigate one
fparke of hir affection, that neither dignitie, nor
death, no not the maieftie of a king coulde perfwade hir to falfifie hir faith, returned *Ninus*
this anfwer. As (my liege) kings haue honour
to countenance their actions, fo poore men haue
honeftie whereby to direct their liues. *Diogenes*
was as defirous of good fame, as *Alexander* was of
glory. Pouertie is as glad to creepe to credite,
as dignitie, and the thoughts that fmoke from a
cottage, are oft as fweete a facrifice to the gods, as
the perfumes of princes: the heauens are equall
allotters of mifhap, and the deftinies impartiall in
their cenfure: for as oft doeth reuenge followe
maieftie for iniuftice, as pouertie for doing amiffe:
the one offendes with intent, the other eyther by
ignorance, or neceffitie: then my Liege, if your

Highneſſe offer me wrong, by taking away my
wife perforce, aſſure your ſelfe that honour is no
priuiledge againſt infamie, neyther will the gods
ſleepe in reuenge of poore *Mænon*: for your
proffers: know this, I account preferment in ill
diſcredite, not dignitie, and the fauour of a Prince
in wickedneſſe, the frowne of God in iuſtice : for
your daughter, I am ſorie the vnbrideled furie of
luſt ſhoulde ſo farre ouerrule the lawe of nature, as
to alienate the loue of a father for ſuch follie : her
I vtterly refuſe, not that I contemne the Princeſſe, /
but that I pitie hir eſtate, and wiſhe hir better
Fortune : for death which your highneſſe threatens,
I ſcorne it, as preferring an honeſt fame before
miſhap, and the loue of my wife before death, were
it neuer ſo terrible : for pouertie denies me to make
other requitall for hir vnfayned affection, than
conſtancie, which I will pay as hir due, though
with the loſſe of my life : why ſhoulde not the
examples which hiſtoriographers pennes downe for
preſidentes, ſerue as trumpettes to incourage poore
men in honeſt and honourable reſolutions : when
Marcus Lepidus the Romane Conſull was driuen
into baniſhment, and hearde that the Senate in
deſpighte had giuen his wife vnto an other, he
preſently died for ſorrowe : when *Nero* the tyrant
(pardon my liege I inferre no compariſons) inflamed
with luſt towardes the wife of *Sylaus*, a Romane,

neither refpecting the law *Iulia* made to the contrarie, by his predeceffor *Auguftus*, neither iuftice
nor the gods, but oppofing himfelfe to the heauens,
reft the poore citizen of his wife, *Sylaus* flewe
himfelfe at the pallace gate: which brought
the Emperour in great hate with his Commons. I inferre not thefe examples as fearefull of your Highneffe disfauour, but as one
determined to followe thefe Romanes in their
fortunes, and eyther with quiet to liue ftill the
hufbande of *Semyramis* in *Babylon*, or to let the
worlde witneffe I neuer was fo cowardly to deliuer
vp fo deare an intereft, but by death. *Nynus*
ftorming at the anfwere which poore *Mænon* made,
did not take his fpeeches as perfwafions from his
follye, but as preparatiues to further choller: for
fo deepe was the vnfatiable defire of filthie luft
ingrauen and imprinted in his minde, and the
fowle imagination / of adulterous thoughtes had fo
blinded his fenfes, that as a man halfe fraught with
a lunacie he became furious, that, in a rage taking
a fword that hoong at his beds head, he rufht vpon
the poore man and flue him: this cruell deede
being thus vniuftly executed, he felt no remorfe in
his confcience, but as a man wholly foulde ouer
vnto mifchiefe, procéeded in his purpofe, and
prefently fent his Secretarie for *Semyramis*: who
no fooner heard the meffage, but fearing that hir

hufband for hir caufe might come to mifhap, in hir
woorft attire, as fhe was, hied to the Court: where
being brought into the kings chamber, *Ninus*
hauing caufed the dead body before to be carried
away, told hir briefly all the matter, howe hir
hufbande was flaine, and that nowe he had fent
for hir not to make hir his concubine but quéene.
Semyramis no fooner heard of the death of hir
hufbande, but fhe fell into a pafme, and was hardly
brought to life, but at laft being reuiued, fhe burft
foorth into fountaines of teares, & into bitter
exclamations againft the tyrant: who fought to
appeafe hir with fundrie fwéete promifes, but féeing
nothing could preuaile, he fent for his daughter
Sarencida to whom he committed the charge of
Semyramis, as of one that fhoulde be a quéene and
hir mother. *Sarencida* as nothing daring (what fo
euer fhe thought) to difobey hir fathers commande,
led hir by the hand into hir chamber, & as womens
perfwafiues are beft confectaries for womens forrowes, did fomewhat mitigate fome parte of hir
griefe, that fhee ceaft from hir teares, till at night
being alone in hir bed, the *Idea* of hir hufbandes
perfon prefented it felfe, though not an obiect to
hir eyes, yet to hir imagination, that ouercome
with the paffions of loue, thinking to take the
benefit of the place and time, & determining to
follow hir hufband in his fortunes, tooke hir knife

in hir / hande, and ſtanding in hir ſmocke by the
bed ſide, fell into theſe furious tearmes. *Semyramis*
this day hath béene the beginning of thy ſorrowes
and the end of thy good fortunes: the fame of
thine honeſtie ſo generally blazed abroade through
all *Babylon*, ſhall this day without deſert be ſpotted
with infamie, the bloudie action of *Ninus* ſhall be
attributed to thée for a fault, and the intent of his
death harbour vnder the ſuſpition of thy diſhoneſty:
if thou liueſt and become queene, yet ſhall this
deede make thée a table talke amongeſt beggers,
honour ſhall not priuiledge thée from the hate of
them which are honeſt, neither ſhall the glorie of a
crowne ſhrowd thée from diſcredit.   Then *Semyramis* ſéeing thou ſéekeſt after fame, ſéeke not to
liue, vſe the knife thou haſt in hand, as a meanes
to requite thy huſbands loue, and to warrant thy
former honeſtie: *Panthea* the wife of *Abradatus*,
ſéeing hir huſbande ſlaine in the campe of *Cyrus*,
ſacrificed hir ſelfe on his dead corps: when *Iulia*
the wife of *Pompey* ſaw but a gowne of hir huſbands
bloudy, ſuſpecting ſome miſhap, fell into a trance &
neuer reuiued.   *Portia* the wife of *Brutus* hearing
of hir huſb̃ads death, choked hir ſelf with hot
burning coales.   *Aria* the wif[e] of *Cæcinna* died
with her condemned huſband before the capitoll.

Let the reſolute loue of theſe noble dames
incourage thée to the like conſtancy, conſider

Semyramis thy hufband is deade, and déedes done can not be reuoked. *Ninus* meanes to make thée his wife : his wife, cowardly wretch as thou art, anfwer to this foolifh obiection which *Pifca* the wife of *Pandoerus* did, who being flaine by the king of *Perfia*, after the flaughter of hir hufbande, he profered hir marriage, but holding, as thou doeft, the inftrument of death in hir hand, fhe vttered thefe wordes : The Gods forbid, that to be a queene, I fhoulde euer wed him that hath béene the / murtherer of my deare hufband. And with this fhée was readie to ftab her felfe to the heart, but ftaying her felfe and paufing a while, fhe beganne as women are prone to conceit reuenge, to thinke with her felfe how in time better to quite the iniury proffered by *Nynus* to her poore hufbande. This Gentlemen, I coniecture was her imagination, for fhe fodainly let fall her knife, leapt into her bed, & paft the reft of the night in a found fléepe. And in déede, had not the fequele proued the contrarie, it might haue been coniectured that the hope of a crowne had bene a great per-fwafion from her defperate refolution : but letting thefe fuppofes paffe, to *Nynus*, who made it his mornings worke, as foone as he was vp to vifite *Semyramis*, and finding her in a better tune than he left her, conceiued fuch ioy in the appeafing of her paffions, that prefently he fommoned all his

Lordes to a Parliament, where hée vnfolded vnto
them the intent hee had to make *Semyramis* quéene,
and therefore craued their confents. The nobilitie
whatfoeuer they thought, durft not gainfaie the
will of their Prince, but affented to his demand, fo
that all things were prepared for the coronation :
but when the brute of *Mænons* death was noifed
abroade in *Babylon*, euerie one after their fundrie
and feuerall imaginations began to conferre of the
action, all generally meruailing that fo honeft a
wife fhuld commit fo hainous a fact: for euerie one
thought her an actor in the tragedie, yet they confidered that ambitious honour was a mortall enemie
to honeftie, and that few women were fo chaft but
dignitie could draw to follie. Well, murmure
what they lift, the kings purpofe tooke effect.
The daie came, and the coronation was moft
folempnely and fumptuouflie perfourmed, the king
conceiuing fuch felicitie in his newe wife, that
hée continued the feaft for tenne dayes : which /
tearme ended, euerie one departed to their home,
and the late married couple liued fo contentedly
to euerie mans coniecture, that *Semyramis* won
her fame halfe loft by her obedience, and efpecially
fhée gained the loue of the commons, for preferment had not pufte her vp with pride, nor dignitie
made her difdainfull of the glorie of a crowne, nor
the title of a quéene had made no metamorphofis

of her minde, but in this, that as fhe grew in
honour, fo fhe increafed in courtefie, bountifull to
all that were poore, and enuious to none that were
noble, preferring the futes of them were wronged,
and féeming as neare as fhée coulde to caufe the
king doe iuftice to all. This her vertuous difpofition not onely ftole the heartes of the commons,
but alfo the loue of her hufband, who to increafe
affection more had a fonne by her called *Nynus.*
Paffing thus three or foure yeeres in great pleafure,
the king furcharged with content, commaunded
his wife to afke whatfoeuer fhe woulde, that was
within the compaffe of his Babylonifh monarch[y],
and it fhould bee graunted her.

Semyramis refufed fuch a proffer, but the king
béeing vrgent, fummoned all his Lordes to the
Court, and there made them priuie what a frée
graunt he made to his wife. The noble men
although fmiling at the fondneffe of the king, that
fo wilfully woulde put a naked fwoorde into a
madde mans hande, yet outwardly feemed to allowe
of his will, fo that *Semyramis* demanded that fhe
might abfolutely without checke or controlement
rule the Babylonian Empire, as fole quéene for
thrée daies. The king who no whit miftrufted
that reuenge could fo long harbour in the heart
of a woman, graunted her requeft, and therefore
prefently with all conuenient fpéede caufed a

ſumptuous ſcaffolde in forme of a Theatre to / be
erected in the middeſt of *Babylon*, whither calling
his nobles and commons by the ſound of a trumpet
vpon the next feſtiuall, which was holden in
honour of their God *Iphis*, he there in preſence
of all his ſubiectes, reſigned vp his crowne and
ſcepter into the handes of *Semyramis*, placing hir
in the Imperiall throne, as ſole quéene, monarch
and gouerneſſe of *Egypt*. *Semyramis* being thus
inueſted with the Diadeame and regall power: firſt
publikely declared the effect of the kings grant,
how ſhe was for the tearme and ſpace of thrée
dayes to reigne as ſoueraigne ouer the land, to
haue as great authoritie to do iuſtice, and to execute
martiall law as hir huſbande : to confirme which,
Ninus as a ſubiect did hir reuerence, and iointly
with the reſt of the nobility, ſwore to performe
whatſoeuer ſhe ſhoulde commande, and to obey hir
as their ſole and ſoueraigne princes.   After the
king had ſolemnely taken his oath, *Semyramis*
vttered theſe or ſuch like ſpéeches to the people.
It is not vnknowne (worthy péeres of *Egypt* and
inhabitantes of *Babylon*) that I liued in my youth
the wife of poore *Mænon* with credit fit for my
degrée, and with fame equall to the honeſty of my
life.   Occaſion neuer armed reporte to ſtaine me
with diſgrace, neither was the wife of *Mænon*
accounted to be prodigall of hir affections, although

perhaps a little proud of hir beautie, the pouertie
of my hufbande neuer touched me with miflike,
nor the proffers of preferrement coulde perfwade
me to inconftancie, but Fortune that is euer fickle
in hir fauours, and enuie that grudgeth at quiet,
féeing we liued fecurely in loue and content, fet
king *Ninus* to be the meanes of my ouerthrow:
for he, inflamed with the fight of my beautie,
yelded prefently to the allaromes of luft, and fought
with the golden baite of dignitie to hale me on to
the wracke of my / honeftie, which by no meanes
he could bring to paffe : ioyning murther with the
pretence of adulterie, hee flew my hufband in his
bed chamber, fo the better to obtaine his purpofe.
After whome I call the Gods to witnes, I haue
liued for no other caufe but to fee this day, neither
hath the gaine of a crowne counteruailed my
former content: the gliftering fhew of dignitie hath
not tickled my minde with delight, the vaine
pleafure of preferment neuer made me proude:
onlie (worthie péeres of *Egypt*) the hope that one
daie I fhould make reuenge of poore *Mænons*
iniurie, hath made me liue in fuch contented
patience, which nowe is come, for it befitteth a
quéene in iuftice to be impartiall, and two mifchiefes
are neuer founde to efcape mifhap : therefore how
faieft thou *Nynus*, quoth fhee, declare héere before
the Lordes and commons of *Egypt*, wert thou not

the fole murtherer of my hufband without my
confent? *Nynus* aunfwered as one halfe afraide
at the countenance of *Semyramis,* I confeffe that
onely *Mænon* was murthered by me, but for the
loue of thée, which I hope thou holdeft not in
memorie while this time.   Yes *Nynus,* and now
will I reuenge the iniurie offered to *Mænon,* and
therefore I command that without further delaie
thy head bee heere fmitten off, as a punifhment
due for murther and adulterie.   The nobilitie and
commons hearing the feuere fentence of *Semyramis,*
intreated for the life of their foueraigne, but it
was in vaine, for fhe departed not from the fcaffolde
till fhee fawe her command executed : which done,
fhe intombed his bodie roiallie, and in fo famous a
fepulchre, that it was one of the feuen wonders of
the world, and after fwaied the kingdome with
politike gouernment vntill her fonne *Nynus* was of
age to rule the kingdome. /

Seignior *Cofimo* hauing ended his tale, *Farneze*
greatly commended the difcourfe, applying the
effect of this hiftorie to the Gentlemen prefent,
telling them that in déede the youth of *Florence*
were greatlie giuen to this folly, as a vice predominant amongeft them.   *Peratio* who meant to
be pleafant with the olde Countie, tolde him that
he had learned this fruit in Aftronomie, that the
influence of *Venus* and *Saturn* kept the fame

conftellation to inferre as wel age as youth, and
that refpect and experience had taught him, that
olde men were like léekes gray headed, and oft
gréene tailde, that they would finde one foote at
the doore for a young wife, when the other ftumbled
in the graue to death, fo that *Diogenes* being
demanded where a man left off from luft: vnleffe,
quoth he, he be vertuous, not vntill the coffin be
brought to his doore, meaning that time neuer
wore out this follie but by death. And yet to
fée, quoth *Benedetto*, what cynicall axiomes age wil
prefcribe to youth, when they themfelues are neuer
able to performe their owne precepts, allowing
more priuiledge to their filuer haires, than to our
greene yéeres, and fhrouding vnder the fhadowe of
vertue the verie fubftance of vice, béeing as intemperate in the froftie winter of their age, as we
in the glowing fummer of our youth, and yet for
that they are olde, and though they cannot deale
more *cafte*, yet will worke more *caute*, and fimplie
conceale that wee rafhlie reueale. They are in age
generally taken for Gods, when compared euen
with youth they are meere deuils. Yet by your
leaue meffieur *Benedetto*, quoth the Ladie *Margeret*,
you fpeake too generally of age, for the verie
conftitution of the naturall temperature of our
bodies is able to infringe your reafons, féeing that
fame *naturalis calor* is ouerpreffed with a cold

drineffe in age, which in youth furthered with
moifture, / caufeth fuch voluptuous motions. *Cupid*
is painted a childe, *Venus* without wrinkles in her
face, and they which calculate the influence of
Saturne, fet not down many notes of venerie.
Howe philofophically you fpeake, quoth *Peratio*,
and yet fmall to the purpofe, for although naturall
heate be extinguifhed in age, yet remaines there
in the minde certain *Scyntillulæ voluptatis*, which
confirmed by a faturnall impreffion, were harder to
root out than were they newly fprong vp in youth,
neither did meffieur *Benedetto* conclude generally
of olde men, but brought in as a premiffe or
propofition, that age as well as youth was infected
with this folly : but well it is Ladie *Margeret*, that
our difcourfe ftretcheth not fo farre as women, nor
to talke of their wanton affections, leaft happilie
we had vntied fuch a labyrinth of their lafciuious
vanities, as might haue made vs fooner defire
our reft then end the difcourfe. You are alwaies
glancing at women, quoth *Cofimo*, not that you are
a Pythagorian, and hate that fexe, for fir I knowe
your lippes can digeft fuch lettuce, but that your
mouth were out of temper if once a daie you had
not a woman in your mouth, héerein refembling
Marcus Læpidus, who made an inuective againft
fumptuoufneffe of diet, himfelfe being called the
glutton of *Rome*: not that hée was fparing in his

chéere, but that *Athens* abftaining from daintie cates, might leaue the market more ftored with delicate diſhes.

Benedetto was nipt on the head with this ſharpe replie, efpeciallie for that all the whole companie laught to ſée how he anſwered with ſilence, & *Farneze* about whom the talke began, made this anſwer, I can not denie Gentlemen, but anger is ſubiect to many fooliſh and intemperat paſſions, & therfore to be comprehēded within the compas of this folly, but either age / or youth, it bréedeth many inormities, ſo that for this night I will take in hand to ſend you all to bed with a farewell of foure verſes, which I read once in the monaſtery of *Santo Marco* in *Venice*: the author I know not, the verſes are theſe.

Quatuor his pænis Certo afficietur adulter,
Aut Egenus erit Subita vel morte peribit,
Aut Cadet in cauſam qua debet Iudice vinci,
Aut aliquod membrum caſu vel Crymine perdit.

The time of the night beeing ſomewhat late, they tooke his ieſt for a charge, and ſolempnly taking their leaue, euerie man departed quietlie vnto his lodging.

The third difcourfe of
Follie.

He morning being come, and the Sun difplaying her radiant beames vpon the gloomie mantle of the earth, *Flora* prefented her glorious obiectes to the eie, and fwéete fmelling parfumes to the nofe, with the delight of fundrie pleafing and odoriferous flowers, when thefe young Gentlemen afhamed that *Tytan* fhould fommon them from their beddes, paffing into the garden, found the olde Countie, his wife and foure daughters walking for health and pleafure in a frefh and gréene arbour: where after they had faluted each other with a mutuall God morrowe, they ioyned all in feuerall parties, amongft the reft *Bernardino* fpying a marigolde opening his leaues a little by the heate of the Sunne, / pulling Ladie *Frances* by the fléeue, began his morning mattens on this manner : The nature of this hearbe, Ladie *Frances*, which we call the marrigolde, and the Grecians *Helitropion*, and the Latiniftes *Sol fequiam*, is thought by the ancient Philofophers to bee framed onely by nature, to teach the duetie of a wife towards her hufband, for féeing that as *Ariftides* faid, a woman was the contrarie of a man : this flower prefents a prefident of her affection, for which waie fo euer the Sunne turneth,

it ftill openeth the leaues by degrées, and as ẙ
Sun declineth, fo it fhutteth : that *Phebus* being
gone to bed, the marrigolde denies any longer to
fhew her glorie : fo faith *Plato*, fhoulde a good
wife imitate her hufbands actions, directing her
felfe after his courfe in his prefence, being pleafant
to content the eie and humour of her hufband in
his abfence with a modeft bafhfulnes, fcarce with
the wife of *Tarquin* to looke out of her windowe.
In déede, quoth the Ladie *Frances*, I haue heard
faie, that young mennes wiues and maidens children
are alwaies wel taught: no doubt fir, your Oecono-
micall preceptes are verie good, and happie is fhe
that heares them and neuer beléeues them: I praie
God your wife may bee a marigolde whenfoeuer
you are married, that to auoide iealoufie, you may
euer weare her pinde on your fléeue. *Peratio* ouer
hearing ftepte in and afked the Ladie *Frances* if
fhe thought *Bernardino* woulde be iealous. I
haue not, quoth the Ladie, fuch affured fight in
phifognomie, as I dare auouch it for truth, but I
promife you fir, the Gentleman is well forehanded
and well foreheaded, two of the nine beauties to
haue a fine finger and a large browe, nowe take
the paines to conclude how you lift. *Peratio*
laught, and *Bernardino* replied, tis no meruaile if
men bée iealous, when *Hefiodus* affirmes, that hee
which / trufteth to the loue of a woman, refembleth

him that hangs by the leaues of trées in Autumne.
But in earneſt *Bernardino*, quoth *Peratio*, what
doeſt thinke of him that is married ?   That hee is
quoth he, areſted with a grieuous action, for no
doubt young Gentlemen ſhoulde flie vp to heauen
if they were not kepte backe with ſuch an areſt :
but for better aunſwere to thy queſtion, take the
replie of *Metellus* to *Pyſo*, that aſked him why
hee married his ſonne being ſo young, and before
hee was wiſe : Becauſe *Pyſo*, quoth hee, if my
ſonne grow to be wiſe, he will neuer marrie : nor
if you were wiſe, quoth the Ladie *Frances*, woulde
yee ſpeake ſo vnreuerently of marriage: but tis no
matter, we ſhall finde you in time like *Crates* the
cynike Philoſopher, who inueighing greatly againſt
this honourable ſocietie, was ſéene begging a péece
of bread at *Lais* doore in *Corinth*.   If the lawe
that *Euphorius* of *Lacedemonia* conſtituted were
kepte, ſuch as refuſed marriage ſhould be baniſhed,
but I thinke *Bernardino*, if you were brought
within the forfaiture of ſuch a ſtatute, you woulde
take that for a ſhifte, which a Lacedemonian
baniſht did, beeing produced before *Lycurgus* for
the like crime.   And what was that madame, quoth
Peratio ?   Marie Sir, quoth ſhée, being aſſigned to
exile, hee brought forth witneſſe that he had begot-
ten thrée children, and vppon that excuſe *Lycurgus*
made the ſtrict lawe againſt adulterie, yet mittigated

before fome parte of the punifhment. I thinke madame, aunfwered *Bernardino*, the Priefte hath a pennie for your banes, your fophiftrie is fo good for marriage. Onelie Sir, quoth fhee, I fpeake it agaynft fuch feuere cenfurers of matrimonie as you are, which for what caufe I knowe not, liuing ftale bachelors, are of *Appolonius Tianeus* opinion, and therefore frame principles. According to your / preceptes, as no doubt one of your fect did who made thefe two verfes :

L'amor del donna il vin del flafco,
Nul fera bon nel matutina guafco.

Such ftoicall Gentlemen as runne into fuch in- conftant and heathenifh conclufions, I had as liefe haue their roome as their companie. *Bernardino* perceiuing the Ladie *Frances* was halfe angrie, thought rather to recant than make her cholerike, and therefore tolde her his meaning was not to condemne mariage, but meerely to ieaft for con- ference fake. Then fir, quoth fhe, all is in ieaft, and fo let vs to the reft of the companie: whome they founde talking with a Cooke that was come to his maifter, to knowe if hée would haue anie extraordinarie difhe pro[ui]ded for dinner. No fir, quoth *Farneze*, I will aunfwere with *Socrates*, if they bée vertuous there is enough, if they bee not, there is too much. The olde Countie tooke occafion

hereof to fpeake of temperaunce in diet, and thus
he began. I remember Gentlemen that *Timotheus*
a Grecian Captaine, hauing fupped with *Plato* in
his Academie, at a fober and fimple repafte, for
their feftiuall fare was Oliues, cheefe, apples, cole
wortes, bread and wine, tolde the next daie certaine noble men his companions, that they which
fupped with *Plato* digeft not his viandes in a long
time, meaning that wife banquet void of exceffe,
not to content the bodie with Epicurifme, but to
decke the minde with philofophicall precepts, fuch
were the feafts of *Socrates*, *Zenocrates*, and other:
the fages which compared the pleafures conceiued
in delicates, to the fauour of perfumes, which for
all their fwéete fmell paffe awaie like fmoake.
The Egyptians vfed in the middeft of their
banquets to bring in the / anatomie of a dead man,
that the horrour of the corps might mitigate
immoderate delightes. Indéede fir, quoth *Bernardino*, I remember that *Alexander* before he fell
into the Perfian delicacy, refufed thofe cookes and
pafterers that *Ada* quéene of *Caria* fent vnto him,
faying to the meffenger, for my dinner I vfe earely
rifing, for my fupper a flender dinner, for he did
vfe to eat but once a day: fo that *Plato* féeing
Dionyfius making two meales, reported in *Athens*
hée fawe nothing in *Sycillia* but a monfter, that did
féede twife before the funne fet. *Cyrus* monarch

of the Perfians, in his childhoode, being demanded
of his grandfather *Aftiage* why he woulde drinke
no wine, aunfwered, for feare they giue me poifon:
for (quoth hée) at the celebration of your natiuitie,
I noted that fome haue made mixture of the wine
with fome inchanted potion, fith at the ende of the
feaft there was not one departed in his right minde.
So did (quoth *Peratio*) *Epaminondas* the greateft
captaine and philofopher in his time, for being
inuited by a friende of his to fupper, the tables
ouercharged with fuperfluitie & fumptuoufneffe
of fare, he told his hoft in great choller that he
thought he had béen requefted, as a friend to dine
competently, not to fuffer iniury by being intertained like a glutton. *Caius Fabritius* a notable
Romane knight, was found by the Samnit ambaffa-
dours that came vnto him, eating of reddifh roafted
in the afhes, and that in a verie poore houfe, and
by the waie to induce a ftrange miracle that Sainct
Ierome reporteth of one *Paule* an heremit, who
liued from fixtéene to fixtie of Dates onely, and
from fixtie to fixe fcore and fiue (at what time he
died) he was fed by a little bread brought to him
by a crowe. Truth (quoth *Farneze*) infinit are
the examples which might perfwade vs to temper-
ance, but fo fonde are we now a dayes as / wee
leaue the ftudie of philofophie to learne out kitching
commentaries, but if we perfeuere ftill in this

diſſolute kind of ſuperfluity; being Chriſtians in name and Epicures in life, we are to feare that in the ende néede and neceſſitie will force vs to forſake it, and as it happened vnto king *Darius,* who when he had liued a long time in delightes, drowning him ſelfe in the ſuperfluitie of the Perſians, not once looking ſo low as hunger and thirſt, as he. fled from *Alexander,* and waxed verie thirſtie, drinking puddle water taken from a riuer tainted with deade carcaſſes, he burſt foorth into this ſpéeche, that in all his life he neuer drancke ſwéeter: ſo will it befall to vs by our inordinate exceſſe, and ſéeing we may beſt ſée this vertue of frugalitie by diſcouering his contrary, we will ſpend this forenoone in diſcourſing the follie of ſuperfluitie or gluttonie: which *Bernardino* I appoint vnto your charge, as one which we all knowe to haue béene an enemie to ſuch diſordered bankets. *Bernardino* not greatly diſcontent at this command, beganne after the gentlemen were ſeated in the arbour, to frame his ſpéech in this manner. *Plato* the prince of the Academickes, who for his ſacred ſentences with his maiſter *Socrates,* amongſt all the Philoſophers, challenged the name of diuine, had alwayes this ſaying in his mouth, that whatſoeuer exceedeth this word neceſſarie is ſuperfluitie, which *genus,* he deuided into two eſpeciall partes of apparell and fare: for the laſt whereof I am

appointed to intreat, thus to the purpofe. Thofe
Gentlemen which build vpon the doctrine of the
Epicures, and place their chiefe felicitie or *fummum
bonum* in the delicacie of fare, confider not that
gluttonie is like to the Lymons in *Arabia*, which
being paffing fwéete to the mouth, are infectious
in the ftomach, like to the floure of *Amyta* which
glorious to / the eye greatly molefteth the fmell,
the fwéete content or rather the bitter pleafures
that proceede from thefe follies, féeding our luft
with a tickling humour of delight: for euerie dram
of pretended bliffe prefents vs a pounde of affured
enormitie, for we are fo blinded with the vale of
this vayne follie, that forgetting our felues we
runne headlong with *Vliffes* into *Cyrces* lappe, and
fo by tafting hir inchaunted potion, fuffer our felues
to be like beafts transformed into fundrie fhapes,
for that was the meaning *Homer* aimed at by the
Metamorphofis, faying: fome were chaunged into
Lyons as by dronkenneffe made furious, fome
into Apes, whom wine had made pleafaunt, fome
into fwine, whofe brutifhe manner bewrayed their
imperfection by fléeping in their pottes, comparing
the alteration of men by ouer much drinke to
no other but a beftiall chaunge of their natures:
befides this difcouerie *Galen, Hypocrates* and other
learned Phifitians approue it at the fource from
whence all difeafes and euill difpofitions of the

body do flow, for fayth *Plutarch* we are ficke of
thofe things whereof we doe liue, and by our
naturall difpofition are wholy giuē to health, if the
diforder of our diet did not infringe the perfect
temperature of our complexions. *Homer* going
about to prooue the immortalitie of the Goddes,
and that they dye not, groundeth his argument
vpon this, becaufe they eate not, as if he woulde
argue, that as eating and drinking maintaines life,
fo they are the efficient caufes of death, and that
more dye of gluttonie than of hunger, hauing oft
more care to digeft meate than care to get it.
Seneca faid that the Phifitians in his time cried out
that life was fhorte and art long, that complaint
was made of nature that fhée had graunted vnto
beaftes to liue fiue or fixe ages, and to limite / mans
dayes but the length of a fpanne, which notwithftanding, being fo fhort and momentarie, was oft
confumd in exceffe, drawing on death by our owne
defires, and offering vp our gorged ftomaches vnto
Atropos as facrifice to intreat that the date of our
yeares bée vntimely preuented, fo that (as the wife
man fayth) more perifhe by furfet than by the
fword: vnto whome (fayth *Salomon*) falleth woe,
affliction, forrowe, ftrife, teares, redneffe of the eyes,
and difeafes? Euen to them that fit long at the
wine, which at the firft pleafeth both the eye and the
taft, but at the laft ftingeth as deadly as a fcorpion.

Heraclytus was of this opinion that the infatiate appetite of gluttonie doth obfcure the interiour vertues of the minde, oppreffing the diuine parte of man with a confufed *chaos* of fundrie delicates, that as the funne eclipfed with darke and vndigefted vapours, hath not the perfection of his brightneffe, fo the bodie ouercharged with fuperfluitie of meates, hath the fenfes fo fotted, as they are not able to pierce by contemplation into the Metaphyficall fecreates of anie honourable fcience. Innumerable alfo be diffolute fafhions and wicked enormities that fpring from gluttony and dronkenneffe, for where this follie is predominant, there is the minde fubiect vnto luft, anger, floth, adulterie, loue, and all other vices that are fubiectes of the fenfuall part: for as the olde Poet fayth,

Cine Cerere & Baccho friget Venus.

And by the way I remember certaine verfes written by our countriman *Dante* to this effect.

Il vitio chi conduce :

Englifhed thus :

A monfter feated in the midft of men,
Which daily fed is neuer fatiat. |
A hollow gulfe of vild ingratitude,
Which for his food vouchfafes not pay of thankes,

But ſtill doth claime a debt of due expence:
From hence doth Venus draw the ſhape of luſt,
From hence Mars raiſeth bloud and ſtratagemes:
The wracke of wealth, the ſecret foe to life,
The ſword that haſtneth on the date of death,
The ſureſt friend to phiſicke by diſeaſe,
The pumice that defaceth memorie,
The miſty vapour that obſcures the light,
And brighteſt beames of ſcience glittring ſunne,
And doth eclipſe the minde with ſluggiſh thoughtes:
The monſter that afoordes this curſed brood,
And makes commixture of theſe dyer miſhaps,
Is but a ſtomach ouerchargd with meates,
That takes delight in endleſſe gluttony.

Well did *Dante* note in theſe verſes the ſundrie miſchiefes that proceede from this folly, ſéeing what expēces to the purſe, what diſeaſes to the perſon, what ruine to the common wealth, what ſubuerſion of eſtates, what miſerie to princes haue inſued by this inſatiate ſinne of gluttonie: We read of the Emperour *Vitellius Spynter* that he was ſo much giuen to ſuperfluity and exceſſe, that at one ſupper he was ſerued with two thouſand ſeuerall kind of fiſhes, and with ſeauen thouſande flying foules, but the heauens ſtorming at ſuch an inſatiable monſter, that ſo highly abuſed the benefites of God, conſpired his ouerthrow, for

Vefpafian did not onely difpoffeffe him of the
imperiall Diademe, but caufed him to be publikly
executed in *Rome*. *Dionyfius* the younger, from
gluttony fell to tyrannie, vntill he was exiled for
his wickednefs out of *Sicilia*. *Mulcaffes* king of
Thunis was fo drowned in pleafure & delight of
fuperfluous banketting, that in the midft of his
miferies when the Emperour *Charles* / had forfaken
him, and left him of a king almoft the outcaft of
the world, yet as *Paulus Iouius* rehearfeth, he
fpent a hundredth crownes vppon the dreffing of a
peacocke, whereat his mufitians playing, he couered
his eyes to reape the greater content: but the
iudgement of God fpéedelie followed this vaine
delicacie, for within two dayes after his owne
fonnes put out his eyes with barres of hoat iron.
Infinit alfo were the examples might be brought
of dronckenneffe, and of his difcommoditie: of
Alexander, how he prepared crownes for them that
excéeded in that filthie vice, and made a great cup
which he called *Alexander*, after his owne name,
wherein he did carrous to his nobles, but *Califtenes*
his deare friend refufing, & faying: for drinking
in *Alexander* I will not ftand in néede of *Efculapius*,
he fell into fuch a furie, that he commanded him
to be put in an iron cage with dogges: which
Califtenes not brooking poifoned him felfe. At
an other dronken feaft he flue his faithfull friende

Clytus, a worthie captaine and a counfellor, to whome hee had fo many times béene beholding for his life: but afterwarde when he came to him felfe, hée was fo grieued for this faƈt, that he fought to fhorten his dayes with his owne fword, and fpent many dayes in continuall teares for his friende: whereby we euidently fée how the beft that infueth of this folly is fhame and repentance. This meant *Heraclytus* to teache his countrie men, when after a mutinous fedition was appeafed, and the commons demanded of him, what antydote were beft to preuent the like misfortune? prefentlye gat him vp to a place where the magiftrate vfed to deliuer Orations to the people, and there in fteade of pronouncing fome eloquent and learned difcourfe, only beganne to féede on a morfell of browne bread, & to drinke a glaffe of cléere water: thus fetting downe a / golden precept by filence, for by this he fignified vnto them that as long as daintineffe and riot and néedleffe expences flourifhed in the citie, fo long fhoulde they ftand in danger of ciuill fedition, but this vaine exceffe abolifhed, a peaceable and perpetuall quiet was like to infue: if this counfell of *Heraclitus* were requifit in a monarchie, what néede haue wee of fuche neceffarie principles, in whofe common wealth nothing is glorious, but fuperfluitie of foode and apparell. Let me borrow a word with you (quoth

Peratio) in this, for in déede if men thoroughly confider the vaine delight diuerfe of our Florentines tooke in trimming and decking out the bodie, which *Epaminondas* called the prifon of the foule, we fhall bee at length forced to confeffe with *Erafmus*, that they rather ferue to whet the eyes of the beholders to wicked defires, than vnto anie honeft opinion or conceit.

Epictetus gaue this onely precept vnto his countrimen at his death : Friendes (quoth he) decke not your bodie with curious fuperfluitie of apparell, but paint them with temperaunce, for the one is but a fhadowe that bleareth the eyes, the other an ornament that inricheth the minde: which counfell the ancient Monarkes and Chiefetaines of the world foretaught vs : for *Auguftus* famous through the whole worlde for his fortunes, and honoured for his maieftie, neuer ware other garmentes than fuche as his wife and daughters made, and thofe verie moderate. *Agefilaus* king of *Lacedemonia* had but one coat for winter and fummer. *Epaminondas* generall captaine of the Thebans, was contented with one onely gowne all the yeare long: this fimplicitie and moderate vfe of apparell in fuch worthie perfonages, might well ferue vs for prefidentes, but that vanity hath fo long / lulled our fenfes a fléep with pleafure, as the cuftome of the fault hath taken away the

féeling of the fact. Well fir (quoth *Bernardino*)
this belongeth to your difcourfe of pride, and
therfore againe to our purpofe, which féeing I
haue confirmed with fufficient reafons & examples
to be an inordinate vice and more follie, I will
nowe alfo ratifie it with a verie briefe and fhort
hiftorie.

Bernardinos Tale.

IN the citie of *Aufpurg* in *Germanie*, there
ruled not long fince a duke whofe name
for reuerence I conceale, & therefore
will tearme him *Don Antonio* : a man of very
honorable parentage, but fo giuen to the filthy
vice of dronkenneffe as he almoft fubuerted the
ftate of the citie, with his gluttonies, for oftimes
he fell into tyranous and barbarous cruelties, as
one that had martiall law in his power, and other
whiles gaue wrong fentence againft the innocent,
as his humour fitted, which exceffe had led him.
But aboue all the reft, a poore man hauing a matter
to plead before him, which he was acertained by
law fhould goe on his fide, *Don Antonio* comming
dronke to the place of iudgment, fléeping in his
furfets, neuer confidered the equitie of the caufe,
but gaue fentence againft the poore man, and
condemned him in fo great a fumme, as fcarfe all
his moueables were able to difcharge: well the

verdict giuen, he had no other remedy but to
abide the cenfure of the iuft iudge, & to make
fale of all that he had to anfwer his condemnation:
which done, fo little remayned that hée had
nothing left to maintaine his wife and childrē :
wherevpon pouertie being the heauieft burden /
a man can beare, prefented vnto him a glaffe of
many miferies, which were apparent to infue by
diftreffed want, wherein after the poore wretch had
a long while gazed, he fell to defpaire, that fling-
ing into his backe fide, he toke the halter out of
his ftable, and running into the field, went to hang
him felfe in a thicket hard adioyning to his houfe:
where yet a little entering into confideration with
him felfe, he began thus to debate.

Infortunate *Ruftico*, for fo we will terme him,
how art thou oppreffed with fundrie paffions,
diftres haling thee on to defpaire, and the care of
thy foule willing thée rather to choofe pouertie than
hell. Well did *Tymon* of *Athens* fée the miferie
of mans life, when hee bought a peece of ground,
wherein hee placed gibbets, and fpent his time in
fuch defperate Philofophie, as to perfwade his
friendes to hang them felues, fo to auoide the
imminent perilles of innumerable misfortunes: fo
Ruftico féeme thou an Athenian, be one of *Tymons*
friendes, liften to his doctrine, follow his counfell,
preuent miferie with death. But alas this is not

sufficient, for in fréeing thy felfe from calamitie,
thou leaueſt thy wife and children in a thouſand
ſorrowes, and further thou cutteſt off all hope
of reuenges. Reuenge, yea reuenge *Ruſtico*, for
aſſure thy felfe, if thou liueſt not, yet God will
reuenge: haue two finnes eſcaped vnpuniſhed? hath
not the accurſed duke to his drunkenneſſe added
iniuſtice? yes, and therefore deſerues to bee reuenged
with thine owne hande: let examples arme thée to
the like attempt. *Philip* king of *Macedonia* was
ſlaine by a meane Gentleman *Pauſanias*, becauſe he
would not let him haue iuſtice againſt *Antipater*,
who had offred him wrong. *Demetrius* hauing
receiued many requeſts of his poore ſubiects, as
he paſſed ouer a bridge / threwe all their ſupplica-
tions into the water, for which cauſe hee became
ſo odious to his ſubiects, that they ſuffered *Pyrrhus*
his enemie to driue him out of his kingdome
without battell. *Ferdinando* the fourth putting to
death a knight more for anger than anie iuſt cauſe,
the Gentleman at the ſentence, cried out: Iniurious
Emperor, I cite thée to appeare before the tribunall
ſeate of God, to anſwere this wrong within thirtie
daies: on the laſt of which expired tearme the
Emperour died. Then comfort thy felfe *Ruſtico*,
let not deſpaire arme thée to ſuch an heatheniſh
reſolution, rather liue to reuenge than die to double
thy miſerie, and féeing the duke hath dealt thus

hardly, vſe him as *Alexander Seuerus* handled his
ſecretarie, who béeing a caterpiller in the Court,
and ſelling the verie fauourable lookes of his
maiſter for coyne, promiſing poore men to proſe-
cute their ſutes, when he neuer mooued their cauſe:
at laſt in requitall of this treacherous dealing was
tied to a poſt and choaked with ſmoake, hauing a
proclamation made before him by ſound of trumpet,
that they which ſell ſmoake ſhoulde ſo periſhe with
ſmoake: the poore man from theſe plaintes fell
into teares, that ouercome with the paſſions hée
fell a ſleepe, where in a dreame was by God re-
uealed vnto him the meanes of reuenge: as ſoone
as he awoake and called vnto minde the viſion,
thinking it to be no fantaſticke illuſion of the brayne,
but a ſtrickt commaunde from the heauenly powers,
preſently went home and waxed contrarye vnto
his woonted cuſtome very merrye, frequenting
dayly the Dukes Palace: where giuing him ſelfe
vnto drinking, he became in time to bée in ſome
fauour with the Duke, who neuer remembred that
hee ſat in iudgement againſt the poore man. On
a time ſéeing that oportunitie fauoured him, he
requeſted the Duke that as he went on hunting,
he would take the paines to viſit his poore houſe,
where he ſhoulde finde no daintie fare, but onely
that he durſt promiſe a cup of good wine. This
worde was enough to perſwade the Duke to a

greater matter, fo that he granted to come. The poore man glad that his purpofe was like to take effect, went home and made a fale of all that hee had euen to his verie fhirt, to the great forrow of his wife, and wonder of his neighbours, which knew not his pretence. As foone as he had pretilie furnifhed him felfe with mony, he bought great ftore of excellent and delicate viandes of ftrong and pleafant wine, and conuaied them home to his houfe, whether within two daies after the Duke forefent his cooke, certifieng the poore man that he would dine with him: who prouiding moft fumptuous fare, fet all his wealth vpon the table at one dinner, and intertained the Duke with fuch a heartie welcome, that he not onely wondered where *Ruftico* got fuch ftore of victuals, but gaue great thankes for his good chéere. *Ruftico* ferued in wine in fuch abundaunce that *don Antonio* fell to his olde vice of dronkennes, and in fuch fort, as he neuer tooke fo much in his life. The poore man féeing him take his drinke fo fréely, went to one of his Trumpetters, and tolde him that the Duke commanded hee fhoulde by founde of Trumpet prefently fummon all the Citizens to appeare at his houfe, eyther without delaie or excufe. Which commande, hee forthwith executed : and the Burgo-maifters & chiefe men of the Citie meruailing what this fhould meane, yet hafting to the houfe of *Ruftico*, they found a fcaffolde erected at the doore, where after they had ftayed a while, *Ruftico* came foorth, and began to fpeake in this manner.

Worthie Citizens and Burgomafters of *Aufpourg*,/ I know you meruaile what the caufe of your com-ming is, efpecially féeing mee that am poore and vnlettered prepare to offer an Oration to fuch politike gouernours, but it is the care of my Countrie, & efpecially of this Citie, which is like to ruinate through the want of the poffeffion of a perfect magiftrate, that driues me to this refolute and defperate attempte : The dutie of a magis-trate, as I haue heard, a certaine Philofopher fhould fet downe, confifteth in three efpeciall pointes, in ruling, teaching and iudging, that hee be wife to gouerne, vertuous to giue infample, and impartiall to iudge : for as *Cicero* faith, fooner fhall the courfe of nature faile, than the fubiects will leaue to follow the fteps of their Prince. If then that common wealth be happy that is gouerned by fuch a king, in what diftreffe is that Citie that wanteth fuch a magiftrate, and hath one that neither ruleth, teacheth, or doth iuftice, but cenfures all things by the pallet. *Philip* of *Macedonia* béeing defired by an olde woman to heare her complaint, anfwered, hee had no leafure. Then, quoth fhe, be not King: meaning that a Prince ought to haue more care ouer the affaires of the common wealth, then

ouer his owne priuate busines : Then worthie
Citizens, what may that Citie saie, whose gouernour
is addicted to his own pleasure, that delights not
in iustice, but in superfluity, that honors not the
seate of iudgement with Philosophie, but polluteth
the place with dronkenesse, that studieth not in
the lawe, but his library is in the kitchin, that
seeketh not to learne wisedome, but to gorge his
stomack with delicates ? such a one, worthie Citisens haue we, for our Duke, our gouernour, our
magistrate, and as hee vttered that word, his poore
wife and children dragged the Duke vpon the
scaffolde, who was all besmeared in his owne
vomite, & resembling rather a brute beast / then
a man, bred loathsomnes to all the people : which
the poore man taking for his aduantage, cried out:
Sée Burgomasters and Citisens of *Auspourg*, your
duke, your magistrate, your gouernour, who is
come vpon the scaffolde to heare the complaints
of the widow and fatherlesse, and to minister
iudgement. This is the man that condemned
me in the halfe of my goods, by iniustice, and
the other halfe I haue solde to present you this
spectacle : the one halfe hee gaue awaie beeing
dronken, and the other this daie hee hath consumed in gluttony. Now citisens, shame you not
at such a sight ? what shall *Germanie, France, Italy*,
and all the bordering Cities report of our towne ?

What ſtraunger will deſire to traffique where there is ſuch a glutton? What Citie can ioy where there is ſuch a gouernour? If you ſuffer this, the common wealth is like to ruinate, and you and your children like to beare the burthen of a ſuperfluous tyrant: See what *Ruſtico* hath done for his Countrie, now vſe him as you pleaſe. The Burgomaiſters by a generall aſſent, gaue commandement that he ſhould be vncouered vpon the ſcaffold til he came to himſelf, and in the meane time they aſſembled themſelues and determined his exile. The duke after he had taken two or three houres ſléepe, finding himſelfe vpon an open ſcaffolde, was aſhamed. But hearing what had happened to him by the meanes of *Ruſtico,* and how the Burgomaiſters had reſolued on his baniſhment, as one féeling the horrour of the faét, deſperatly went into the poore mans backe ſide and hanged himſelfe. Which newes being brought to the Burgomaiſters, with a generall voice they created *Ruſtico* gouernour of the Citie. /

This ſhort and ſwéete tale of *Bernardino* greatlie pleaſed the Countie and the reſt of the companie, all praiſing the pollicie of the poore man, that had made ſo ſpéedie and ſharpe a reuenge. Well, quoth the olde Counteſſe, wee haue ſo long diſcourſed of gluttonie, that our ſimple cheere hauing ſo good a ſauce as hunger, will proue verie good

delicates, therefore Gentlemen, féeing wee muſt
either make our Cooke cholerike, or elſe leaue our
preſent parle, let vs at this time not diſturbe his
patience, but hie vs in to dinner: and repaſt being
taken, willingly wee will continue our diſcourſe.
Then feignior *Farneze* and the reſt hauing
their ſtomackes armed to ſuch a combat,
willingly obeied, and ſo for this
time we will leaue them.

FINIS.

I. NOTES AND ILLUSTRATIONS.

** *See general explanatory remarks prefixed to Notes and Illustrations in Vol. II., pp. 301-2.*

ALCIDA: GREENES METAMORPHOSIS.

Title-page, l. 11, '*sawsed*' = sauced.

Page   5, l. 2, '*Sir Charles Blount*'—see Index of Names, as before : l. 3, '*indewed*' = endowed, as before — see Glossarial-Index, *s.v.* : l. 7, '*Mirmidones*'—see Index of Names, as before: l. 9, '*Courtelax*' = Fr. *coutelas*, cutlass, a short, broad, crooked, and rather heavy sword. Nares quotes Fairfax's Tasso (ix. 82)—

> "His curtlax by his thigh, short, hooked, fine."

  „   6, l. 13, '*resolution*' = bravery: l. 15, '*patronage*'—note verbal use : l. 17, '*intended*' = stretched to, dedicated to: l. 25, '*rest*' = stake, card term. So p. 9, l. 8: l. 26, '*momentany*' = momentary — the words are frequently interchanged.

  „   7, l. 2, '*boord Iest*' = Table jesting.

  „   8, l. 4, '*supposes*' = a game so called : l. 6,

'*indifferent*' = impartial: l. 11, '*broad*' = outspokenly: l. 12, '*fondly*' = foolishly: l. 15, '*little secrecie*' = woman's tendency to blab what ought to be kept secret: l. 18, '*Algorisme*' = Arith. Alguarismo or Guarismo in the science of Arithmeticke (Florio's Sp. Dict.)

Page 9, l. 22, '*plies*' = bend or turn (Fr. *plier*): l. 18, '*R.A.*'—see Index of Names, as before.

  „ 10, l. 16, '*Ed. Percy*'—*ibid.*

  „ 11, l. 7, '*cooling card*'—see Glossarial-Index, *s.v.*, for prior examples: l. 14, '*Vertue[s]*'—cf. l. 12, and 'their' in the line itself: l. 18, '*ouer-read*' = read over attentively: last l., '*Bubb Gent*'—see Index of Names, as before.

  „ 12, last l., '*G. B.*'—*ibid.*

  „ 13, l. 8, '*Florint*'—*sic*, by misprint doubtless.

  „ 15, l. 6, '*speedy cut*'—short cut is our phrase: l. 10, '*Constellation*' = planet (in Astrology): l. 13, '*Taprobane*' = Sumatra.

  „ 16, l. 8, '*hull*' = drive before—not used in its then and now nautical sense: l. 15, '*Canapus*' = Canopus: last l., '*Champion*' = plain country, champagne.

  „ 17, l. 9, '*continent*' = interior?

  „ 18, l. 17, '*three legs*' = two, and a staff.

  „ 19, l. 6, '*Midaes*'—qy. an error for Admetus: l. 10, '*Oast*' = host. So 'Oastesse' p. 20, l. 26, and p. 21, l. 11: l. 24, '*proportion*' = the measure—we should say 'proportions.'

Page 20, last l., ' *salues* ' = salutations (Latin *salve*).

„ 21, l. 4, '*dumpes*' = melancholy, *ut freq.* : l. 22, ' *heralts* ' = heralds.

„ 22, l. 7 , '*catastrophe*' = finish : l. 11, ' *obliuie* ' = oblivion : l. 24, ' *leueld* ' = plotted out, delineated, mapped out.

„ 23, l. 13, '*courted it*' = vaunted it in court : l. 16, '*foregarded*' = guarded beforehand : l. 23, ' *reuies* ' = stakings and re-stakings against the adversary — a card figure or metaphor.

„ 24, l. 9, '*a table*' = a picture, *ut freq.* : l. 24, ' *Gigglets* ' = giddy, wantonly disposed girl. Cotgrave says, *s.v.* Gadrouillette, 'A minx gigle[t], callet, Gixie, (a feigned word applicable to any such cattle) : l. 25, ' *brau'd* ' = adorned : *ibid.*, ' *Creeple* ' = the famous blacksmith god Vulcan : *ib.*, ' *horne*,' = usual symbol of cuckoldry : but why ?

„ 25, l. 22, '*poesies*' = verses rather than (brief) posies.

„ 26, l. 19, ' *Fiordespine* '—Editor can't find out what flower this Italian word represents. The two ' e's ' don't seem Italian. Possibly it may have been meant for *Fior di spina*, the blossom of the thorn (qy. the hawthorn blossom; though the hawthorn has a different name).

, 27, l. 1, '*glorious*'—contemporaneously adjectives were not unfrequently used where we should use adverbs : l. 17, ' *curious* ' = artful ? l. 25, ' *barran* '—see separate lists, as before.

Page 28, l. 3, '*fond*' = foolish, *ut freq.*: l. 8, '*Margarites*' = pearls, *ut freq.*

„ 29, l. 14, '*betweene*'—misprinted 'lewtene' in the original : l. 19, '*freshwater soldier*'—an epithet then used, and not difficult to understand of an island now at peace within itself, and not invaded.

„ 32, l. 13, '*Thesides*'—some error here, *ut freq.*, in proper names and others : l. 14, misprinted—'bring on lewd lookes' in the original : l. 17, 'hee was'—read '[s]hee was.'

„ 33, l. 6, '*blind Osyphrage*' = the bone breaker, *i.e.* the osprey or sea-eagle, then said to be short-sighted by comparison with the true eagle, and by some to be a mongrel, and a kind of vulture. See Holland's Pliny x. 3, and xxx. 7 : l. 11, '*lure*' = used in hawking, etc. : l. 16, '*tablet*' = picture : l. 19, '*Sapho a Queene*'—how this error arose Editor knoweth not, nor of any classical origin for it : l. 25, '*randon*' = random—note spelling : l. 26, '*feareth*' = causal verb, not unfrequently, *i.e.* caused (a prince) to fear.

„ 34, l. 3, '*heat*' = heated—verb ending in *t*, as before : l. 4, '*Zathe*'—see separate lists of names, etc., as before.

„ 36, l. 1, '*since*'—seems superfluous here : l. 3, '*boote compare*' = compare with advantage (cf. Sherwood, *s.v.*)

„ 37, l. 9, '*salue*' = salutation, as before : l. 11,

' *Though* '—superfluous, as ' since ' before
(p. 36, l. 1).

Page 39, l. 2, ' *no* '—misprinted ' not ' in the original:
but it may have been = knew not [of any]
other, etc. : l. 8, ' *iumpe* ' = agree : l. 19,
' *from* '—misprinted ' for ' in the original,
albeit it may have been meant as a co-
relative of the ' for hunting ' of the previous
clause (l. 16). ' For ' was then used in the
sense of ' against.' Cf. Holland's Pliny
i. 195E, " to cut his throat, so making him
sure *for* telling tales " : also Abbot's Shak.
Grammar, §§ 147 and 154.

„ 40, l. 19, ' *frowning* '—cf. p. 44, last l.—in the
original misprinted ' fermning,' which is
nonsense.

„ 42, l. 11, ' *before*,' *i.e.* before [that], etc., heart
[else they would die] : l. 24, ' *supersedeas* '
= Law term—a writ commanding one to
forbear from doing that which in appear-
ance of law ought to be done. Here =
the supersedence or superseding.

„ 43, ll. 7-9—probably repetitions by misprint
here.

„ 44, l. 9, ' *conquered* '—*sic* — qy. misprint for
' conqueror ' ?

„ 45, l. 9, ' *discontent* ' = ed—verb ending in t, *ut
freq.* : l. 16, ' *standish* ' = dish for holding
pens, sand, etc., as well as ink, *ut freq.* :
l. 19, ' *polt foote* ' = club foot, *ut freq.*

„ 46, l. 11, ' *in red letters* ' = a synonym for ' by
a rubric ' : l. 19, ' *I think : suppose* '—read,

IX.   23

as it would be now printed, ' I think ——— : suppose.'

Page 47, l. 20, '*fondling*' = foolish one.

      48, l. 5, '*lewd*'—here used in our sense of ' poor,' it being then ordinarily used = base or vile.

  „ 49, l. 6, '*carefull*' = full-of-care : l. 12, '*rebut*' = repulse : l. 21, '*tried*' = as a cause, and judged : l. 28, '*frownes*'—qy. misprint for ' frowes ' of Bacchus, *i.e.* the half-mad or delirious Bacchantes.

  „ 50, l. 20, '*decipherst*' = expoundest.

  „ 53, l. 5, '*quit*' = quite.

  „ 55, l. 5, '*interseamed*' — properly 'interlined,' but more loosely, as here, = interspersed : or qy. = intersown ? l. 9, '*as*'—example of its use where we should use ' that ' : l. 24, '*aspect*'—used astrologically as = intent.

  „ 56, l. 6, '*steeme*' = esteem : l. 16, '*wrest*' = an old instrument for tuning, its name explaining its mode of action : l. 21, '*flittering*' = fluttering.

  „ 57, l. 1, '*euer*'—misprinted ' euery ' in the original : last l., '*Minion*' (Fr. *mignon*)— was used, like its original, in a good sense —here = dainty one, etc.

  „ 58, l. 18, '*feat=ly*' = feat-like, whence it sometimes means the same as 'neatly,' but here is rather equivalent to dexterously, successfully, artfully.

  „ 61, l. 2, '*Adamant*' = loadstone, *ut freq.* : l. 20, '*feature*' = person *ut freq.*

Page 62, l. 26, '*crimes*' — misprint doubtless for 'reines' or some such word : l. 27, '*curiositie*' = over carefulness—good example.

„ 64, l. 11, '*Niese*' = eyas, a young (nestling) hawk, *ut freq.* : l. 13, '*bate*' = flutter.

„ 65, l. 2, '*tainteth*' = tenteth—a surgical term, a 'tent' being a linen roll which is used to enlarge or search or stop a wound— generally = probeth : l. 24, '*tries*' = proves. So, *e.g.*, pp. 67, l. 12, 74, l. 3, 77, l. 2 : l. 25, '*solemne saint*' = a saint in outward solemnity.

„ 66, l. 13, '*grow*'—misprinted 'grew' in the original.

„ 67, l. 13, '*indifferent*' = impartial, unprejudiced, or free.

„ 68, l. 5—remove comma (,) after ' feare ' and place after 'amazed' : l. 6, '*doubted*' = feared—excellent example : l. 20, '*muses*' = musings. Cf. p. 69, l. 9: l. 22, '*ensueth*' = followeth.

„ 69, l. 15, '*frumpe*' = quip or jest, *ut freq.* : l. 17, '*property*' = qualities.

„ 70, l. 1, '*inferred*' = brought in: l. 19, '*Enthymema*' — a logical form — an argument where one of the (two) premises of the syllogism is understood, *i.e.* not stated : l. 20, '*affecting*' = loving : l. 21, '*Paramour*' = lover (in good sense).

„ 71, l. 5, ' *Penses* ' = pansies. So Shakespeare : " pansies that's for thoughts " (Hamlet iv. 5). Pascall's ' Pensees ' has made the

word immortal : l. 9, '*agnomination*' = an
added name or nickname.

Page 72, l. 3, '*Heart's ease.*' Cf. Henry V., IV. i. 254:
and Romeo and J., IV. v. 104.

„   73, l. 3, '*reddest Margarites*'—more applicable
to the opal.

„   74, l. 18, '*misling*' = small-dropping — our
'mizzling.'

„   75, l. 13, '*Sethin*' = shittim-wood, as before.

„   76, l. 5, '*fetch*' = trick or snare.

„   78, l. 11, '*Justes and Turneyes*' = jousts and
tournaments : l. 17, '*to grace . . . daughters*'—a noteworthy example of a singular
verb after a plural nominative placed after
it.   This is caused by the real objective
'companie' immediately preceding, though
it is to be remarked that the preceding
objectives are two and therefore would
seem to suggest a plural verb.

„   84, l. 17, '*string*' = one band, etc. [supporting
it] : last l., '*the North-west Ilands*'—see
separate lists, as before.

„   85, l. 3, '*Polipe stones*'—what ? see *ibid.*: l. 4,
'*Adamants*' = diamonds : ll. 25-6, punc-
tuate (by transposition) 'reioyced, ...
maine ' : l. 26, '*scowred*' — now vulgar
cant word = left them.

„   87, l. 13, '*imprest*' = impresa or motto : l. 18,
'*impalls*' = impales—used heraldically, as
surrounding within one border or circum-
ference.   So when a husband and wife's
coats of arms are put side by side within

one coat of arms, they are said to be impaled.

Page 90, l. 11, '*nusled*' = nurtured.

" 91, l. 20—read '*heart*' [had].

" 92, l. 22, '*settle*'—qy. fettle ?

" 93, l. 6, '*while*' = during.

" 94, l. 23, '*cooling card*'—see Glossarial-Index, *s.v.*, for prior examples : l. 26, '*fondling*' = foolish one : l. 27, '*comfortures*' = comforts.

" 95, l. 10, '*loues*'—qy. error for 'loue' through '*s*' of thought*s*?

" 96, l. 21, '*matches*' = mates.

" 97, l. 13, '*Aphorismes*'=maxims : l. 26, '*wring Troylus by the hand*' = fervent hand-shaking.

" 98, l. 4, '*blacke*' = smoke ? : l. 5, '*nothing lesse*' —a common phrase at that time = nothing so little as that, not that at all. Cf. Richard II., II. ii. 34.

" 99, l. 12, '*lated*' = belated : l. 22, '*drad*' = dreaded : l. 24, '*start*'—read 'start ;'.

" 100, l. 23, '*ambages*' = circumlocutions.

" 101, l. 21—'*smell*' ends his speech: l. 23, '*infer*' = bring in.

" 102, l. 2, '*solaced*' = was solacing himself or herself : l. 9, '*amordelayes*' = love lays.

" 103, l. 18, '*maine*' = the number sought for by the throw or throws at dice.

" 104, l. 3, '*wheare the*'—misprinted in the original ' wheat, the '—qy. whereat : l. 16, '*Deire*' = deer.

" 105, l. 11, '*tolde*' = said . . . [that] : *ibid.*, '*flat*' —see Glossarial-Index, *s.v.*, for prior examples, *freq.* : l. 17, ' *nipped* ' = reproved, *ut freq.*

Page 108, l. 7, ' *tried* ' = proved : l. 22, ' *while* ' = until —excellent example.

„ 109, l. 2—perhaps the supplied 'the' is useless —the phraseology of the day answered to ours in saying ' into position.'

„ 111, l. 11, ' *serues they* '—read as though 'serves [that] they.'

„ 112, l. 18, ' *cockbotes* '=small boats. See Glossarial-Index, *s.v.*, for prior examples.

MOURNING GARMENT.

Page 119, *George Clifford, Earle of Cumberland*—see Index of Names, as before : l. 6, ' *ouerweaned* '=over-ween, but in causal sense, *i.e.* made the Niniuites to overween (themselves). Cf. l. 16 and p. 124, l. 1 : l. 8, ' *surcoats* ' = outer or upper coat : *ibid.*, ' *bisse* '—see Glossarial-Index, *s.v.*, for prior examples.

„ 120, l. 1, ' *affectes* ' = affections. So p. 122, l. 11, *et freq.*

„ 121, l. 4, ' *coniectures* ' = throwing together, conclusions : l. 12, ' *fond* ' = foolish—he means [only] half, etc. : l. 14, ' *weede* ' = garment. In supplement to a former note (see Glossarial-Index, *s.v.*) add Hamlet iv. 7, " his sables and his *weeds*," neither implying mourning, besides " maiden weeds " and " woman's weeds " in Twelfth Night v. 1,

and other places in Shakespeare : l. 24,
'*condigne*' = merited, fitting.

Page 122, l. 8, '*dispute of*' = to maintain the thesis of.

„ 123, l. 1, '*Eris*'—qy. Ens : l. 24, '*Hermia*' =
Hermias, a male friend : l. 26, '*moale*' =
(here) a sort of knot or formless swelling
in the thread, such as is easily noticed in
fine cloth, and corresponding with the
Latin *mola*. Usually it is = a rusty stain
or mould : *ibid.*, '*orient*'—here used in
sense of Eastern, for Eastern pearls were
considered the better. This use of Greene
is found in the translation of Levinus
Lamnius's Herball to the Bible. Cochineal
is spoken of as a ' most . . . orient red '
and as ' a most orient colour.'

„ 124, l. 13, Avicen or Avicenna is alleged to have
died of intemperance.

„ 125, l. 9, '*communis*'—read 'commune': l. 25,
'*censures*' = judgments.

„ 127, l. 8, '*sometimes*' = some time.

„ 128, l. 2, '*leueld*' = laid out, plotted out, *ut freq.*:
l. 4, '*Callipolis*'—none of the cities so
called were or are so placed: l. 5, '*tramelles*'
= nets, *i.e.* locks of hair : l. 8, ' *talents* ' =
talons.

„ 131, l. 5, '*pleasant*'—misprinted ' present ' in
original : l. 7, '*Adamant*' = diamond, *ut
freq.* : l. 8, ' *Syern*'—misprint by transposition for ' Syren ' : l. 15, ' *Salerne*'—a
noted medical school. The *Regimen Sani-
tatis Salerni* was a book of great note and

popularity in its day : l. 18, ' *Coleworts* ' = cabbages.

Page 132, l. 9, ' *rauening* ' = preying on his own (*i.e.* his father's) estate, prodigal : l. 11, ' *bated* ' —to ' bate ' as a hawking term was not only to ' flutter ' but to ' fly off and at something.' Here it seems the latter, from the after expression ' checkt to the fist ' : l. 14, ' *meacock* ' = an effeminate dastardly fellow : l. 24, ' *couet* '—read ' couet[s] ' : last l., ' *cut* ' = go (vulgarly).

„   133, l. 5, ' *Micher* ' = truant, though staying at home. A derivative sense was a ' sneak,' also a ' niggard ' (see Cotgrave, *s.v.* Chiche), which seems its meaning here.

„   135, l. 18, ' *preiudice* ' = ill, as elsewhere.

„   136, l. 1, ' *decipher* ' = expound : l. 11, ' *yerksome* ' = irksome : l. 14, ' *braue* ' = bravado.

„   139, l. 1, ' *Aconitum* '—used for ' poison ' in general : l. 5, ' *like the Curlew* ' — see Glossarial-Index, *s.v.* : last l., ' *witty* ' = wise.

„   140, l. 14, ' *discurations* ' = discurrations, discursive discourses : l. 16, the odd ω and context = his great O's, or as we should say in his notes of admiration, his exclamations in various tones of O and Oh.

„   141, l. 8, ' *trauailed* ' = travelled.

„   142, l. 13, ' *Huswife* ' = [to be or as a] Huswife : l. 19, ' *side* ' = long : *ibid.*, ' *plighted* ' = pleated : l. 21, ' *whittle* ' = knife — still an American word : *ibid.*, ' *chape* ' = metal band at top of scabbard or knife covering :

l. 27, '*whigge*' = preparation of fermented whey.

Page 143, l. 6, '*parell*' = apparell : l. 7, '*doone*' = do : l. 12, '*alderleefest*' = dearest of all, *i.e.* lief = dear, liefer = dearer, liefest = dearest, alder = of all : l. 14—probably should be line[s] as dissyllable : l. 17, '*Buxsame*' = buxom: l. 21, '*the*'—misprinted 'thee' in original : last l., '*gawdy*' = joyous. But it was also used as now for fine or well decorated.

„ 144, l. 3, '*bent*' = a coarse grass. Parkinson gives an engraving of it and calls it 'Bent, or Corn Reed grass, or of some Windle-strawes,' 1640 : l. 4, '*gent*' = neat, pretty.

„ 145, l. 6, '*swink*' = to labour, but really = to swill or drink fully (metaph.) : l. 23, '*gramercies*' = great or grateful thanks (Fr. *grand merci*).

„ 146, l. 1, '*antipechargein*' — *i.e.* a compound, αυτι πηγαργειν (from ἀντίπηξ, an osier basket or cradle, and ἀργέω, I am inactive), to lie inactive in a cradle, or basket : l. 15, '*takes him*' — 'him' is the Damme, or more probably the young one; in the latter case it is an instance of idiomatic use overcoming grammar, for either of the 'hims' is by the foretext a 'she' : l. 26, '*non*'—a variant of a familiar line.

„ 147, l. 3, '*fact*' = heinous fact, *ut freq.* : l. 8, '*discouered*' = shown.

„ 148, l. 25, '*feature*'—the singular number here,

et freq., shows that the word was used in its primary sense of ' (her) making.'

Page 149, l. 13, ' *bewrayed* ' = betrayed, *ut freq.* : l. 16, ' *at gaze* '—said of deer, who when first roused stand and look at the unexpected or terrifying sight : l. 18, ' *tramels* '—another instance bearing out that it was used—as before explained—as netlike knots or locks of hair: l. 24, ' *vncouth* ' = strange : last l., ' *bauine* '—see Glossarial-Index, *s.v., freq.*

„ 150, l. 3, ' *curiously* ' = carefully : l. 4, ' *period* ' = made a full stop at. This is (*meo judicio*) an example of a figurative mode of speech, exemplified elsewhere and in Hamlet's—

" And stand a comma 'twixt their amities."

„ 151, l. 18, ' *liefe* ' = dear : l. 14, ' *by* '—we should write ' on,' but it may be presumed Greene uses it in the sense of ' through the influence of.' See Abbot's Shakesp. Gr. p. 99 : l. 24, ' *Aarches* ' = eyebrows or lashes.

„ 152, l. 2, ' *taint* ' = stain, or as we might say superficial covering. We have a similar thought in ' glaunces . . . glazed with a blush,' at p. 150, l. 22. In l. 27 also ' *stain*,' *i.e.* that which stains or renders the beauty of Alexis a thing of no account : l. 23, ' *disgrac'd* '—remove the comma.

„ 153, l. 14, ' *deciphered* ' = unfolded, *ut freq.* :

l. 21, '*partial*' = imperfect, telling only in part.

Page 154, l. 22, '*conuents*' = coming together, assemblies.

  „ 155, l. 5, ' *scaffold* ' = scaffolding : l. 16, '*phere*' = mate : l. 19, ' *bias* ' — adaptation of a bowling term : l. 20, ' *lemman* ' = one lovep or beloved, without (here) any injurious signification, the king having offered marriage.

  „ 156, l. 17, '*censure*' = decision or doom.

  „ 157, l. 8, ' *hang-by* ' = dependant, or perhaps here a thing hung up out of use, neglected : l. 9, '*momentany*' = Latin *momentanum*. See Glossarial-Index, *s.v.* : l. 19, '*Alexis*'—he being 'afar off on a hill ' must have had acute ears : l. 22, ' *dapperest* '— then, as shown by Cotgrave and Minsheu, it meant as now 'neatest ' and most spruce, or smartest. According to them also 'dapper' meant ' pretty and dainty ' : l. 23, ' *brooke* ' = bear, submit to. So p. 156, l. 28, *et freq.*

  „ 158, l. 7, '*frumpe*' = lie—sometimes ' taunt ' : l. 12, '*shee*'—probably an error for ' soe,' etc. Up to that moment Alexis could not be called ' *her* Alexis ' — the next sentence by its more emphatic repetition confirms this: l. 24, '*passionate*' = sorrowful, as not unfrequently, and as shown by ' sorrowes.'

  „ 160, l. 7, ' *clip* ' = embrace.

  „ 161, l. 9, '*liefe*' = dear, *ut freq.* : l. 13, '*giglot*'

= a merry, wanton lass, *ut freq.* But cf. Nares and Halliwell-Phillipps, as earlier Minsheu and Holyoke's Rider and Kersey. It had lighter and darker meanings.

Page 162, l. 25, ' *his wrongs* ' = the wrongs done by him : last l., '*willow*'—used as appropriate in like manner as Shakespeare conjoins a willow with Ophelia's death.

„ 163, l. 14, ' *Sagunta* '—unknown—there was a Saguntum in Spain.

„ 164, l. 1, ' *shee* '—he was thinking of Circe. See p. 163, l. 26.

„ 165, l. 4, ' *rest* '—not the gaming metaphor here : l. 6, ' *braue* ' = more finely attired : l. 22, ' *could* ' = could do as—therefore ' shew ' perhaps not needed.

„ 166, l. 14, ' *equipage* ' = habiliments, dress.

„ 168, l. 15, ' *circumquaque* ' = circumlocutions ; but where did Greene get it ?

„ 169, l. 14, ' *Porphuer* '—doubtless our porphyry (*porphyrites* in Latin ; *porphyre* Fr.): l. 25, ' *Cator* ' = caterer : l. 26, ' *affects* ' = affections, *ut freq.*

„ 170, l. 4, '*feature*'—see Glossarial-Index *s.v.*, *freq.* : l. 13, ' *most deepest* '—double superlative, *ut freq.*

„ 171, l. 3, ' *Metaphusicall* ' = beyond nature, as in Macbeth I. v. 28. See Glossarial-Index, *s.v.* : l. 8, ' *canker.*' See Glossarial-Index, *s.v.*, *freq.* : l. 11, ' *Layes* ' = Lais : l. 19, ' *vaded* '—see Glossarial-Index, *s.v.*, for distinction between ' fade ' and ' vade.'

Page 172, l. 13, '*Synamond*' = cinnamon.

" 173, l. 15, '*meacocke*' : l. 16, '*milksop*'—see Glossarial-Index *s.v., freq.*

" 174, l. 1, '*ietting*' = strutting, showing off : l. 20, '*iumpt*' = agreed, *ut freq.* : l. 23, '*Aconiton*' = poison in general, *ut freq.*

" 175, l. 4, '*Chrisocoll*'—see Glossarial-Index, *s.v.*, for prior examples : *ib.*, '*Aurifolium*'— unknown plant-name.

" 176, l. 24, '*copesmates*' = associates, as before.

" 177, l. 6, '*cassier*' = cashier : l. 19, '*Master*'— oddly misprinted 'Mistris' in the original —perchance 'M' only in the Author's MS.

" 178, l. 12, '*Pomice-stone*' = pumice-stone : l. 26, '*Caldes*' = Chaldees or Chaldeans.

" 179, l. 12, '*Calipses*' = Calipsos : l. 17, '*apply*' —as *freq.*, our 'to' not used.

" 180, l. 20, '*only*'—we transpose and say 'his only care.'

" 181, l. 2, '*angelles*' = coins so called.

" 182, l. 7, '*Bayard*' = steed, *ut freq.*

" 183, l. 10, '*patch*' = a fool : l. 18, '*fetches*' = stratagems : l. 22, '*Gripes*' = vultures.

" 185, l. 9, '*laie*' = lying-place : l. 13, '*Haggard*,' see Glossarial-Index, *freq.* : l. 21, '*quick*' = living.

" 186, l. 14, '*trencher-flyes*'—a figure from fly-fishing, caught by food.

" 187, l. 20, '*swine*'—here and elsewhere he follows the Lord's Parable.

" 188, l. 21, '*demisheth*' = diminisheth or famisheth.

Page 189, l. 2, '*Lombard*' = the banker and pawn-broker, etc., of the day : l. 20, '*Baaron*'—see separate lists, as before.

„   190, l. 3, '*Oliphant*' = elephant—this, the Scotch pronunciation of 'elephant' at the date, gave point to a contemporary epigram on one of the Jameses *liasons* with one 'fair frail lady' named Oliphant: l. 18, '*Liquonico*' —see separate lists, as before.

„   193, l. 20, '*bewray*' = betray or reveal, *ut freq.* : last l., '*induction*' = beginning, or our in-*tro*duction.

„   194, l. 17, '*fond*' = foolish, *ut freq.*

„   196, l. 3, '*Christolite*'—note spelling—perhaps a compositor's error from the likeness to Christ or to Christal. Cf. p. 195, l. 9 : l. 4, '*orient*'—another instance where it seems used in the conventional sense of 'bright': l. 9, '*giglot*'—as before; see Glossarial-Index, *s.v.* : l. 26, '*necessary euill*'—here he uses the saying of the philosopher whom he before quoted as describing women as *mala necessaria.*

„   197, l. 15, '*Pathetical*' = that can move the feelings (not as now merely the feeling of pity).

„   198, l. 20, '*preiudice*' = ill, as before.

„   199, l. 15, '*Hidaspis*'—several times in Greene we have had 'Hidaspis' as a serpent—not so elsewhere, though it must be some-where contemporaneously. Probably some one has spoken of Hydaspis (a river of

Parthia and India) as a serpent—much as the 'Links of the Forth' at Stirling has been—and so brought about the error. It is odd, and yet congruous with this, that each notice in Greene (as here) can be adapted to a river, as for instance that its thirst is insatiable and can swallow up anything.

Page 200, l. 8, ' *abiect* ' = cast down : l. 17, '*maimed*' = tamed.

„ 201, l. 17, '*gree*'—misprinted 'greee' in the original.

„ 2 02, l. 1, ' *Her* '—misprinted ' His ' in the original.

„ 203, l. 16, '*loue*'—misprinted 'liue' in original; but qy. is the 'nay' of l. 17 only as spoken understood ? and does l. 18 refer to l. 15 ? If so 'liue' must be meant.

„ 204, l. 5, '*deawes*' = dews—misprinted 'drawne,' unless 'drawne' be held = by (voluntary) effort, not falling naturally.

„ 205, l. 24, '*pretended*' = brought forward.

„ 206, l. 8, ' *remorse* ' = pity, *ut freq.* : l. 10, '*bate*' = flutter or fly off (Fr. *battre*), *ut freq.* : l. 16, ' *slipperness* ' = slipperiness — Sir Thomas More uses the former form, Donne the latter.

„ 207, l. 14, '*Adamants*' = diamonds, *ut freq.* : l. 19, ' *metaphysicall* ' = beyond nature, as in l. 25, 'supernatural.'

„ 208, l. 26, ' *Cyancynatus* ' — read Cyncynatus = Cincinnatus.

Page 209, l. 6, '*trencher flyes*' = parasites, *ut freq.* :
l. 19, '*hang-byes*'—see on p. 157, l. 8 :
l. 27, '*remorse*'—see on p. 206, l. 8—
excellent examples.

„ 210, l. 15, '*instances*' = examples. Cf. " wise
saws and modern *instances* ": l. 18, '*and
my*'—probably either '[had] my ' or ' and
[had] my.'

„ 211, ll. 12, 25, '*discontent*' = ed—ending in 't,'
as usual : l. 17, '*think nothing*' = think
nothing [ill] ; but qy. did Greene write
' nothing [of it] if,' etc. : l. 24, '*fond*' =
foolish, *ut freq.*

„ 212, l. 1, '*iet*' = to carry one's body in a stately
manner ('incedere magnificè,' Baret): *ibid.*,
'*surcoates*'—see on p. 119, l. 7 : l. 23,
'*careful*' = full of care.

„ 214, l. 8, '*thus*'—throughout in the original :
after 'thus ': l. 9, '*linne*' = cease.

„ 215, l. 21, '*Nor Shepheards weeds*,'—evidently
a verb lacking—qy. 'Nor [wear the] shepheards,' etc. We have such an Alexandrine
in l. 5, and so elsewhere.

„ 216, l. 12, '*affects*' = affections, *ut freq.*: l. 19,
'*she*'—misprinted ' we ' in the original,
and as elsewhere, corrected by Dyce.

„ 217, l. 3, '*is fickle*'—error for '*as* fickle ': l. 12,
'*snares*' —— misprinted ' thares ': l. 15,
'*With*'—misprinted 'Which' in the original : but if we change 'same,' l. 14, to
'sawe'. or even';' 'which' might stand :
l. 19, '*molest* '—used as substantive, having

a less active signification than molestation.

Page 218, l. 7, '*A doe*' = Ado — such A's being frequently separated contemporaneously : l. 9, '*And,*' superfluous to sense and measure ; but Greene may, as did Shakespeare similarly, have made 'And therefore' his first foot : l. 13, '*passion*' = grief as passionate, frequently contemporaneously. Cf. 'sigh,' l. 11 : l. 22, '*dumpes*' = sorrows.

„ 219, l. 3, '*wild*' = willed.

„ 220, l. 11, '*with him,*' *i.e.* with Diogenes, not with the man.

„ 221, l. 17, '*frumps*' = mocks, flouts, taunts : l. 20, '*Bayard*' = horse, *ut freq.*: l. 22, '*Hipanchian*'—no such name. Possibly Greene meant to write Hipparchus (the Athenian comic poet), or Hipparchus the author of an Egyptian Iliad; and some slight evidence in favour of the latter is afforded by the mention of Ennius immediately after.

„ 225, l. 4, '*president*' = precedent. When did the distinction between 'president' and precedent' come in ?

„ 227, l. 3, '*Robert Carey, Esq.*'—see Index of Names, as before : l. 15, '*ouerslipt*' = slipt over, or allowed themselves to slip over " my follies " without notice.

„ 228, l. 7, '*vaine*' = vein : l. 10, '*Cooling Card*' —see Glossarial-Index, *s.v.*, for prior ex-

amples : l. 20, ' *Martinize* '—the reference
is to the Martin Mar-Prelate books, to
which Greene several times alludes : *ibid.*,
' *faie* ' = faith (Fr. Sp. Port.) : l. 21, '*gogs
wounds* ' = Gods wounds—an attempted
inoffensive oath : l. 25, ' *iumpe* ' = agree.

Page 229, l. 15, ' *rest* ' = card term at primero, *i.e.*
setting my stake, or the amount one stakes
on the cards in hand, on which one rests.

  „ 230, l. 4, ' *alate* ' = lately : l. 9, ' *Tomliuclin* ' =
corruption of Tom o' Lincoln ? : l. 13,
read ' if [a] good man ' : l. 22, ' *houre-
glasse* '—a hit at the Martinists and Puri-
tans.

  „ 231, l. 6, ' *quaint* '—see Glossarial-Index, *s.v.*,
for examples : l. 14, ' *louemates* ' = associates :
l. 21, ' *stale . . . check* '—a sort of equivoque
on the chess terms stale-mate and checkmate : l. 23, ' *marched in the Mercers
books* ' = gone into debt for dress.

  „ 232, l. 14, ' *were* '—qy. misprint for ' went ' ?
l. 19, ' *ouer-read* ' = read over sarcastically
and skimmingly : l. 20, ' *frumpe* ' = taunt,
etc., *ut freq.* : l. 23, ' *fazion* ' *alias* fashion,
corrupted forms of farcins, farcy. This is
shown by the words 'scabd Iades.' Shakespeare has ' fashions ' in same sense (T. of
Sh. iii. 2).

  „ 233, l. 11, ' *runnes over him* ' = crushes him.

  „ 235, l. 11, ' *denounced* ' = our ' announced.' So
also p. 256, l. 25.

  „ 236, l. 7, ' *countermanded* ' = checked : l. 9,

'*Ieronimo Farnese*'—Farnese is also intro-
duced into ' Mamillia.'

Page 237, l. 6, '*indifferent*' = impartial : l. 8, '*Bernardine*'—mistake for Bernardino : l. 14,
'*Countie*' = count—so spelt throughout
the book : l. 15, '*Grange*' = farm place.
Cf. ' Countrie cottage ' below : l. 22, '*centurie*'—another form of error for ' centry '
or ' sentry ' = a watch-tower or other small
place. Cf. Cotgrave, *s.v.* Guerite : last l.,
'*base Court*'—a lower court, said by some
to be in front, but more generally behind
the building, etc. Cf. Cotgrave, *s.v.* Basse-
cour.

„ 238, l. 3, '*censure*' = judgment, *ut freq.*

„ 239, l. 8, '*sit a while*'—According to the old
couplet—

> " After dinner sit awhile,
> After supper walk a mile."

„ 240, l. 1, '*Antipelargein*'—see Glossarial-Index,
s.v., for note : l. 3, '*counterfeit*' = picture,
as frequently : l. 11, '*ants egg* . . . . *Sciatica*,'
i.e. no good at all : l. 23, '*reuoked*' = called
back.

„ 241, l. 12, '*therefore to be*'—to be read as
though it were ' [are] or [you are] to be.' So
l. 26, ' holy [as] to die ' : l. 15, '*preuent*' =
= go before, as often : l. 19, '*Zodiaock*'—
note spelling of ' Zodiac.' See Index of
Names, *s.n.* Phaeton : l. 23, '*Saturnists*'
= sullen and morose ones.

„ 242, l. 26, '*youth his folly*'—an early example

of the supposed origin of the apostrophe, 'youth's.'

Page 243, l. 22, '*pontificalibus*' = one may judge by your habits what other things you profess.

„   244, l. 8, '*iumpt*' = agreed with: l. 18, '*fondnesse*' = folly, as 'fondlings,' p. 242, l. 17, is 'foolish ones' : l. 27, '*Chronography*' = History in Chronicles.

„   246, l. 1, '*Anthropomasia*'—probably a misprint for 'Anthropomastis' or -mastix : l. 3, '*alluding the reason*' = applying. So p. 268, l. 14 : l. 17, '*Nemroth*' = Nimrod.

„   247, l. 21, '*his my prescription*'—qy. his = its (*i.e.* fame's) and 'prescription' = writing (or name written) before them, etc. ?

„   248, l. 9, '*appech*' = appeach, accuse : l. 24, '*pirking*' = perking : l. 25, '*for*' (1st) = on account of : l. 26, '*shadowes*' = pictures.

„   249, l. 8, '*braue*' = bravado : l. 9, '*Thrasonically*' = boastfully : l. 22, '*appeached*'—see on p. 248, l. 9 : l. 24, '*induce*' = bring in or introduce.

„   250, l. 5, '*side gowne*' = long gown : last l., '*neate*' = nice.

„   251, l. 1, '*cursier*' = courser—see l. 3.

„   252, l. 4, '*masse*' = master. So p. 253, l. 26 : l. 6, '*eode*' = eodē : l. 20, '*vntrust*' = strings of clothes (then used instead of buttons) unfastened.

„   254, l. 16, '*euer*' = always : l. 22, '*Calco*,' etc. —on this and other 'slips' of Greene, see annotated Life in Vol. I.

Page 255, l. 25, '*lineaments*'—a good example of its
  more general meaning than that in which
  it is now used.

" 257, l. 4, '*ouerweene*' = think too highly.

" 258, l. 13, '*featured*' = well made up in body.

" 259, l. 16, '*water boughes*' = low set or near
  to the water : l. 17, '*Margarite*' = pearl :
  l. 26, '*misse*' = amisse, ill, or misfortune.

" 260, l. 22, '*impalied*' = impaled with fame as
  with a crown : l. 26, '*Antonius*' = An-
  toni[n]us.

" 261, l. 24, '*in*' = in [the penalties of] a penal
  statute.

" 262, l. 5, '*for*' = instead of giving her coyne
  . . . . he left her advice, etc. : l. 15, '*complexion*' = temperament, *ut freq.*

" 263, l. 13, '*mate*' = checkmate—the winning
  close of a game at chess.

" 264, l. 7, '*resolve*' = dissolve : l. 16, '*fynde*' =
  fiend.

" 265, l. 14, '*Morice*' = morris—a lively dance
  derived, as its other name Morisco more
  clearly implies, from the Moors—danced
  in England on May-day and other festi-
  vities : l. 17, '*strawne*' = strawen, adj. of
  straw = made of straw : l. 24, '*for*' =
  against : l. 27, '*pompes*' = pumps, slighter-
  soled shoes for dancing, as still in use :
  ibid., '*start-ups*'—Nares describes them as
  "a kind of rustic shoes with high tops, or
  half-gaiters." Cf. Halliwell-Phillips, *s.v.*,
  extract from Thynne. The meaning is

that what were being used for 'dancing,'
and so named ' pompes,' were so heavy as
rather to resemble ' start-ups.'

Page 266, l. 26, *despight'* = framed in despight of, or,
to spite or dull all other created beauty.

  „   267, l. 10, '*in pudding time* ' = in season.   See
Nares, *s.v.*, and Withel's Dict., 1608, p. 3 :
l. 22, '*earnest penny* ' = engagement penny.

  „   268, l. 2, ' *enuie* ' = hatred, as commonly.   Cf.
St. Mark xv. 10.

  „   269, l. 1, ' *regiment* ' = government, *ut freq.*

  „   270, l. 8, '*doome not* ' = judge not : *ibid.*, ' *least* '
—Did   Greene   mean   'in   the   smallest
matter ' ? or is ' least ' = lest—a common
spelling, and should it be followed by ——
as showing he left the sentence in his
rage imperfect, and more terrible because
of its imperfection ?

  „   271, l. 2, '*plackardes* ' = signs, *i.e.* sign-boards :
l. 21, ' *cut ouer* '—a vulgarism still.

  „   272, l. 18, ' *did* ' = [he, Selides] did.

  „   273, l. 3, ' *braues* ' = bravados, *ut freq.* : l. 8,
'*infer*' = bring in (so p. 285, l. 15): l. 20,
' *enuie* ' = hatred, as before : l. 22, ' *comicall* '—see Glossarial-Index, *s.v.*, for a full
note : l. 25, ' *palmers* ' = pilgrims.

  „   274, l. 13, '*abiect* ' = fallen, vilest: l. 16, '*flawe*'
= wind—see Glossarial-Index, *s.v.*

  „   275, l. 16, ' *prickes* ' = pens or quills : l. 20,
' *vntimelie* ' = too late discovered.

  „   277, l. 13, ' *created* ' = created [king].

  „   278, l. 20, ' *tainted* ' = stained or tinted.

Page 279, l. 10, '*neate*' = handsome and 'orderly' dressed : l. 25, '*meane*' = medium : *ibid.*, '*grees*' = agrees.

„ 280, l. 24, '*plackard*' = sign.

„ 281, l. 13, '*tabling*'—see Glossarial-Index, *s.v.*

„ 285, l. 5, '*Cullen*' = Cologne : last l., '*alay*' = alloy.

„ 286, l. 12, '*drie blowes*'—elsewhere 'dry bobs' —see Glossarial-Index, *s.v.*: l. 25, '*Masse*' = Master, as before.

„ 287, l. 2, '*counterfet*' = picture.

„ 289, l. 12, '*simpler*' = maker up of simples.

„ 293, l. 8, '*appaled*' = pale : l. 15, '*Pen sicke*' = sick of writing—see Glossarial-Index on Dyce's (mis)reading.

„ 294, l. 3, '*knee-stead*'—see Glossarial-Index, *s.v.*, for full Note.

„ 296, l. 1, '*seethim*'—see Glossarial-Index for prior examples.

„ 299, l. 4, '*paramour*'—see Glossarial-Index, *s.v.*, for good and bad use of this word. Cf. here p. 302, ll. 16, 23 : l. 24, '*race*' = raze.

„ 300, l. 5, '*lemman*' = mistress . l. 26, '*trie*' = prove.

„ 302, l. 1, '*lotted*' = allotted : l. 12, '*for*' = from : l. 13, '*popiniay*' = parrot.

„ 304, l. 15, '*blasing*' = blasoning.

„ 305, l. 5, '*markes*' = sea-marks, lighthouses : l. 27, '*standish*' = inkstand : but see Glossarial-Index, *s.v.*

„ 307, l. 6, '*doom*' = sentence.

Page 308, l. 21, '*presence*' = the presence or audience
of the king : l. 23, '*common*' = commune.

„   310, l. 9, '*then*'—misprinted 'them' in the
original : l. 19, '*make*' = mate : l. 24,
'*appeached*' = accused, *ut freq.*: l. 27, '*call*'
= summons—a sporting term, on which
see Glossarial-Index, *s.v.*

„   312, l. 5, '*deaws*' = dews.

„   314, l. 20, '*fraught*' = distraught.

„   315, l. 9, '*pasme*' = spasm : l. 20, '*confectaries*'
= confections.

„   317, l. 4, '*abiection*' — see Glossarial-Index,
s.v.: l. 16, '*quite*' = requite : l. 24, '*supposes*' = suppositions.

„   318, l. 7, '*brute*' = report : l. 9, '*conferre*' =
consult : l. 23, '*coniecture*' — misprinted
' coniectured.'

„   321, l. 9, '*allaromes*' = alarums : l. 13, '*pretence*' = intent, purpose.

„   322, l. 4, '*onely*' = ' Mænon was murthered by
me onely' : l. 6, '*while*' = until : l. 17,
'*Astronomie*'—this science then included
astrology, as here.

„   323, l. 1, '*constellation*'—The co-aspects of the
stars, *i.e.* planets, as differing from the
aspect of one planet, which in astrology
might be neutralized by the aspect (or
position) of another : l. 7, '*where*' = our
when : l. 27, '*infringe*' = break, *ut freq.*

„   325, l. 11, '*either*' — misprinted 'neither' in
the original.

„   326, l. 11, '*arbour*'—context shows that this

was not used as we now do, but as
Chaucer, Shakespeare (Jul. Cæsar iii. 2),
and Dryden used it, for walks benched
with grass seats, and shaded with trees.

Page 327, l. 23, ' *beauties to haue* ' = 'beauties [being]
    to haue.'

  „   329, l. 3, ' *banes* ' = bans — the whole phrase
    means—'has an [earnest] penny for de-
    claring your bans,' *i.e.* you are thinking of
    being married.

  „   330, l. 5, ' *cole-wortes* ' = cabbages : l. 9, ' *anato-*
    mie '—from the after word ' corps ' it might
    be thought that Greene has here made
    a slip, and that ' anatomie ' was here made
    = corse ; but he used it = skeleton (as in
    Comedy of Errors v. 1 : K. John iii. 4) :
    l. 22, ' *pasterers* ' = pastry-bakers.

  „   331, l. 19, ' *induce* ' = bring in : l. 26, ' *fonde* ' =
    foolish, *ut freq.*: l. 27, ' *kitching* ' = kitchen.

  „   333, l. 7, ' *floure* ' = flower : l. 27, ' *as* '—mis-
    printed ' at ' in the original.

  „   334, l. 21, ' *preuented* ' = anticipated.

  „   335, l. 17, ' *Cine* ' = sine : l. 26, ' *vild* ' = vile.

  „   336, l. 21, ' *Spynter* ' — Was Greene's ancient
    history at fault ?   I cannot find Vitellius
    was so called ; nor was he killed by order
    of Vespasian, but by the soldiery who
    entered Rome.

  „   337, l. 18, ' *his* ' = its: l. 27, ' *brooking* ' = bearing.

  „   338, l. 4, ' *fact* '—see Glossarial-Index for many
    examples of use as if from ' fascinus.'

  „   340, l. 19, ' *which* ' = [into] which.

Page 341, l. 2, '*iust*'—may have been used ironically; but qy. misprint for [un]iust ?

  „ 342, l. 7, '*drunkennesse*'—misprinted in original ' drunken messe.'

  „ 343, l. 24, ' *on hunting* ' = our ' a-hunting.'

  „ 344, l. 6, '*pretence* '= intention or design.

  „ 345, l. 10, ' *ruinate* '—used by Shakespeare in Comedy of Errors iii. 2, etc. : l. 24, '*pallet*' = palate.

  „ 347, l. 18, ' *backside* '—as p. 341, l. 11, shows = the 'backside' of a house, though it meant ' back garden,' and generally = back court. Sherwood's English Dictionary has " a Backside or back court," and Cotgrave, *s.v.*, has a " back yard or base-court." See ' Base-court' in Glossarial-Index, *s.v.*

II. Proverbs, Proverbial Sayings, Phrases, ETC.

Page   8, l. 12, ' *soyle her owne nest.*'

  „ 16, l. 23, ' *taking heart at grasse* ' [= grace], *ut freq.*

  „ 19, l. 4, ' *the Hood makes not the Monke, nor the apparell the man.*'

  „ 27, l. 18, ' *afford a pound of pride then an ounce of humility.*'

  „ 29, l. 8, ' *as the Deere at the gaze* ': l. 18, ' *freshwater soldier* '—see Notes and Illustrations : l. 21, ' *he could not tell on which eare to sleepe, but builded Castles in the ayre, and cast beyond the moone.*'

Page 30, l. 9, '*nipped on the pate.*'

„ 31, l. 11, '*dally with the flye in the candle, sport with the Salamander in the heate of Aetna.*'

„ 32, l. 5, '*loue is without law and therefore aboue all lawe.*'

„ 33, l. 12, '*the more beauty, the more pride*': l. 24, '*Loue . . . . hath no lack.*'

„ 35, l. 4, '*take heart at grasse*': l. 28, '*you shall not iudge colours for me.*'

„ 36, l. 1, '*wee count our penny good siluer*': l. 4, '*taking opportunity by the forehead*'—'*thinking to strike the yron at this heate.*'

„ 37, l. 5, '*fancie is a Shrew*' . . . . '*many like that neuer loued.*'

„ 38, l. 11, '*I see fire cannot be hidden in the Flaxe without smoke,*' . . . . '*I perceiue, in faith neighbour, by your lippes what lettice you loue*': l. 21, '*not inferring comparisons, because they be odious*': l. 23, '*There are more Maydes then Maulkin,*' etc.

„ 39, l. 5, '*nipped on the pate.*'

„ 40, l. 11, '*I stood to my tackling*': l. 17, '*with a loth to depart.*'

„ 41, l. 19, '*setting his rest*' = a card term: l. 25, '*hammering in his head.*'

„ 48, l. 14, '*Autumne showres are euer out of season.*'

„ 49, l. 10, '*I was neuer of that minde to count him martiall, that at the first shoote could yeeld vp the keyes of the Citie.*'

„ 50, l. 14, '*looke on thy feete and so fall thy*

plumes' — usually, as here, said of the peacock.

Page 62, l. 24, '*best Clarkes are not the wisest men.*'

  „   63, l. 2, '*I will cast at all*'—a dicing and gambling phrase.

  „   64, l. 24, '*all is not gold that glisters.*'

  „   65, l. 1, '*the Mariners sound at the first, for feare of a Rocke ; the Chirurgion tainteth betimes, for his surest proofe : one fore-wit is worth two after : it is not good to beware when the act is done : too late commeth repentance*': l. 9, '*he killed her with kindnesse*': l. 27, '*hee makes a vertue of his neede.*'

  „   66, l. 3, '*The cloth is neuer tried, until it come to the wearing, nor the linnen neuer shrinkes, till it comes to the wetting*' : l. 21, '*Trie then Eriphila ere thou trust*' : l. 23, '*prooue ere thou put in practise : cast the water before thou appoint the medecine : doe all things with deliberation : goe as the Snaile, faire and softly : haste makes waste : the malt is euer sweetest, where the fire is softest : let not wit ouercome wisedome, nor the hope of a husband be the hasard of thine honestie.*'

  „   67, l. 1, '*cast not thy credite on the chance of a stranger*' : l. 3, '*wade not too far where the foord is vnknowne*' : l. 8, '*know this, it is too late to call againe the day past.*'

  „;   68, l. 7, '*spill his pottage*' : l. 8, '*the law of necessitie*' : l. 11, '*the straight tree pressed downe groweth alwayes crooked*' : l. 13, '*kind cannot haue his course.*'

Page 69, l. 8, '*no pardon, where is no offence.*'

   „   70, l. 16, '*haue two strings to a bowe*' : l. 23, '*you harpe still . . . on one string.*'

   „   72, l. 19, '*a blinde man might haue seene the the creeples hault.*'

   „   73, l. 1, '*the fayrest and greenest herbes haue the most secret operation*' : l. 24, '*in many words lyeth mistrust and in painted speech deceit is often couered.*'

   „   75, l. 16, '*al things are not made of one mould.*'

   „   76, l. 1, '*it is hard taking the fowle when the net is descried, and ill catching of fish when the hooke is bare, and as impossible to make her beleeue that will give no credit, and to deceiue her that spieth the fetch. When the string is broken, it is hard to hit the white ; when a man's credite is called in question, it is hard to perswade one*' : l. 10, '*a woman may knit a knot with her tongue, that shee cannot vntie with all her teeth, and when the signet is set on, it is too late to breake the bargaine : therefore I had rather mistrust too soone then mislike too late*' : l. 19, '*the Wolfe hath as smooth a skin as the simple sheepe, the sowre Elder hath a fairer barke then the sweete Juniper : where the sea is calmest, there it is deepest, and where the greatest colour of honestie is, there oftentimes is the most want : for Venus vessels haue the loudest sound when they are most emptie.*'

   „   79, l. 25, '*The Turtle chooseth, but neuer changeth.*'

   „   80, l. 5, '*a woman hauing crackt her loyaltie is*

halfe hanged ': l. 22, ' *if I should stand to
my penyworth* ' = stand to the bargain I've
made.

Page 81, l. 1, ' *wittie but the other more wise* ': l. 3,
' *cannot the Cat catch mise, but shee must haue
a bell hanged at her eare ? he that is afraid
to venter on the Buck, for that he is wrapt
in the bryers, shall neuer haue hunters hap :
and hee that puts a doubt in loue at euery
chance shall neuer haue louers lucke* ': l. 10,
' *I will sit beside the saddle* '—apparently
(from this example) it means sit ' beside '
and not ' in ' the saddle—*i.e.* fail or perhaps
not make the attempt : l. 26, ' *there was but
one heart in two bodies.* '

„   82, l. 13, ' *so many faces, so many fancies* ':
l. 22, ' *early in a morning stepped into her
bed chamber* '—to be noted as then no un-
common reception-room (so-to-say).

„   83, l. 22, ' *may not a woman looke, but she must
loue ?* '

„   89, l. 15, ' *as the burnt childe dreads the fire.* '

„   91, l. 26, ' *she waded so farre, that she was ouer
her shooes.* '

„   94, l. 9, ' *hee could espie a pad in the strawe, and
discerne a glowing coale, from cold cinders.* '

„   95, l. 3, ' *it is good to looke before thou leape, and
to sound the Ford before thou venter to wade* ':
l. 6, ' *gaze not at starres, lest thou stumble
at stones* ': ' *looke not into the Lions denne,
lest for thy presumption, thy skinne be pulled
ouer thine eares.* '

Page 97, l. 10, '*thy Logike prooue not worth a lowse*' :
l. 21, '*lay they not their lookes to intrap,
when they meane to keep the fowle for tame
fooles.*'

„ 98, l. 5, '*God wot.*'

„ 100, l. 10, '*your sorrow is like the raine that came
too late.*'

„ 101, l. 19, '*the colour clapt to the eye, hindreth
the sight, the flower put in the nostrill,
hindreth the smell.*'

„ 102, l. 5, '*like the Lapwing, that cryeth farthest
from her nest.*'

„ 104, l. 24, '*making a womans resistance.*'

„ 107, l. 27, '*shee was with childe of this late and
dangerous newes.*'

„ 108, l. 24, '*hoping all shall be troden vnder foote.*'

„ 111, l. 1, '*whose hearts are full of holes.*'

„ 123, l. 11, '*though my showers come in Autumne*' :
l. 24, '*had not ridden them with a snaffle,*'
i.e. tenderly and lightly.

„ 125, l. 11, '*sit downe and blowe his fingers*' :
l. 13, '*fooles will haue bolts*'—allusion to
the proverb : l. 18, '*a dog will haue a
barking tooth.*'

„ 129, l. 6, '*basted him Calends in his forehead*' =
in his younger virile age Time marked its
course on his forehead and nowhere else :
l. 17, '*not laughing once a yeare with*'
Apollo.'

„ 130, l. 2, '*thought it good sleeping in a whole
skinne*' : l. 25, '*commendable prodigality
that grew from the Bonnet and the Tongue*' :

l. 28, '*Chaucer*'—see Index of Names, *s.n.*

Page 131, l. 13, '*thoughts in his fist*' = keeps his thoughts close except on proper occasion, when he readily opens his hand, or gives them. See 'The Secretary,' p. 138, l. 6.

„ 133, l. 27, '*thinke no smell good, but their Countries smoake.*'

„ 135, l. 1, '*young wits were wandring*': l. 11, '*hast not eaten bread with one tooth*' = not come to an age when you are all but toothless : '*nor hath the blacke Oxe trodden vpon thy foote*' = not worn with age or (as here probably) with cares : l. 15, '*what a long haruest thou shouldest reape for a little corne,*' etc.: l. 23, '*Fortune daunceth attendance on thy will*'—a phrase still used from the delays and consequent impatience of the suitor fidgets and moves about (so metaph. ' daunceth ').

„ 138, l. 10, ' *Trust not him that smyles,*' etc. Cf. Shakespeare's " Smile, and smile, and be a villain"—Hamlet i. 5.

„ 145, l. 7, '*hunger needs no sauce, and thirst turnes water into wine*': l. 10, ' *theres more mault in the floore.*'

„ 153, l. 11, ' *Beauty is like smoake in the straw,*'etc.

„ 154, l. 4, '*as she respected King nor Kesar.*'

„ 155, l. 14, '*inequality in marriage was oft enemy to Loue*': l. 17, ' *the meane . . . . a merry song*': l. 25, '*I shall buy gold too deare.*'

Page 156, l. 1, '*the higher was my seat, the sorer shall be my fall.*'

„ 157, l. 3, '*desires aboue Fortunes, are the fore-pointers of deep fall*': l. 11, '*keepe a Calender of their affection.*'

„ 163, l. 19, '*like rust on yron that neuer leaues fretting till it be consumed.*'

„ 167, l. 3, '*Better fill a man's belly then his eye*': l. 22, '*leade Apes in hell*'—Is the origin of this phrase to be found either in the custom of itinerant showmen leading an ape or apes (= monkey) as an employment and for gain, or from the custom of young unmarried women having them as a source of amusement? In the latter case, '*in hell*' was added as the place of amusement ironically: last l., '*what needes the hand a Taber, when hee meanes to catch the Hare?*'

„ 170, l. 2, '*A beautifull man, why he is a pearle in a woman's eye.*'

„ 173, l. 15, '*To pinne*,' etc. = a phrase probably derived from the custom of pinning or fastening favours on the sleeve.

„ 174, l. 14, '*Loue careth not for Cowards : faint heart neuer wonne faire Lady*': l. 17, '*a Souldier for my money.*'

„ 176, l. 7, '*being already ouer the shooues in a little loue forsooth*': l. 15, '*commanded his horses to be put to grasse.*'

„ 177, l. 13, '*his will stood for a law.*'

„ 178, l. 3, '*buy repentance with too deare a*

price': l. 17, '*there are more maydes then Maulkin*': l. 20, '*the idle life is the mother of all mischiefe*': l. 25, '*lye at racke and manger*' = to eat (and do nothing).

Page 179, l. 20, '*yet may ye stoppe before you come to the bottome.*'

   „ 180, l. 8, '*see day light at euery hole*': l. 17, '*not wring him by the finger, the blacke Oxe,*' etc.: l. 23, '*all went vpon wheels.*'

   „ 181, l. 1, '*too many by one*': l. 5, '*then the post began to bee painted*' = he began to run up bills, 'scores' being chalked, in taverns at least, on posts and behind doors.

   „ 182, l. 9, '*Are women's courtesies such sharpe showres?*': l. 10, '*all is not Golde that doth glister*': l. 11, '*euery Orient* [Eastern] *stone is not a Diamond*': '*all Drugges that are deare, are not precious, nor euery woman that can flatter, is not faithfull*': l. 14, '*Did you at the first decke mee with Roses, and now doe you beate mee with Nettles?*'

   „ 183, l. 11, '*straine further then thy sleeue would reach.*'

   „ 186, l. 9, '*needes beyond the Moone*': l. 10, '*they doe smyle that haue gained*': l. 16, '*pay thee with a cappe and a knee*' = by off-capping and bending the knee: l. 24, '*hauing bought witte at too deare a rate.*'

   „ 188, l. 13, '*thoughts reach at starres, stumble at stones*': l. 14, '*such as gaze at the heauens, fall on the earth.*'

Page 189, l. 10, '*the starres determine, but God disposeth.*'

   ,, 191, l. 1, '*promise mountaines and performe Molehills*': l. 22, '*thou art but one Swallow, and makest not Summer*': l. 26, '*say, Had I wist is a little too late.*'

   ,, 193, l. 19, '*There is no hap past hope*': l. 23, '*the foulest weedes haue oft the most vertuous operation, so the hoode makes not the Monke, nor the apparell the man.*'

   ,, 195, l. 16, '*women's thoughts are like babies fancies.*'

   ,, 196, l. 8, '*such a wanton as she would neuer want one.*'

   ,, 197, l. 9, '*the outward shew did not alwaies manifest the inner man.*'

   ,, 206, l. 25, '*bought wit is best.*'

   ,, 207, l. 8, '*Ah Father, had I reuerenced my God as I honoured my goddesse.*'

   ,, 209, l. 3, '*thought not that measure was a merry meane*': l. 8, '*as Doues flocke where the house is faire ; so where the carrion is, thither such hungry Eagles resort*': l. 11, '*empty vessels . . . . haue loud sounds*': l. 12, '*painted streakes . . . . haue rusty blades*': l. 13, '*glorious flowres . . . . haue no smell*': l. 15, '*by drawing too oft, the Well waxed drie*': l. 22, '*wit hath hee purchased with great repentance.*'

   ,, 210, l. 21, '*rubbe the sore afresh . . . . by recounting . . . . offences.*'

   ,, 212, l. 18, '*that nature likes best seldome seene*'

= as we should express it, 'that [that]' or 'that [which].' There is an ellipsis of '[is] seldome,' the [is] being understood from the previous 'are' : l. 26, ' *bought wit . . . . better late than neuer.*'

Page 213, l. 9, '*as kindly as his stomake would suffer.*'

„ 216, l. 2, ' *I stretcht beyond the compasse of my sleeue.*'

„ 218, l. 13, '*rubd the scarre afresh*' . . . . '*suffered the Caterpillers of time to consume the blossomes of his young thoughts.*'

„ 221, l. 19, ' *rid mee without a spurre* ' : l. 27, ' *Euery one dippes not his finger with Homer in the bason.*'

„ 228, l. 13, ' *if Diogenes stirre his stumpes,*' etc. . . . . ' *if the fox preach, tis to spie which is the fattest goose,*' etc.

„ 230, l. 13, ' *Diogenes hath taught me, that to kicke an asse,*' etc.

„ 231, l. 25, ' *haue made the tauerne to sweate with riotous expences.*'

„ 232, l. 14, ' *if I were not beyond,*' etc.

„ 233, l. 12, ' *a mans conscience is a thousand witnesses.*'

„ 236, l. 14, ' *sweeter was the deaw that dropt from peace, than the showers that powred downe from wars.*'

„ 239, l. 16, ' *tis a whetstone to sharp fancie.*'

„ 240, l. 11, '*an ant's egge,*' etc.—see Notes and Illustrations *in loco.*

„ 243, l. 17, '*women's fancies . . . men's fauors*' : l. 27, '*Parrats spake not what they thinke.*'

Page 244, l. 5, '*follie treading vpon our heeles*' . . .
'*taking time by the forehead.*'

„ 246, l. 2, '*deepely bred by the bone*': l. 14,
'*pride as ill befitteth a crowne as a cottage.*'

„ 248, l. 16, '*gazing at a starre you stumble at
a stone.*'

„ 249, l. 1, '*knewe scarse a speare from a spigot.*'

„ 250, l. 2, '*as fit a harbour for pride vnder a
scholler's cap as vnder a souldiours helmet.*'

„ 251, l. 7, '*no touch in Padua,*' etc.: l. 13, '*Peratio
looke to your owne last,*' etc. : l. 26, '*Peratio
thought to push him with the pike,*' etc.

„ 253, l. 10, '*English Gentleman . . . . painted
naked,*' etc.

„ 254, l. 13, '*the coule makes not the monk, nor
the gray weede the frier*': l. 23, '*take his
ease in his Inne.*'

„ 256, l. 14, '*thought Fortune had beene tied to
his thoughtes*': l. 25, '*kings might determine but God dispose.*'

„ 257, l. 5, '*consideration, the enemie of vntimely
attempts*': l. 27, '*Fortune euer commeth
at the sight of a scepter.*'

„ 258, l. 20, '*bring not contempt to such a royall
dignitie by too muche familiaritie.*'

„ 262, l. 3, '*a vertue of necessitie.*'

„ 263, l. 1, '*the priuiledge of honour is sealed
with the signet of time*': l. 15, '*accuse
not fates or Fortune as thy foes.*'

„ 264, l. 11, '*the frost nippeth the budde,*' etc. (a
number here together): l. 27, '*teares are
no cures for distresse.*'

Page 267, l. 15,   *I will rather marre the plaie then
your market* ' : l. 22, ' *so hired her before
the Constable.* '

„   268, l. 3, ' *pearked so highe with Danida's
Parrat,* etc.

„   269, l. 1, ' *more blossomes die the first nippe
in a morning,* ' etc., etc. : l. 19, ' *his skin
pulled ouer his eares* ' : l. 25, ' *Is not the
print of a lyon's clawea seale of his safetie?* '

„   270, l. 9, ' *flung from them in a rage.* '

„   273, l. 8, ' *a fooles coat to procure perpetual shame.* '

„   276, l. 18, ' *neuer shrinke at this shot.* '

„   277, l. 18, ' *the gaie coates of kings couers much
care* ' . . . l. 20, ' *the plowman hath more
ease then a king* ' . . . l. 23, ' *we haue as
much health with feeding on the browne
loafe as a Prince hath with all his delicates,
and I steale more sweete naps in the
chimney corner in a weeke then (God saue
his maiestie),* ' etc.

„   279, l. 1, ' *pouertie slept quietly at his plough beame.* '

„   280, l. 16, ' *hittest the crow by hap* ' : l. 26,
' *step thou not farther than thy scrip.* '

„   282, l. 9, ' *Fortune is blinde* ' : l. 27, ' *ioyne in
thee both pouertie and pride.* '

„   283, l. 1, ' *Report* . . . *a blister on her tongue* ' :
l. 11, ' *thy haruest is out of the grasse.* '

„   285, l. 18, ' *you may smell their pride by their
perfumes* ' : l. 23, ' *crosse Benedetto ouer the
thumbs.* '

„   286, l. 8, ' *wring water out of a stone* ' : l. 11,
' *hee burnt but his owne clothes.* '

Page 287, l. 27, '*brooke companions.*'

  „ 289, l. 4, '*discouer where his shoe wroong him.*'

  „ 290, l. 3, '*couering an inuenomed hooke with a faire baite.*'

  „ 291, l. 3, '*forgetting our God for the gaine of a goddesse.*'

  „ 292, l. 10, '*apply their wittes and wils.*'

  „ 300, l. 9, '*loue filleth not the hand with pelfe, but the eie with pleasure.*'

  „ 304, l. 25, '*shadowe thy misse*' = cover thy fault.

  „ 306, l. 11, '*hot loue is soone colde.*'

  „ 307, last l., '*looke twise . . . before he refused.*'

  „ 308, l. 17, '*like so proper a man*' . . . '*setting her husbande . . . foorth in print.*'

  „ 309, l. 4, '*it is not richesse to haue much, but to desire little.*'

  „ 311, l. 17, '*take time now by the forehead.*'

  „ 313, l. 27, '*I inferre no comparisons.*'

  „ 319, l. 7, '*stole the heartes of the commons.*'

  „ 323, l. 3, '*like leekes gray headed and . . . greene tailde.*'

  „ 324, l. 23, '*your lippes can digest such lettuce.*'

  „ 325, l. 4, '*nipt on the head.*'

  „ 327, l. 11, '*young mennes wiues and maidens children are alwaies wel taught*': l. 17, '*weare her pinde on your sleeue.*'

  „ 329, l. 15, '*as liefe haue their roome as their companie.*'

  „ 334, l. 14, '*life shorte, art long.*'

  „ 338, last l., '*Let me borrow a word.*'

A. B. G.

END OF VOL. IX.